Copyright, 1926, by
LOUIS F. BENSON

PRINTED IN U. S. A.

Christian Song

Edited by
Louis F. Benson, D.D.

The Century Co.
New York and London
1926

Preface

¶ It has come about once again that the first step toward attaining an effective congregational song is very much what it was in Luther's and Calvin's time; that of getting the hymn book into the hands of the people. Its abiding-place at present is in the pew-racks of our churches, to be taken into our hands as the Minister announces a hymn, and retained, it may be, till pretty near the hymn's end.

¶ The use of the hymnal as a companion of our private devotion, its place in the home circle, the thought of it as a book to be owned and loved and read, seem almost to have passed away.

¶ Under such conditions congregational song cannot be expected to prosper. Hymnody is not an ordinance that dwells in the church and waits (in the pew-racks) till a congregation gathers to exercise it. It is a spiritual function, and therefore personal first of all. Congregational song becomes spiritual only as each individual Christian brings his personal offering to the sanctuary, and contributes it to the common song of brotherhood. To do this he must first have made himself familiar with the hymns. He must come prepared to sing them out of his heart. If he has to make up his mind, as the hymn proceeds, whether he even agrees with its sentiments a sincere and hearty congregational song is not attainable.

¶ If we ask how this cloud of indifference to our Christian hymns has arisen, it may be that the modern fad of printing the words within the braces of the tune is partly responsible; for so they become hardly more than a libretto to the music. Strung out like prose in long lines across the page and crowded together between the staves one hardly thinks of them as poetry, and no one who could escape would willingly read poetry so printed. No better device could be invented for breeding a spirit of inattention to the words of our hymns. It is regrettable that some few good hymns, by reason of their varying and irregular rhythms, have to be so set up.

¶ But there are causes for this modern neglect that go deeper. In a desire to meet every occasion and cover every sermon theme, our church hymnals are grown too large, too encyclopædic. They are cumbersome to the hand;

iii

they present a hopeless task to the memory; they include too many utility hymns, too much of what Coleridge called religious thoughts expressed in verse, which makes so little appeal to the heart that only the call of duty could suggest singing it.

¶ Doubtless the serious call to take our part in the church song as a Christian duty has been kept before us ever since William Law's day, but it is little to the point and ought to be superfluous. The spirit of song is elusive of the canons of Christian ethics. St. Paul's injunction to let the word of Christ dwell in us richly, that we may speak to one another in Psalms and hymns and spiritual songs, and to Him in thanksgivings, is much more to the point. For the heart that is so filled finds in song the natural expression of its gratitude, not as a duty but as a pleasure.

¶ The church hymnal, therefore, best fulfils its function when it contributes to that pleasure by lifting Christian hymnody above the sphere of duty, and presenting it in such a way as will evoke and nourish the spirit of song in hearts that too readily lose the joy of salvation. And such is the main purpose of the present book: to make our hymnody more interesting by excluding what fails to appeal to the common heart, and to make it more lyrical by excluding whatever fails to appeal to the spirit of song.

¶ The book aims to be quite a limited selection of Christian lyrics (as distinguished from thoughts in verse), set to music that has charm. Some hymns are excluded that are familiar only in the sense that we of the pulpit persist in giving them out to serve our own ends in spite of the fact that they obstruct the spirit of song: and some beautiful lyrics are omitted, (such as Thring's "The radiant morn hath passed away" and Wordsworth's "The day is gently sinking") because of the observation that practically their effect is depressing.

¶ The hymns retained have been submitted to the fourfold test of reverence, spiritual reality and wholesomeness, lyrical beauty and (not least) cheerfulness. And those have been preferred that breathe out something of the spirit of eternal youth. The inclusion of much material new to our hymnals is more of a venture of faith, that must be tried by the same tests. Such of it as comes from the Editor's own hand is here by the will of his publishers.

¶ The Editor's aim (possibly his obsession) has been to rid our hymnody of the burden of sorrow and disillusionment and the pervading shadow of death, which are an inheritance from the peculiar type of experience developed in the great Evangelical Revival. The intensity of mood it engendered bred morbid views of life and craved death as a relief from life's distresses. The hymn writers of the Revival (a main source of our own hymnody) formed a habit which hardened into an Evangelical tradition of weighting their song with the burden of self pity and of pursuing every theme into the grave. And it is surprising to what extent the tradition still lingers, even after all the winnowings hymnody has had.

¶ But the habit of pitying one's self and living within the foreshadow of death, so detrimental to bodily health, is not any more edifying to the spirit. A resolute cheerfulness is as Christian as it is winsome, and makes a lovely atmosphere to work in. Blest is any ministry, to use Lord Balfour's words, that "serves the great cause of cheering up"; and what ministry is better fitted to such an end than that of a cheerful Christian Song?

¶ To this mission of good cheer in Christ the present book is consecrated. It acknowledges our human sin and feels its burden, but holds it up to the light of God's fatherly countenance. It cherishes fondly the hope of heaven, but not in the spirit of disillusionment with life pervading what an eminent psychologist is unkind enough to call "hymns of the Weary Willie type." Its recast of Faber's "O Paradise" will exemplify its point of view. To this cheerful "obsession" of the Editor even the text of the hymns has had to submit. Many a depressing verse has gone, or even a phrase. The "weary wanderer" of Blatchford's lovely hymn becomes "every traveller"; in "O day of rest and gladness," "life's dry, dreary sand" looms less suggestively: such ameliorations being of course duly noted.

¶ In choosing the tunes the Editor has been guided by no theory of Christian Song except that it is the family and community song of the Brotherhood. And in the interests of a general participation in it a very large proportion of the tunes have been transposed to lower keys, better adapted to a body of mixed voices. Believing that every hymn has somewhere its one best musical expression, he has diligently sought to find it, whether familiar or unfamiliar. Flippant tunes and dull ones and what is accounted correct liturgical music, he has religiously avoided. Some Welsh tunes, and some of the newest English type based on folk-songs, have been made very welcome. Each hymn is dealt with after its kind. If it is sentimental, as most good songs are, it is set to a melody that conveys the sentiment.

¶ The collects that precede each section of the book have been composed with a view of suggesting that music becomes religious only from a religious motive and when associated with holy words and thoughts. The numerous foot-notes are designed to awaken more interest in what is being sung.

¶ The canticles that follow the hymns are as a rule set to the chants most familiarly associated with them, with a view of facilitating the use of the only form of music the church can claim as her own. The prose Psalms are arranged for what is called "responsive reading," but is better thought of as responsive devotions; for responsive reading in itself is hardly a form of delivery that appeals to the intelligence. The indexes for immediate use are at the front of the book, where the left hand can find them while the right still holds the book open.   The indexes for casual reference lie between the hymnal and the Psalter, where they are most out of the way.

¶ It remains to express thanks to all those who have graciously permitted the use of their hymns or tunes.   It is a pleasure to acknowledge the skillful revision of the harmonies by Mr. Edward Shippen Barnes, Choirmaster of St. Stephen's Church, Philadelphia, and also his sympathetic adjustment of some strains here and there that failed to anticipate the associations into which they are now brought.

LOUIS F. BENSON

CONTENTS

The Hymns

I. TIMES OF WORSHIP

II. THE ETERNAL GOD

III. OUR LORD JESUS CHRIST

IV. THE HOLY SPIRIT

Contents

V. THE CHURCH

VI. THE KINGDOM

VII. THE SPIRITUAL LIFE

VIII. IMMORTAL LIFE

IX. OCCASIONAL HYMNS

X. CANTICLES, VERSICLES, ETC.

The Psalter

Index of First Lines

ix

Index of First Lines

x

Index of First Lines

Index of First Lines

xii

Index of First Lines

Index of Canticles, Versicles, Etc.

Alphabetical Index of Tunes

xv

Metrical Index of Tunes

Metrical Index of Tunes

Morning

A Collect for the Morning

O God, our Creator and Preserver, who hast refreshed our bodies by the slumber of the night: Restore our souls also by Thy ministries of grace, and strengthen us for new service in this new day. Cause us to hear Thy loving-kindness in the morning, for in Thee do we trust: make us to know the way wherein we should walk, for we lift up our souls unto Thee; through Jesus Christ our Lord. Amen.

2 SOLDIERS OF CHRIST S. M.

Rev. WILLIAM P. MERRILL in *The Hymnal*, 1895

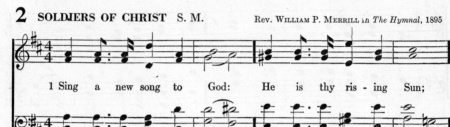

1 Sing a new song to God: He is thy ris - ing Sun;

His is the ra-diance of thy dawn; His the new day be - gun. A-MEN.

Sing a new song at morn;
  Join the glad woods and hills;
Join the fresh winds and seas and plains,
  Join the bright flowers and rills.

Waken, cold lips, and sing;
  Waken, dull mind, and pray;
Lift up, O man, thy heart and eyes;
  Brush slothfulness away.

4 Cast every weight aside;
  Battle with every sin;
Fight with the faithless world without,
  Thy careless heart within.

5 Look up beyond these clouds;
  Thither thy pathway lies;
Up and away now, for Thy goal
  Beckons from yonder skies.

Adapted for this book from a poem, "Begin with God,"
by Rev. HORATIUS BONAR, 1861

3 (ST. AGNES) C. M.

1 O Father, hear my morning prayer,
  Thine aid impart to me,
That I may make my life to-day
  Acceptable to Thee.

May this desire my spirit rule;
  And, as the moments fly,
Something of good be born in me,
  Something of evil die;

3 Some grace that seeks my heart to win
  With shining victory meet;
Some sin that strives for mastery
  Find overthrow complete.

4 That so throughout the coming day
  The hours shall carry me
A little farther from the world,
  A little nearer Thee.

Mrs. FRANCES A. PERCY, 1896

4 LUCIUS C. M.

George Kingsley, 1853: slightly varied

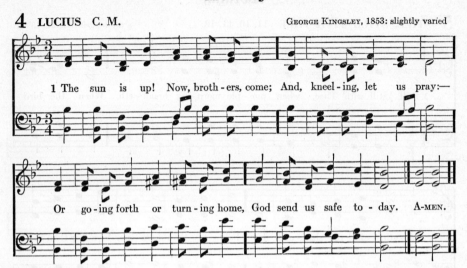

1 The sun is up! Now, broth-ers, come; And, kneel-ing, let us pray:—
Or go-ing forth or turn-ing home, God send us safe to-day. A-men.

Jam Lucis Orto Sidere

2 His hand be like a bridle-rein,
Held firm but lovingly,
His grace enfold us, to restrain
Our eyes from vanity.

3 God cleanse our lives from innermost,
God guard them from outside;
For fear life's simpler ways be lost
In luxury or pride.

4 That when the day is done, and night
Comes down by His decree,
His praise be still our heart's delight,
Our hearts from care still free.

5 Now let us rise, for it is meet
That all together say,
Praise Father, Son, and Paraclete,
For ever and alway.

An anonymous 15th century
Latin hymn, translated for this book

ST. AGNES C. M.

Rev. John B. Dykes, 1866

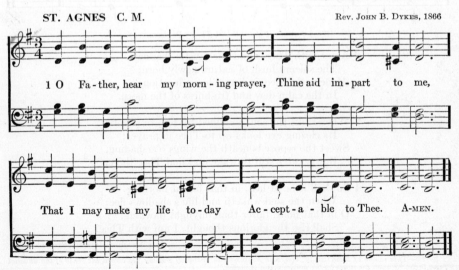

1 O Fa-ther, hear my morn-ing prayer, Thine aid im-part to me,
That I may make my life to-day Ac-cept-a-ble to Thee. A-men.

5 **STILL, STILL WITH THEE** 11. 10. 11. 10.

Sir Joseph Barnby, 1883

1 Still, still with Thee, when pur-ple morn-ing break-eth, When the bird wak-eth, and the shad-ows flee; Fair-er than morn-ing, love-lier than the day-light, Dawns the sweet con-scious-ness, I am with Thee. A-men.

When I awake, I am still with Thee —Ps. cxxxix: 18

2 Alone with Thee, amid the mystic shadows,
The solemn hush of nature newly born;
Alone with Thee, in breathless adoration,
In the calm dew and freshness of the morn.

3 When sinks the soul, subdued by toil, to slumber,
Its closing eye looks up to Thee in prayer;
Sweet the repose beneath the wings o'ershading,
But sweeter still to wake and find Thee there.

4 So shall it be at last, in that bright morning
When the soul waketh and life's shadows flee:
O in that hour, fairer than daylight dawning,
Shall rise the glorious thought, I am with Thee.

Mrs. Harriet Beecher Stowe, 1852

Note—*This is one of some twenty American hymns set to music by Barnby "to record his sense of the unusual favor bestowed upon his tunes by the musicians of America."*

6 WENTWORTH 8. 4. 8. 4. 8. 4. FREDERICK C. MAKER, 1876

1 The sun is on the land and sea, The day be-gun;
Our morn-ing hymn be-gins with Thee, Blest Three in One:
Our praise shall rise con-tin-ual-ly Till day is done. A-MEN.

His praise shall continually be in my mouth.—Ps. xxxiv: 1

2 Thy love was ever in our view,
   Like stars, by night;
   Thy gifts are every morning new,
   O God of light;
   Thy mercy, like the heavens' blue,
   Fills all our sight.

3 We do not know what grief or care
   The day may bring:
   The heart shall find some gladness there
   That loves its King;
   The life that serves Thee everywhere
   Can always sing.

4 All glory to the Father be,
   With Christ the Son,
   And, Holy Spirit, unto Thee,
   For ever One;
   All glory to the Trinity
   While ages run.

Rev. LOUIS F. BENSON, 1897

5

7 CANONBURY L. M.

Arranged from ROBERT A. SCHUMANN'S
Nachtstücke No. 4, 1839

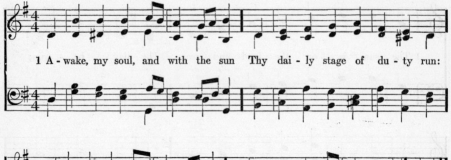

1 A - wake, my soul, and with the sun Thy dai - ly stage of du - ty run:

Shake off dull sloth, and joy - ful rise To pay thy morn-ing sac - ri - fice. A-MEN.

2 In all thy converse be sincere;
Thy conscience as the noontide clear;
Think how all-seeing God thy ways
And all thy secret thoughts surveys.

3 By influence of the light divine
Let thy own light to others shine;
Reflect all heaven's propitious rays
In ardent love and cheerful praise.

4 Wake and lift up thyself, my heart,
And with the angels bear thy part,
Who all night long, unwearied, sing
High praise to the Eternal King.

5 Lord, I my vows to Thee renew;
Disperse my sins as morning dew;
Guard my first springs of thought and will,
And with Thyself my spirit fill.

6 Direct, control, suggest, this day,
All I design, or do, or say;
That all my powers, with all their might,
In Thy sole glory may unite.

7 Praise God from whom all blessings flow;
Praise Him, all creatures here below;
Praise Him above, ye heavenly host:
Praise Father, Son, and Holy Ghost.

Bishop THOMAS KEN, 1674
with some of the changes he made in 1709

NOTE—*The "Long-metre Doxology" appeared originally as the last verse of this and of No. 12.*

8 (BROOKFIELD) L. M.

1 O God, I thank Thee for each sight
Of beauty that Thy hand doth give,
For sunny skies, and air and light;
O God, I thank Thee that I live.

2 That life I consecrate to Thee;
And ever, as the day is born,
On wings of joy my soul would flee,
And thank Thee for another morn;

3 Another day in which to cast
Some silent deed of love abroad,
That, greatening as it journeys past,
May do some earnest work for God;

4 Another day to do, to dare,
To tax anew my growing strength,
To arm my soul with faith and prayer,
And so reach heaven and Thee at length.

MRS. CAROLINE A. MASON, published in 1891

9 MOZART L. M.

Arranged from the "Kyrie" in the *Twelfth Mass*, attributed to MOZART

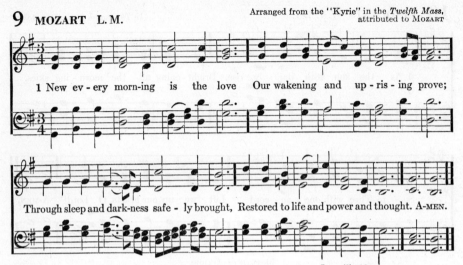

1 New ev-ery morn-ing is the love Our wakening and up-ris-ing prove;

Through sleep and dark-ness safe - ly brought, Restored to life and power and thought. A-MEN.

His compassions fail not; they are new every morning.—LAM. iii: 22.

2 New mercies, each returning day,
Hover around us while we pray;
New perils past, new sins forgiven,
New thoughts of God, new hopes of heaven.

3 If, on our daily course, our mind
Be set to hallow all we find,
New treasures still, of countless price,
God will provide for sacrifice.

4 The trivial round, the common task,
Will furnish all we ought to ask;
Room to deny ourselves, a road
To bring us daily nearer God.

5 Only, O Lord, in Thy dear love,
Fit us for perfect rest above,
And help us, this and every day,
To live more nearly as we pray.

From the opening hymn of
Rev. JOHN KEBLE's *The Christian Year*, 1827

BROOKFIELD L. M.

THOMAS B. SOUTHGATE, 1855

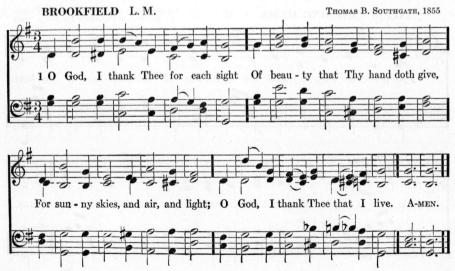

1 O God, I thank Thee for each sight Of beau-ty that Thy hand doth give,

For sun - ny skies, and air, and light; O God, I thank Thee that I live. A-MEN.

7

10 INNOCENTS 7. 7. 7. 7.

In *The Parish Choir*, Nov. 1850

1 As the sun doth dai - ly rise, Bright-ening all the morn - ing skies,

So to Thee with one ac - cord Lift we up our hearts, O Lord! A-MEN.

MATUTINUS ALTIORA

2 Day by day provide us food,
For from Thee come all things good:
Strength unto our souls afford
From Thy living Bread, O Lord!

3 Be our Guard in sin and strife;
Be the Leader of our life;
Lest like sheep we stray abroad,
Stay our wayward feet, O Lord!

4 Quickened by the Spirit's grace
All Thy holy will to trace,
While we daily search Thy word,
Wisdom true impart, O Lord!

5 Praise we, with the heavenly host,
Father, Son, and Holy Ghost;
Thee would we with one accord
Praise and magnify, O Lord!

An anonymous Latin hymn, translated by "O. B. C.";
recast by EARL NELSON in 1864

TALLIS'S EVENING HYMN L. M.

Adapted from a canon by THOMAS TALLIS
in Archbishop PARKER'S Psalter, c. 1560

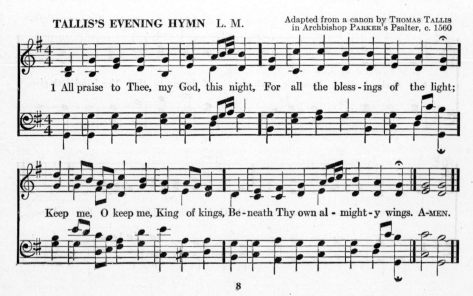

1 All praise to Thee, my God, this night, For all the bless - ings of the light;

Keep me, O keep me, King of kings, Be-neath Thy own al - might - y wings. A-MEN.

11 HURSLEY L. M.

In *Katholisches Gesangbuch*, Vienna, c. 1774
arranged by William H. Monk, 1861

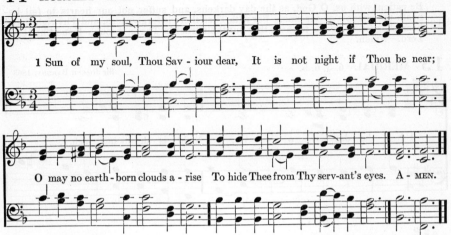

1 Sun of my soul, Thou Sav - iour dear, It is not night if Thou be near;

O may no earth - born clouds a - rise To hide Thee from Thy serv-ant's eyes. A - MEN.

2 When the soft dews of kindly sleep
My wearied eyelids gently steep,
Be my last thought, how sweet to rest
For ever on my Saviour's breast.

3 Abide with me from morn till eve,
For without Thee I cannot live;
Abide with me when night is nigh,
For without Thee I dare not die.

4 If some poor wandering child of Thine
Have spurned to-day the voice divine,
Now, Lord, the gracious work begin;
Let him no more lie down in sin.

5 Watch by the sick; enrich the poor
With blessings from Thy boundless store;
Be every mourner's sleep to-night,
Like infants' slumbers, pure and light.

6 Come near and bless us when we wake,
Ere through the world our way we take,
Till in the ocean of Thy love
We lose ourselves in heaven above.

From the Evening Hymn in
Rev. John Keble's *The Christian Year*, 1820

12 TALLIS'S EVENING HYMN L. M.

1 All praise to Thee, my God, this night,
For all the blessings of the light;
Keep me, O keep me, King of kings,
Beneath Thy own almighty wings.

2 Forgive me, Lord, for Thy dear Son,
The ill that I this day have done;
That with the world, myself, and Thee,
I, ere I sleep, at peace may be.

3 O may my soul on Thee repose,
And with sweet sleep mine eyelids close;
Sleep that may me more vigorous make
To serve my God when I awake.

4 When in the night I sleepless lie,
My soul with heavenly thoughts supply;
Let no ill dreams disturb my rest,
No powers of darkness me molest.

5 Praise God from whom all blessings flow;
Praise Him, all creatures here below;
Praise Him above, ye heavenly host:
Praise Father, Son, and Holy Ghost.

Bishop Thomas Ken, 1674; his text of 1709

9

Evening

A Collect for the Evening

Be patient with us, O God, as the day darkens, and suffer not our hearts to fail beneath the shadow of our sins. For with Thee there is forgiveness, and Thy right hand beareth gifts of peace to them that put their trust in Thee; through Jesus Christ our Lord. Amen.

13 MERRIAL 6. 5. 6. 5.

Sir Joseph Barnby, 1868

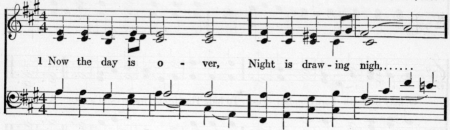

1 Now the day is o - ver, Night is draw - ing nigh,......

Shad - ows of the eve - ning Steal a - cross the sky. A - men.

Alternative tune, LYNDHURST, No. 370

2 Now the darkness gathers,
   Stars begin to peep;
Birds and beasts and flowers
   Soon will be asleep.

3 Jesus, give the weary
   Calm and sweet repose:
With Thy tenderest blessing
   May our eyelids close.

4 Grant to little children
   Visions bright of Thee;
Guard the sailors tossing
   On the deep blue sea.

5 Comfort every sufferer
   Watching late in pain;
Those who plan some evil
   From their sin restrain.

6 Through the long night watches
   May Thine angels spread
Their white wings above me,
   Watching round my bed.

7 When the morning wakens,
   Then may I arise,
Pure, and fresh, and sinless
   In Thy holy eyes.

8 Glory to the Father,
   Glory to the Son,
And to Thee, blest Spirit,
   Whilst all ages run.

Rev. Sabine Baring-Gould, 1865

NOTE—*Mr. Baring-Gould wrote this hymn especially for the children of his Sunday school at Horbury Bridge, England.*

Evening

FRIEDRICH F. FLEMMING's setting of
Horace's "Integer Vitæ," 1810

1 Now God be with us, for the night is clos-ing: The light and dark-ness are of His dis-pos-ing; And 'neath His shad-ow here to rest we yield us, For He will shield us. A-MEN.

DIE NACHT IST KOMMEN DRIN WIR RUHEN SOLLEN

2 Let evil thoughts and spirits flee before us;
Till morning cometh, watch, O Master, o'er us;
In soul and body Thou from harm defend us,
    Thine angels send us.

3 As Thy beloved, soothe the sick and weeping,
And bid the prisoner lose his griefs in sleeping;
Widows and orphans, we to Thee commend them,
    Do Thou befriend them.

4 We have no refuge, none on earth to aid us,
Save Thee, O Father, who Thine own hast made us;
But Thy dear presence will not leave them lonely
    Who seek Thee only.

5 Father, Thy Name be praised, Thy kingdom given,
Thy will be done on earth as 'tis in heaven;
Keep us in life, forgive our sins, deliver
    Us now and ever.

REV. PETRUS HERBERT, 1566
Translated by CATHERINE WINKWORTH, 1863

15 AR HYD Y NOS 8. 4. 8. 4. 8. 8. 8. 4.

A Welsh traditional melody;
in E. JONES's *Relics of the Welsh Bards*, 1784

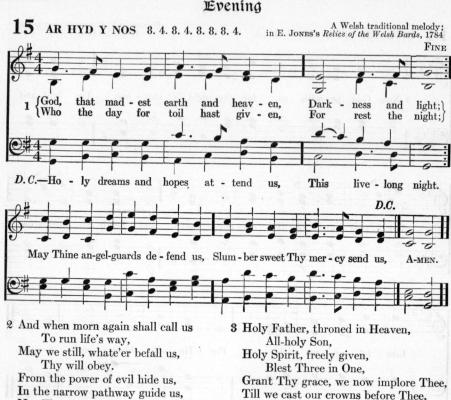

1 {God, that mad-est earth and heav-en, Dark-ness and light;}
  {Who the day for toil hast giv-en, For rest the night;}

D.C.—Ho-ly dreams and hopes at-tend us, This live-long night.

May Thine an-gel-guards de-fend us, Slum-ber sweet Thy mer-cy send us, A-MEN.

2 And when morn again shall call us
　　To run life's way,
May we still, whate'er befall us,
　　Thy will obey.
From the power of evil hide us,
In the narrow pathway guide us,
Nor Thy smile be e'er denied us,
　　The livelong day.

3 Holy Father, throned in Heaven,
　　All-holy Son,
Holy Spirit, freely given,
　　Blest Three in One,
Grant Thy grace, we now implore Thee,
Till we cast our crowns before Thee,
And in worthier strains adore Thee,
　　While ages run.

Verse 1 by Bishop REGINALD HEBER, 1827;
verses 2 and 3 added by Rev. WILLIAM MERCER, 1864

SEYMOUR 7. 7. 7. 7.

Arranged from the opening chorus
in CARL M. VON WEBER's *Oberon*, 1827

1 Soft-ly now the light of day Fades up-on my sight a-way;

Free from care, from la-bor free, Lord, I would com-mune with Thee. A-MEN.

16 ST. EDMUND 6. 4. 6. 4. 6. 6. 6. 4.

Sir ARTHUR SULLIVAN's setting of "I'm but a Stranger Here," 1872

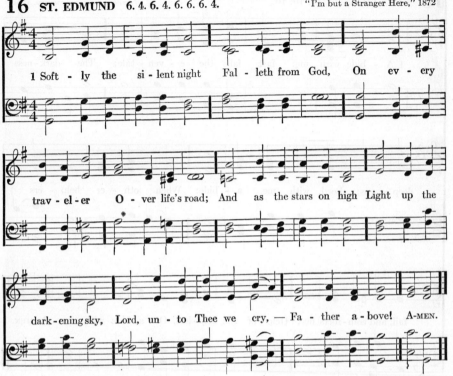

1 Soft - ly the si - lent night Fal - leth from God, On ev - ery trav - el - er O - ver life's road; And as the stars on high Light up the dark - ening sky, Lord, un - to Thee we cry, — Fa - ther a - bove! A-MEN.

Our Father which art in heaven.—ST. MATT. vi, 9

2 Slowly on failing wing
  Daylight has passed;
Sleep, like an angel kind,
  Folds us at last.
Peace be our lot this night,
Safe be our slumbers light,
Watched by Thine angels bright,
  Father above!

3 And when the gleam of morn
  Touches our eyes,
And the returning day
  Bids us arise,
Happy beneath Thy will,
Steadfast in joy or ill,
Lord, may we serve Thee still,
  Father above!

Rev. AMBROSE N. BLATCHFORD, 1875
with the third line revised

17 (SEYMOUR) 7. 7. 7. 7.

1 Softly now the light of day
  Fades upon my sight away;
Free from care, from labor free,
  Lord, I would commune with Thee.

2 Thou, whose all-pervading eye
  Naught escapes, without, within,
Pardon each infirmity,
  Open fault, and secret sin.

3 Soon for me the light of day
  Shall for ever pass away;
Then, from sin and sorrow free,
  Take me, Lord, to dwell with Thee.

4 Thou who, sinless, yet hast known
  All of man's infirmity;
Then, from Thine eternal throne,
  Jesus, look with pitying eye.

Bishop GEORGE W. DOANE, 1824

Evening

WILLIAM H. MONK, for
Hymns ancient and modern, 1861

18   EVENTIDE   10. 10. 10. 10.

1 A - bide with me: fast falls the e - ven - tide; The dark - ness deep - ens; Lord, with me a - bide: When oth - er help - ers fail, and com - forts flee, Help of the help - less, O a - bide with me. A - MEN.

Abide with us; for it is toward evening, and the day is far spent.—ST. LUKE xxiv, 29

2 Swift to its close ebbs out life's little day;
Earth's joys grow dim, its glories pass away;
Change and decay in all around I see;
O Thou who changest not, abide with me.

3 I need Thy presence every passing hour;
What but Thy grace can foil the tempter's power?
Who like Thyself my guide and stay can be?
Through cloud and sunshine, O abide with me.

4 I fear no foe, with Thee at hand to bless:
Ills have no weight, and tears no bitterness.
Where is death's sting? where, grave, thy victory?
I triumph still, if Thou abide with me.

5 Hold Thou Thy cross before my closing eyes;
Shine through the gloom, and point me to the skies:
Heaven's morning breaks, and earth's vain shadows flee:
In life, in death, O Lord, abide with me.

Rev. HENRY F. LYTE, 1847

19 ST. ANATOLIUS 7. 6. 7. 6. 8. 8.

ARTHUR H. BROWN, 1862

1 The day is past and o - ver: All thanks, O Lord, to Thee;

I pray Thee that of - fence - less The hours of dark may be.

O Je - sus, keep me in Thy sight, And save me thro' the com - ing night. A - MEN.

2 The joys of day are over:
  I lift my heart to Thee,
And call on Thee that sinless
  The hours of gloom may be.
O Jesus, make their darkness light,
And save me through the coming night.

3 The toils of day are over:
  I raise the hymn to Thee,
And ask that free from peril
  The hours of fear may be.
O Jesus, keep me in Thy sight,
And guard me through the coming night.

4 Lighten mine eyes, O Saviour,
  Or sleep in death shall I,
And he, my wakeful tempter,
  Triumphantly shall cry,
"He could not make their darkness light,
Nor guard them through the hours of
  [night."

5 Be Thou my soul's Preserver,
  O God, for Thou dost know
How many are the perils
  Through which I have to go.
Lover of men, O hear my call,
And guard and save me from them all.

Arranged and translated from an early Greek Service Book
  by Rev. JOHN M. NEALE, 1853, 1862

20 EVENING PRAYER 8. 7. 8. 7.

GEORGE C. STEBBINS, 1878

1 Sav-iour, breathe an eve-ning bless-ing, Ere re-pose our spir-its seal;

Sin and want we come con-fess-ing: Thou canst save, and Thou canst heal. A-MEN.

Copyright by Geo. C. Stebbins. Renewal, 1919, Hope Publishing Co., owner

2 Though destruction walk around us,
  Though the arrow past us fly,
  Angel-guards from Thee surround us;
  We are safe if Thou art nigh.

3 Though the night be dark and dreary,
  Darkness cannot hide from Thee;
  Thou art He who, never weary,
  Watchest where Thy people be.

4 Now unto the holy keeping
  Of that changeless love of Thine,
  Whether waking, Lord, or sleeping,
  Humbly we ourselves resign.

Verses 1-3 by JAMES EDMESTON, 1820:
verse 4 written for this book

VESPERS 8. 7. 8. 7.

From "Buona notte, buon dormir!"
in FRIEDRICH FLOTOW's *Martha*, 1847

1 Lo! The day of rest de-cli-neth, Gath-er fast the shades of night;

May the Sun that ev-er shi-neth Fill our souls with heavenly light. A-MEN.

21 VESPER HYMN 8. 7. 8. 7. D.

Sir J. A. STEVENSON's setting of
"Hark! the vesper hymn is stealing," 1818

1 { Now, on land and sea de-scend-ing, Brings the night its peace pro-found; }
  { Let our ves-per hymn be blend-ing With the ho-ly calm a-round. }

REFRAIN

Ju - bi - la - te! Ju - bi - la - te! Ju - bi - la - te! A - men.

Let our ves-per hymn be blend-ing With the ho-ly calm a-round. A-MEN.

2 Soon as dies the sunset glory,
　Stars of heaven shine out above,
Telling still the ancient story,—
　Their Creator's changeless love.—REF.

3 Now, our wants and burdens leaving
　To His care who cares for all,

Cease we fearing, cease we grieving:
　At His touch our burdens fall.—REF.

4 As the darkness deepens o'er us,
　Lo! eternal stars arise;
Hope and faith and love rise glorious,
　Shining in the spirit's skies.—REF.

Rev. SAMUEL LONGFELLOW, 1859; arranged for this book

22 VESPERS 8. 7. 8. 7.

Under His wings shalt thou trust.—Ps. xci, 4

1 Lo! the day of rest declineth,
　Gather fast the shades of night;
May the Sun that ever shineth
　Fill our souls with heavenly light.

2 Softly now the dew is falling;
　Peace o'er all the scene is spread:

On His children, meekly calling,
　Purer influence God will shed.

3 While, Thine ear of love addressing,
　Thus our evening hymn we sing,
Father, grant Thine evening blessing,
　Fold us safe beneath Thy wing.

Rev. CHANDLER ROBBINS, 1845

23 ST. LEONARD C. M. D.

HENRY HILES, 1867

1 The shad-ows of the eve-ning hours Fall from the dark-ening sky;

Up - on the fra-grance of the flowers The dews of eve-ning lie:

Be - fore Thy throne, O Lord of heaven, We kneel at close of day;

Look on Thy chil-dren from on high, And hear us while we pray. A-MEN.

I will lay me down in peace.—Ps. iv, 9

2 Slowly the rays of daylight fade;
    So fade within our heart
The hopes in earthly love and joy
    That one by one depart.
Slowly the bright stars, one by one,
    Within the heavens shine;
Give us, O Lord, fresh hopes in heaven,
    And trust in things divine.

3 Let peace, O Lord, Thy peace, O God,
    Upon our souls descend;
From midnight fears and perils, Thou
    Our trembling hearts defend:
Give us a respite from our toil,
    Calm and subdue our woes;
Through the long day we labor, Lord,
    O give us now repose.

ADELAIDE ANNE PROCTER, 1862:
verse 3, line 7, varied

24 EVENING PRAISE 7. 7. 7. 7. 4. with Refrain

WILLIAM F. SHERWIN, 1877

1 Day is dy-ing in the west; Heaven is touch-ing earth with rest; Wait and wor-ship while the night Sets her eve-ning lamps a-light Through all the sky.

REFRAIN.

Ho-ly, Ho-ly, Ho-ly, Lord God of Hosts! Heaven and earth are full of Thee; Heaven and earth are prais-ing Thee, O Lord Most High! A-MEN.

2 Lord of life, beneath the dome
Of the universe, Thy home,
Gather us who seek Thy face
To the fold of Thy embrace,
For Thou art nigh.—REF.

3 While the deepening shadows fall,
Heart of love, enfolding all,
Through the glory and the grace
Of the stars that veil Thy face,
Our hearts descend.—REF.

4 When for ever from our sight
Pass the stars, the day, the night,
Lord of angels, on our eyes
Let eternal morning rise,
And shadows end.—REF.

MARY A. LATHBURY, 1877

25 AURELIA 7. 6. 7. 6. D.

SAMUEL S. WESLEY's setting of
"Jerusalem the Golden," 1864

1 This night, O Lord, we bless Thee For Thy pro-tect-ing care,

And, ere we rest, ad-dress Thee In low-ly, fer-vent prayer:

From e-vil and temp-ta-tion De-fend us through the night,

And round our hab-i-ta-tion Be Thou a wall of light. A-MEN.

Yea, the Almighty shall be thy defence.—JOB xxii, 25

2 On Thee our whole reliance
　From day to day we cast,
To Thee, with firm affiance,
　Would cleave from first to last;
To Thee, through Jesus' merit,
　For needful grace we come,
And trust that Thy good Spirit
　Will guide us safely home.

3 What may be on the morrow
　Our foresight cannot see;
But be it joy or sorrow,
　We know it comes from Thee.
And nothing can take from us,
　Where'er out steps may move,
The staff of Thy sure promise,
　The shield of Thy true love.

REV. JAMES DRUMMOND BURNS, 1856

In God's House

A Collect for Sunday

O God, who hast given us this day of rest: Grant that Thy constant presence may hallow it, and that Thy love may draw all our hearts to Thee; for we are Thine, and not another's, and this is the day which Thou hast made. Help us, O Lord, to keep this day unspotted from the world, in remembrance of Jesus Christ, risen from the dead. Amen.

26 **MENDEBRAS** 7. 6. 7. 6. D.

A German melody: arranged by LOWELL MASON, 1839

1 { O day of rest and gladness, O day of joy and light, O balm of care and sad - ness, Most beau - ti - ful, most bright;}

On thee, the high and low - ly, Through a - ges joined in tune,

Sing Ho - ly, Ho - ly, Ho - ly, To the great God Tri - une. A-MEN.

Alternative tune, AURELIA, opposite

2 On thee, at the creation,
　The light first had its birth;
On thee, for our salvation,
　Christ rose from depths of earth;
On thee our Lord, victorious,
　The Spirit sent from heaven;
And thus on thee, most glorious,
　A triple light was given.

3 Thou art a port protected
　From storms that round us rise;
A garden intersected
　With streams of Paradise;

Thou art a cooling fountain
　Amid the desert sand;
From Thee, like Pisgah's mountain,
　We view our promised land.

4 New graces ever gaining
　From this our day of rest,
We reach the rest remaining
　To spirits of the blest.
To Holy Ghost be praises,
　To Father, and to Son;
The Church her voice upraises
　To Thee, blest Three in One.

Bishop CHRISTOPHER WORDSWORTH, 1862
with one line varied

21

In God's House

27 ACCESS 10. 10. 10. 10.

Uzziah C. Burnap: composed in 1898
published in 1925

1 Fa - ther, once more with - in Thy Ho - ly Place We bring the sins which,
kneel - ing, we con - fess; Not worth - y yet to look up - on Thy face,
Yet loath to rise un - til Thy hand doth bless. A - MEN.

I said, I will confess my transgressions unto the Lord; and Thou forgavest the iniquity of my sin. —Ps. xxxii, 5

2 Father, once more within Thy House of Hope
    We turn from sin to find a glad release:
  In Thy forgiveness there is strength to cope
    With all that robs the spirit of Thy peace.

3 Father, once more within Thy House of Prayer
    We kneel before Thee at the open way;
  And, leaving both our hopes and burdens there,
    We wait till Thou shalt teach us how to pray.

4 Father, once more within Thy House of Praise
    We bring our gifts to Thee from whom they came;
  We lift our hearts and our hosannas raise
    To welcome Him who cometh in Thy Name.

Rev. Louis F. Benson, 1897

22

28 EVENING SHADOWS S. M. D.

J. T. MUSGRAVE, 1900

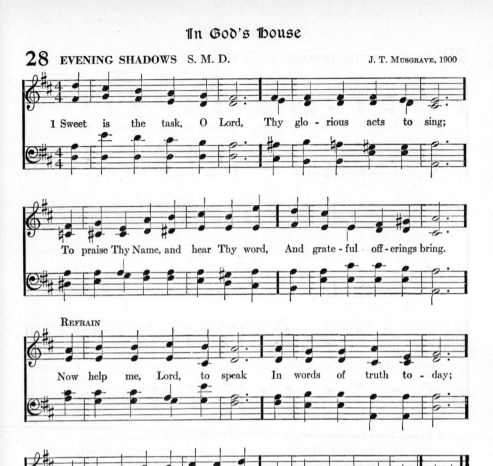

1 Sweet is the task, O Lord, Thy glorious acts to sing;
To praise Thy Name, and hear Thy word, And grateful offerings bring.

REFRAIN

Now help me, Lord, to speak In words of truth today;
Keep true my voice when Thee I praise, And trustful when I pray. A-MEN.

I will sing praise unto the Lord while I have my being. My meditation of Him shall be sweet.—Ps. civ, 33, 34

2 Sweet at the dawning hour
   Thy boundless love to tell,
And, when the night-wind shuts the
      flower,
   Still on the theme to dwell.—REF.

3 Sweet, on this day of rest,
   To join in heart and voice
With those who love and serve Thee
      best,
   And in Thy Name rejoice.—REF.

4 To songs of praise and joy
   Be every Sabbath given,
That such may be our blest employ
   Eternally in heaven.—REF.

HARRIET AUBER, 1829
with a refrain adapted from HORATIUS BONAR

29 HYMN TO THE TRINITY 6.6.4.6.6.6.4.

Felice de Giardini, 1769

1 Come, Thou Al - might - y King, Help us Thy Name to sing,
Help us to praise: Fa - ther, all - glo - ri - ous, O'er all vic - to - ri - ous,
Come, and reign o - ver us, An - cient of Days. A - MEN.

2 Come, Thou Incarnate Word,
　Gird on Thy mighty sword,
　　Our prayer attend:
　Come, and Thy people bless,
　And give Thy word success;
　Spirit of holiness,
　　On us descend.

3 Come, Holy Comforter,
　Thy sacred witness bear
　　In this glad hour:
　Thou who almighty art,

　Now rule in every heart,
　And ne'er from us depart,
　　Spirit of power.

4 To the great One in Three
　Eternal praises be
　　Hence evermore.
　His sovereign majesty
　May we in glory see,
　And to eternity
　　Love and adore.

Printed in a tract bound up with
George Whitefield's hymn book, 1757

30 SABBATH 7.7.7.7.7.7.

Lowell Mason, 1834

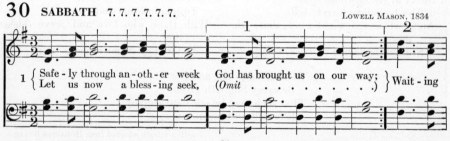

1 { Safe - ly through an - oth - er week
　 Let us now a bless - ing seek,
God has brought us on our way;
(Omit . . . .) } Wait - ing

In God's House

In His courts to - day: Day of all the week the best, Em - blem of e - ter-nal rest.

Day of all the week the best, Em - blem of e - ter - nal rest. A - MEN.

2 While we pray for pardoning grace,
  Through the dear Redeemer's Name,
Show Thy reconcilèd face;
  Take away our sin and shame;
From our worldly cares set free,
May we rest this day in Thee.

3 Here we come Thy Name to praise,
  Let us feel Thy presence near;
May Thy glory meet our eyes,

While we in Thy house appear:
Here afford us, Lord, a taste
Of our everlasting feast.

4 May Thy gospel's joyful sound
  Conquer sinners, comfort saints;
May the fruits of grace abound,
  Bring relief for all complaints:
Thus may all our Sabbaths prove,
Till we join the Church above.

Rev. JOHN NEWTON, 1774, each verse varied

NOTE—*This hymn was written "For Saturday Evening;" and has been since adapted to Sunday use.*

DIX 7. 7. 7. 7. 7. 7. Arranged from CONRAD KOCHER's "Treuer Heiland," 1838

1 { Safe - ly through an - oth - er week God has brought us on our way; }
  { Let us now a bless - ing seek, Wait - ing in His courts to - day; }

Day of all the week the best, Em - blem of e - ter - nal rest. A - MEN.

In God's House

31 **MURIEL** 7. 6. 7. 6.

Thomas Morley; first printed in
The Book of Common Praise, 1909

1 The earth is hushed in si - lence, Its cares now flee a - way;

Let all things bow in rev - 'rence On this the Lord's own day. A - MEN.

2 The bells are sweetly ringing,
   Their clear-toned voices say,
"Ye people, come and worship
   On this the Lord's own day."

3 O call of love and duty!
   Who would not praise and pray,
And thank the Lord of heaven
   On this His chosen day!

4 He cheers the weary-hearted,
   He shows the heavenly way
To those who kneel before Him
   On this His holy day.

5 Come, all ye thankful people:
   Why should our hearts delay
To greet the Lord of heaven
   On this His holy day!

Anonymous in Ginn and Co.'s *Fifth Reader:
Educational Music Course,* 1897

SOHO C. M.

Sir Joseph Barnby, 1881

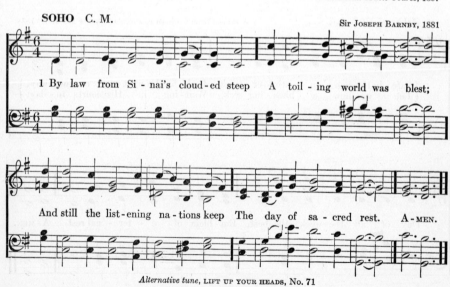

1 By law from Si - nai's cloud - ed steep A toil - ing world was blest;

And still the list - ening na - tions keep The day of sa - cred rest. A - MEN.

Alternative tune, LIFT UP YOUR HEADS, No. 71

32 DOMINICA S. M.

Sir Herbert S. Oakeley, 1874

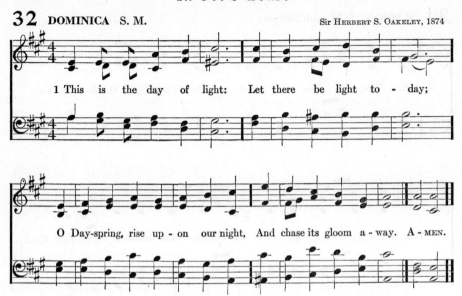

1 This is the day of light: Let there be light to - day;

O Day-spring, rise up - on our night, And chase its gloom a - way. A - MEN.

This is the day which the Lord hath made.—Ps. cxviii, 24

2 This is the day of rest:
　Our failing strength renew;
On weary brain and troubled breast
　Shed Thou Thy freshening dew.

3 This is the day of peace:
　Thy peace our spirits fill;
Bid Thou the blasts of discord cease,
　The waves of strife be still.

4 This is the day of prayer:
　Let earth to heaven draw near:
Lift up our hearts to seek Thee there;
　Come down to meet us here.

5 This is the first of days:
　Send forth Thy quickening breath,
And wake dead souls to love and praise,
　O Vanquisher of death!

Rev. John Ellerton, 1867

33 (SOHO) C. M.

Wherefore the Lord blessed the sabbath day, and hallowed it.—Exodus xx, 11

1 By law from Sinai's clouded steep
　A toiling world was blest;
And still the listening nations keep
　The day of sacred rest.

2 Renewed to peace, and power and joy,
　Man's soul is free this day;
Nor task nor care our minds employ;
　We need but love and pray.

3 Let wheel and anvil silent stand,
　Leave furrow, field and mart,
Give rest to weary head and hand
　And lift to heaven the heart.

4 Be life upborne by light and love
　As tides enlarge the sea;
Let grief and sin see God above
　And all men brothers be.

5 Man may not live by bread alone,
　Him angel hands sustain;
But gifts from heaven are not our own
　Till God within us reign.

6 So on this holy day of days,
　With free, fraternal mind
We bring Thee, Lord, our hymn of praise,
　And leave the world behind.

Rev. Theodore C. Williams, (1855–)

34 MARION S. M. with Refrain

ARTHUR H. MESSITER, 1885

1 Re - joice, ye pure in heart, Re - joice, give thanks, and sing;
Your fes - tal ban - ner wave on high, The cross of Christ your King.

REFRAIN

Re - joice, re - joice, Re - joice, give thanks, and sing. A - MEN.
Re - joice, re - joice,

Both young men and maidens; old men and children: let them praise the name of the Lord.—Ps. cxlviii, 12

2 Bright youth and snow-crowned age,
   Strong men and maidens meek,
Raise high your free exulting song,
   God's wondrous praises speak.—REF.

3 With all the angel choirs,
   With all the saints on earth,
Pour out the strains of joy and bliss,
   True rapture, noblest mirth.—REF.

4 With voice as full and strong
   As ocean's surging praise,
Send forth the hymns our fathers loved,
   The psalms of ancient days.—REF.

5 Yes on, through life's long path,
   Still chanting as ye go,
From youth to age, by night and day,
   In gladness and in woe.—REF.

6 Still lift your standard high,
   Still march in firm array,
As warriors through the darkness toil
   Till dawns the golden day.—REF.

7 Then on, ye pure in heart,
   Rejoice, give thanks, and sing,
Your festal banner wave on high,
   The cross of Christ your King.—REF.

Rev. EDWARD H. PLUMPTRE, 1865

35 LIEBSTER JESU, WIR SIND HIER 7. 8. 7. 8. 8. 8.

JOHANN RUDOLPH AHLE, 1664

1 { Bless - ed Je - sus, at Thy word We are gath - ered all to hear Thee; }
  { Let our hearts and souls be stirred Now to seek and love and fear Thee; }

By Thy teachings sweet and holy, Drawn from earth to love Thee sole - ly. A - MEN.

LIEBSTER JESU, WIR SIND HIER

2 All our knowledge, sense, and sight
  Lie in deepest darkness shrouded,
Till Thy Spirit breaks our night
  With the beams of truth unclouded.
Thou alone to God canst win us,
Thou must work all good within us.

3 Glorious Lord, Thyself impart!
  Light of light, from God proceeding,
Open Thou our ears and heart,
  Help us by Thy Spirit's pleading,
Hear the cry Thy people raises,
Hear, and bless our prayers and praises.

TOBIAS CLAUSNITZER, 1671
Translated by CATHERINE WINKWORTH, 1858

*Alternative tune to Hymn 34,
omitting the refrain*

FESTAL SONG S. M.

WILLIAM H. WALTER, 1894

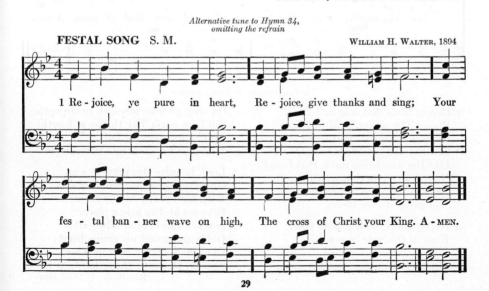

1 Re - joice, ye pure in heart, Re - joice, give thanks and sing; Your

fes - tal ban - ner wave on high, The cross of Christ your King. A - MEN.

In God's House

36 IVES 7. 7. 7. 7. D.   An Irish melody, arranged by ELAM IVES, JR., 1846

1 Pleas-ant are Thy courts a-bove, In the land of light and love;

Pleas-ant are Thy courts be-low, In this land of sin and woe.

O my spir-it longs and faints For the con-verse of Thy saints,

For the bright-ness of Thy face, For Thy ful-ness, God of grace. A-MEN.

A PARAPHRASE OF PSALM LXXXIV

2 Happy birds that sing and fly
Round Thy altars, O Most High!
Happier souls that find a rest
In a heavenly Father's breast!
Like the wandering dove, that found
No repose on earth around,
They can to their ark repair,
And enjoy it ever there.

3 Happy souls! their praises flow
Even in this vale of woe;
Waters in the desert rise,
Manna feeds them from the skies:

On they go from strength to strength,
Till they reach Thy throne at length;
At Thy feet adoring fall,
Who hast led them safe through all.

4 Lord, be mine this prize to win;
Guide me through a world of sin;
Keep me by Thy saving grace;
Give me at Thy side a place.
Sun and Shield alike Thou art;
Guide and guard my erring heart:
Grace and glory flow from Thee;
Shower, O shower them, Lord, on me.

Rev. HENRY F. LYTE, 1834

In God's House

37 ELM C. M.   J. VARLEY ROBERTS, 1889

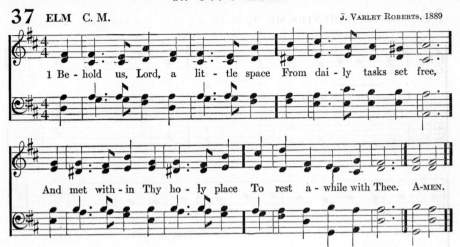

1 Be - hold us, Lord, a lit - tle space From dai - ly tasks set free,

And met with - in Thy ho - ly place To rest a - while with Thee. A-MEN.

2 Around us rolls the ceaseless tide
   Of business, toil, and care;
And scarcely can we turn aside
   For one brief hour of prayer.

3 Yet these are not the only walls
   Wherein Thou mayst be sought;
On homeliest work Thy blessing falls,
   In truth and patience wrought.

4 Thine is the loom, the forge, the mart,
   The wealth of land and sea;
The worlds of science and of art,
   Revealed and ruled by Thee.

5 Then let us prove our heavenly birth
   In all we do and know;
And claim the kingdom of the earth
   For Thee, and not Thy foe.

6 Work shall be prayer, if all be wrought
   As Thou wouldst have it done;
And prayer, by Thee inspired and taught,
   Itself with work be one.

Rev. JOHN ELLERTON, 1870

WINCHESTER OLD C. M.   Adapted from CHRISTOPHER TYE, 1553
                                              in THOMAS ESTE's *Psalmes*, 1592

1 Be - hold us, Lord, a lit - tle space From dai - ly tasks set free,

And met with - in Thy ho - ly place To rest a - while with Thee. A - MEN.

38 AUDITE AUDIENTES ME C. M. D.

Sir Arthur Sullivan, 1875

Voices in unison

1 Prayer is the soul's sin - cere de - sire, Un - ut - tered or ex - pressed;

Organ

The mo - tion of a hid - den fire That trem-bles in the breast.

Voices in harmony

He pray - eth best who lov - eth best All things both great and small;

For the dear God who lov - eth us, He made and lov - eth all. A - MEN.

2 Prayer is the burden of a sigh,
  The falling of a tear,
The upward glancing of an eye
  When none but God is near.
    He prayeth best, etc.

3 Prayer is the simplest form of speech
  That infant lips can try;
Prayer the sublimest strains that reach
  The Majesty on high.
    He prayeth best, etc.

4 Prayer is the Christian's vital breath,
  The Christian's native air,
His watchword at the gates of death;
  He enters heaven with prayer.
    O Thou, by whom we come to God,
      The Life, the Truth, the Way,
    The path of prayer Thyself hast trod;
      Lord, teach us how to pray.

James Montgomery, 1819; the rhythm of
line 2 is revised; with a verse from Coleridge's
The Ancient Mariner, used as a refrain

In God's House

39 EPHRATAH C. M. D.

Uzziah C. Burnap, in *The Hymnal*, 1895

1 My Lord, my Love, was cru-ci-fied, He all the pains did bear;

But in the sweet-ness of His rest He makes His serv-ants share.

How sweet-ly rest Thy saints a-bove Which in Thy bo-som lie;

The Church be-low doth rest in hope Of that fe-lic-i-ty. A-MEN.

Copyright, 1895, by The Trustees of The Presbyterian Board of Publication

"A Song of Praise for the Lord's Day"

2 Thou, Lord, who daily feed'st Thy sheep,
  Mak'st them a weekly feast;
Thy flocks meet in their several folds
  Upon this day of rest.
Welcome and dear unto my soul
  Are these sweet feasts of love;
But what a Sabbath shall I keep
  When I shall rest above!

3 I bless Thy wise and wondrous love,
  Which binds us to be free;
Which makes us leave our earthly snares,
  That we may come to Thee.
I come, I wait, I hear, I pray,
  Thy footsteps, Lord, I trace;
I sing to think this is the way
  Unto my Saviour's face.

Rev. John Mason, 1683

33

40 DALEHURST C. M.

ARTHUR COTTMAN, 1872

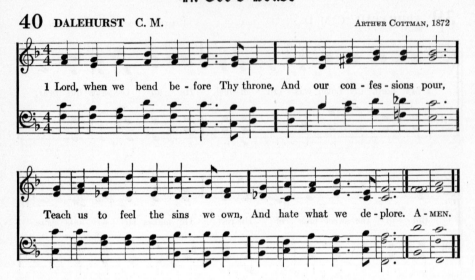

1 Lord, when we bend be - fore Thy throne, And our con - fes - sions pour,

Teach us to feel the sins we own, And hate what we de - plore. A - MEN.

2 Our broken spirits pitying see,
    And penitence impart;
Then let a kindling glance from Thee
Beam hope upon the heart.

3 When our responsive tongues essay
    Their grateful hymns to raise,
Grant that our souls may join the lay,
And mount to Thee in praise.

4 When we disclose our wants in prayer,
    May we our wills resign;
And not a thought our bosom share
Which is not wholly Thine.

5 Let faith each meek petition fill,
    And waft it to the skies;
And teach our hearts 'tis goodness still
That grants it, or denies.

Rev. JOSEPH D. CARLYLE, 1802

RETREAT L. M.

THOMAS HASTINGS, 1842

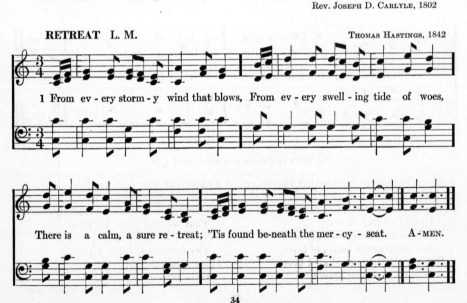

1 From ev - ery storm - y wind that blows, From ev - ery swell - ing tide of woes,

There is a calm, a sure re - treat; 'Tis found be-neath the mer - cy - seat. A - MEN.

41 ALMSGIVING 8. 8. 8. 4.

Rev. JOHN B. DYKES, 1865

1 My God, is a - ny hour so sweet, From blush of morn to eve - ning star,

As that which calls me to Thy feet, The hour of prayer? A - MEN.

2 Blest is that tranquil hour of morn,
  And blest that solemn hour of eve,
When, on the wings of prayer upborne,
  The world I leave.

3 Then is my strength by Thee renewed;
  Then are my sins by Thee forgiven;
Then dost Thou cheer my solitude
  With hopes of heaven.

4 No words can tell what sweet relief
  There for my every want I find;
What strength for warfare, balm for grief,
  What peace of mind!

5 Lord, till I reach yon blissful shore,
  No privilege so dear shall be
As thus my inmost soul to pour
  In prayer to Thee.

CHARLOTTE ELLIOTT, 1835 (her text of 1836)

42 (RETREAT) L. M.

There I will meet with thee, and I will commune with thee from above the mercy seat.—EXODUS xxv, 22

1 From every stormy wind that blows,
  From every swelling tide of woes,
  There is a calm, a sure retreat;
  'Tis found beneath the mercy-seat.

2 There is a place where Jesus sheds
  The oil of gladness on our heads,
  A place than all besides more sweet;
  It is the blood-stained mercy-seat.

3 There is a spot where spirits blend,
  Where friend holds fellowship with friend,
  Though sundered far; by faith they meet
  Around the common mercy-seat.

4 Ah, whither could we flee for aid,
  When tempted, desolate, dismayed,
  Or how the hosts of hell defeat,
  Had suffering saints no mercy-seat?

5 There, there on eagle wings we soar,
  And time and sense seem all no more,
  And heaven comes down our souls to greet,
  And glory crowns the mercy-seat.

6 O may my hand forget her skill,
  My tongue be silent, cold, and still,
  This bounding heart forget to beat,
  If I forget the mercy-seat.

Rev. HUGH STOWELL, 1827, 1831

43 POSTLUDE   4. 4. 10. 4. 8. 10.   ALFRED REGINALD ALLEN, 1915

1 O Ho - ly One, Our prayers are done, And with Thy bless - ing may our

wor - ship cease. To all that waits Be - yond the shel - ter of Thy gates

Now let - test Thou Thy ser - vants go in peace. A - MEN.

Copyright, 1925

*Now lettest Thou Thy servant depart in peace.—*St. LUKE ii, 29

2   O Glorious One,
    Our songs are done;
The world is calling and its cares
    increase.
With lips that praise
And hearts that softly sing always,
Now lettest Thou Thy servants go in
    peace.

3   O Changeless One,
    When day is done
Breathe through the dark Thy pardon
    and release.
Thou wilt forget,
But lest some shame may linger yet,
Now lettest Thou Thy servants go in
    peace.

REV. LOUIS F. BENSON, 1897

NOTE—*The composer of this tune, a radiant personality, became a major in the American forces in the World War, and was killed in action at Montfaucon, France, September 30, 1918.*

44 (DENNIS) S. M.

1 Still, still with Thee, my God,
    I would desire to be;
By day, by night, at home, abroad,
    I would be still with Thee.

2 With Thee when dawn comes in
    And calls me back to care,
Each day returning to begin
    With Thee, my God, in prayer.

3 With Thee amid the crowd
    That throngs the busy mart,
To hear Thy voice, where time's is loud,
    Speak softly to my heart.

4 With Thee when day is done,
    And evening calms the mind;
The setting as the rising sun
    With Thee my heart would find.

5 With Thee when darkness brings
    The signal of repose,
Calm in the shadow of Thy wings,
    Mine eyelids I would close.

6 With Thee, in Thee, by faith
    Abiding, I would be;
By day, by night, in life, in death,
    I would be still with Thee.

REV. JAMES DRUMMOND BURNS, 1857:
the rhythm of the opening line is revised

45 GARDEN CITY S. M.

HORATIO W. PARKER, 1890

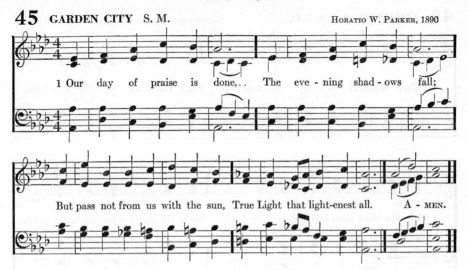

1 Our day of praise is done,.. The eve-ning shad-ows fall;

But pass not from us with the sun, True Light that light-enest all. A - MEN.

2 Around the throne on high,
   Where night can never be,
The white-robed harpers of the sky
   Bring ceaseless hymns to Thee.

3 Too faint our anthems here;
   Too soon of praise we tire;
But O the strains how full and clear,
   Of that eternal choir!

4 Yet, Lord, to Thy dear will
   If Thou attune the heart,

We in Thine angels' music still
   May bear our lower part.

5 'Tis Thine each soul to calm,
   Each wayward thought reclaim,
And make our life a daily psalm
   Of glory to Thy Name.

6 A little while, and then
   Shall come the glorious end;
And songs of angels and of men
   In perfect praise shall blend.

Rev. JOHN ELLERTON, 1868 (his text of 1871)

DENNIS S. M.

Arranged from HANS G. NÄGELI, by LOWELL MASON, 1845

1 Still, still with Thee, my God, I would de - sire to be,

By day, by night; at home, a - broad, I would be still with Thee. A - MEN.

37

46 EMMELAR 8. 7. 8. 7. D.

Arranged from HENRY BRINLEY RICHARDS (1819—)

1 Part in peace! is day be-fore us? Praise His Name for life and light;
Are the shad-ows length-ening o'er us? Bless His care who guards the night.
Part in peace! with deep thanks-giv-ing; Ren-dering, as we home-ward tread,
Gra-cious ser-vice to the liv-ing, Tran-quil mem-ory to the dead. A-MEN.

Alternative tune, FABEN, No. 55

2 Part in peace! such are the praises
   God, our Maker, loveth best;
Such the worship that upraises
   Human hearts to heavenly rest.
Part in peace! our duties call us;
   We must serve as well as praise;
Ask not what may here befall us;
   Leave to God the coming days.

MRS. SARAH FLOWER ADAMS, 1841

47 SICILIAN MARINERS 8. 7. 8. 7. 8. 7.

In MERRICK and TATTERSALL'S *Psalms*, 1794, as a Sicilian Melody

1 {Lord, dis-miss us with Thy bless-ing; Fill our hearts with joy and peace:}
{Let us each, Thy love pos-sess-ing, Tri-umph in re-deem-ing grace;}

O re-fresh us, O re-fresh us, In this dry and bar-ren place. A-MEN.

2 Thanks we give and adoration
　For Thy gospel's joyful sound:
　May the fruits of Thy salvation
　In our hearts and lives abound:
　Ever faithful, ever faithful
　To the truth may we be found;

3 Of Thy love some gracious token
　Grant us, Lord, before we go;
　Bless Thy word which has been spoken,
　Life and peace on all bestow:
　O direct us and protect us
　In the paths we do not know.

Anonymous, 1773 (ascribed to Rev. JOHN FAWCETT):
verse 3 arranged from Rev. THOMAS KELLY, 1804

ABBOTT 8. 7. 8. 7. 8. 7.

CHARLES S. YERBURY, 1908

1 {Lord, dis-miss us with Thy bless-ing; Fill our hearts with joy and peace;}
{Let us each, Thy love pos-sess-ing, Tri-umph in re-deem-ing grace;}

O re-fresh us, O re-fresh us, In this dry and bar-ren place. A-MEN.

48 ST. MATTHIAS 8. 8. 8. 8. 8. 8.

WILLIAM H. MONK, for
Hymns ancient and modern, 1861

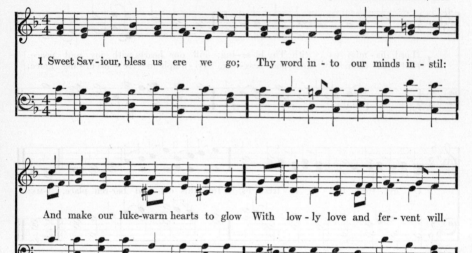

1 Sweet Sav-iour, bless us ere we go; Thy word in-to our minds in-stil:

And make our luke-warm hearts to glow With low-ly love and fer-vent will.

Through life's long day and death's dark night, O gen-tle Je-sus, be our Light. A-MEN.

2 The day is done, its hours have run;
And Thou hast taken count of all,
The scanty triumphs grace hath won,
The broken vow, the frequent fall.
Through life's long day and death's dark
night,
O gentle Jesus, be our Light.

3 Grant us, dear Lord, from evil ways
True absolution and release;
And bless us, more than in past days,
With purity and inward peace.
Through life's long day and death's dark
night,
O gentle Jesus, be our Light.

4 Do more than pardon; give us joy,
Sweet fear, and sober liberty,
And loving hearts without alloy,
That only long to be like Thee.
Through life's long day and death's dark
night,
O gentle Jesus, be our Light.

5 For all we love, the poor, the sad,
The sinful, unto Thee we call;
O let Thy mercy make us glad;
Thou art our Jesus, and our All.
Through life's long day and death's dark
night,
O gentle Jesus, be our Light.

Rev. FREDERICK W. FABER, 1849

NOTE—*Written as the "Evening Hymn" for The Oratory, London.*

49 ELLERS 10. 10. 10. 10.   EDWARD J. HOPKINS, 1868

1 Sav - iour, a - gain to Thy dear Name we raise With one ac - cord our
part - ing hymn of praise; We stand to bless Thee ere our wor - ship cease;
Then, low - ly kneel - ing, wait Thy word of peace. A - MEN.

The Lord shall give His people the blessing of peace.—Ps. xxix, 10

2 Grant us Thy peace upon our homeward way;
 With Thee began, with Thee shall end the day:
 Guard Thou the lips from sin, the hearts from shame,
 That in this house have called upon Thy Name.

3 Grant us Thy peace, Lord, through the coming night;
 Turn Thou for us its darkness into light;
 From harm and danger keep Thy children free,
 For dark and light are both alike to Thee.

4 Grant us Thy peace throughout our earthly life,
 Our balm in sorrow, and our stay in strife;
 Then, when Thy voice shall bid our conflict cease,
 Call us, O Lord, to Thine eternal peace.

Rev. JOHN ELLERTON, 1866 (his text of 1868)

The Eternal God
God's Greatness

Almighty God, whose fatherhood is clothed with majesty and whose love is made perfect in holiness: Inspire our hearts with the reverence that is Thy due, and hallow our lips lest they take Thy Name upon them lightly; that so our offering of praise may go up with acceptance: before Thy throne, and our minds may be drawn unto Thyself, whose strength is the confidence of our faith; through Jesus Christ our Lord. Amen.

50 REGENT SQUARE 8. 7. 8. 7. 4. 7.

HENRY SMART, 1867

1 Praise, my soul, the King of heav-en, To His feet Thy trib-ute bring;

Ran-somed, healed, re-stored, for-giv-en, Who, like me, His praise should sing?

Praise Him, praise Him, Praise Him, praise Him, Praise the Ev-er-last-ing King. A-MEN.

A PARAPHRASE OF PSALM CIII

2 Praise Him for His grace and favor
To our fathers in distress;
Praise Him, still the same for ever,
Slow to chide, and swift to bless;
Praise Him, praise Him,
Glorious in His faithfulness.

3 Father-like, He tends and spares us;
Well our feeble frame He knows;
In His hands He gently bears us,
Rescues us from all our foes;
Praise Him, praise Him,
Widely as His mercy goes.

4 Angels, help us to adore Him;
Ye behold Him face to face;
Sun and moon, bow down before Him;
Dwellers all in time and space,
Praise Him, praise Him,
Praise with us the God of grace.

Rev. HENRY F. LYTE, 1834

God's Greatness

1 Ho - ly, Ho - ly, Ho - ly! Lord God Al - might - y! Ear - ly in the
morn - ing our song shall rise to Thee; Ho - ly, Ho - ly, Ho - ly!
Mer - ci - ful and Might - y! God in Three Per - sons, bless-ed Trin - i - ty! A - men.

They rest not day and night, saying, Holy, Holy, Holy, Lord God Almighty,
which was, and is, and is to come.—REV. iv, 8

2 Holy, Holy, Holy! All the saints adore Thee,
   Casting down their golden crowns around the glassy sea;
Cherubim and seraphim falling down before Thee,
   Who wert, and art, and evermore shalt be.

3 Holy, Holy, Holy! Though the darkness hide Thee,
   Though the eye of sinful man Thy glory may not see,
Only Thou art holy; there is none beside Thee
   Perfect in power, in love, and purity.

4 Holy, Holy, Holy, Lord God Almighty!
   All Thy works shall praise Thy Name, in earth and sky and sea;
Holy, Holy, Holy! Merciful and Mighty!
   God in Three Persons, blessèd Trinity!

Bishop REGINALD HEBER, published in 1827

The Eternal God

52 MIRIAM 7. 6. 7. 6. D.   Joseph P. Holbrook, 1865

1 O God, the Rock of A - ges, Who ev - er - more hast been,

What time the tem - pest ra - ges, Our dwell - ing - place se - rene:

Be - fore Thy first cre - a - tions, O Lord, the same as now,

To end - less gen - er - a - tions, The Ev - er - last - ing Thou! A - MEN.

Alternative tune, MEIRIONYDD, No. 142

They shall be changed: but Thou art the same, and Thy years shall not fail.—Ps. cii, 27

2 Our years are like the shadows
  On sunny hills that lie,
Or grasses in the meadows
  That blossom but to die;
A sleep, a dream, a story
  By strangers quickly told,
An unremaining glory
  Of things that soon are old.

3 O Thou who canst not slumber,
  Whose light grows never pale,
Teach us aright to number
  Our years before they fail;
On us Thy mercy lighten,
  On us Thy goodness rest,
And let Thy Spirit brighten
  The hearts Thyself hast blessed.

Bishop Edward H. Bickersteth, 1860

44

God's Greatness

53 **ANCIENT OF DAYS** 11. 10. 11. 10.   J. Albert Jeffery, 1886

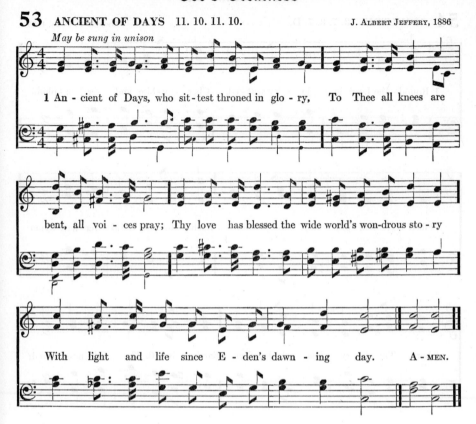

May be sung in unison

1 An - cient of Days, who sit-test throned in glo - ry, To Thee all knees are

bent, all voi - ces pray; Thy love has blessed the wide world's won-drous sto - ry

With light and life since E - den's dawn - ing day. A - men.

2 O Holy Father, who hast led Thy children
    In all the ages, with the fire and cloud,
Through seas dry-shod, through weary wastes bewildering;
    To Thee, in reverent love, our hearts are bowed.

3 O Holy Jesus, Prince of Peace and Saviour,
    To Thee we owe the peace that still prevails,
Stilling the rude wills of men's wild behavior,
    And calming passion's fierce and stormy gales.

4 O Holy Ghost, the Lord and the Life-giver,
    Thine is the quickening power that gives increase;
From Thee have flowed, as from a pleasant river,
    Our plenty, wealth, prosperity and peace.

5 O Triune God, with heart and voice adoring,
    Praise we the goodness that doth crown our days;
Pray we that Thou wilt hear us, still imploring
    Thy love and favor, kept to us always.

Bishop William C. Doane, for the Bicentenary of Albany, 1886

The Eternal God

54 MOULTRIE 8. 7. 8. 7. D.   GERARD F. COBB, 1885

1 Round the Lord in glo-ry seat-ed, Cher-u-bim and ser-a-phim

Filled His tem-ple, and re-peat-ed Each to each the al-ter-nate hymn:

"Lord, Thy glo-ry fills the heav-en, Earth is with Thy ful-ness stored;

Un-to Thee be glo-ry giv-en, Ho-ly, Ho-ly, Ho-ly Lord!" A-MEN.

One cried unto another, and said, Holy, Holy, Holy.—ISA. vi, 3

2 Heaven is still with glory ringing,
    Earth takes up the angels' cry,
"Holy, Holy, Holy!" singing,
    "Lord of Hosts, the Lord Most High!"
"Lord, Thy glory fills the heaven,
    Earth is with Thy fulness stored;
Unto Thee be glory given,
    Holy, Holy, Holy Lord!"

3 With His seraph train before Him,
    With His holy Church below,
Thus conspire we to adore Him,
    Bid we thus our anthem flow:
"Lord, Thy glory fills the heaven,
    Earth is with Thy fulness stored;
Unto Thee be glory given,
    Holy, Holy, Holy Lord!"

Arranged from Bishop RICHARD MANT's
"Bright the vision that delighted," 1837

God's Greatness

55 FABEN 8. 7. 8. 7. D.

JOHN H. WILLCOX, 1849

1 Praise the Lord! ye heavens, a-dore Him; Praise Him, an-gels, in the height;

Sun and moon, re-joice be-fore Him; Praise Him, all ye stars and light.

Praise the Lord! for He hath spo-ken; Worlds His might-y voice o-beyed:

Laws which nev-er shall be bro-ken For their guid-ance hath He made. A-MEN.

O praise the Lord of heaven: praise Him in the height.—Ps. cxlviii, 1

2 Praise the Lord! for He is glorious;
　Never shall His promise fail:
God hath made His saints victorious;
　Sin and death shall not prevail.
Praise the God of our salvation;
　Hosts on high, His power proclaim;
Heaven and earth and all creation,
　Laud and magnify His Name.

3 Worship, honor, glory, blessing,
　Lord, we offer unto Thee;
Young and old, Thy praise expressing,
　In glad homage bend the knee.
All the saints in heaven adore Thee;
　We would bow before Thy throne:
As Thine angels serve before Thee,
　So on earth Thy will be done.

Verses 1 and 2 were printed in an anonymous tract, *circa* 1801:
verse 3 was added by EDWARD OSLER, 1836

47

The Eternal God

56 **ST. ANNE C. M.**

The melody is from *Supplement to the New Version,* 1708; and probably by Dr. CROFT

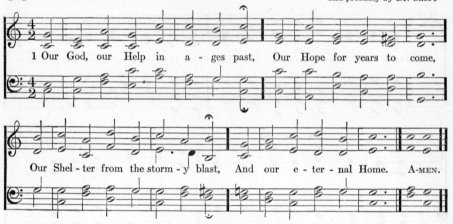

1 Our God, our Help in a - ges past, Our Hope for years to come,

Our Shel - ter from the storm - y blast, And our e - ter - nal Home. A-MEN.

For a lower setting see No. 237

A PARAPHRASE OF PSALM XC

2 Under the shadow of Thy throne
Thy saints have dwelt secure;
Sufficient is Thine arm alone,
And our defence is sure.

3 Before the hills in order stood,
Or earth received her frame,
From everlasting Thou art God,
To endless years the same.

4 A thousand ages in Thy sight
Are like an evening gone;
Short as the watch that ends the night
Before the rising sun.

5 Time, like an ever-rolling stream,
Bears all its sons away;
They fly forgotten, as a dream
Dies at the opening day.

6 Our God, our Help in ages past,
Our Hope for years to come;
Be Thou our Guard while troubles last,
And our eternal Home.

Rev. ISAAC WATTS, 1719

BURG 8. 7. 8. 7. Iambic

EMILY S. PERKINS, 1921

1 Our God, He is a God of might, His power is nev - er fail - ing;

He safe - ly leads us in the fight, 'Gainst ev-ery foe pre - vail - ing. A-MEN.

Copyright, 1921, by Emily S. Perkins

48

57 KING EDWARD S. M.

EDWIN A. SYDENHAM, 1883

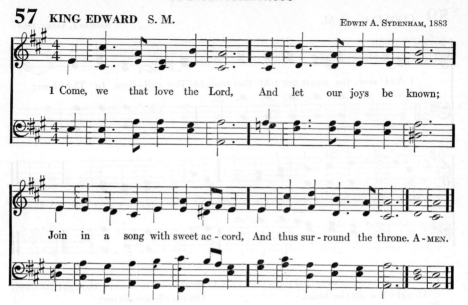

1 Come, we that love the Lord, And let our joys be known;
Join in a song with sweet ac-cord, And thus sur-round the throne. A-MEN.

Let the righteous be glad; let them rejoice before God.—Ps. lxviii, 3

2 Let those refuse to sing
   That never knew our God;
   But children of the heavenly King
   May speak their joys abroad.

3 The men of grace have found
   Glory begun below;
   Celestial fruits on earthly ground
   From faith and hope may grow.

4 The hill of Zion yields
   A thousand sacred sweets,
   Before we reach the heavenly fields,
   Or walk the golden streets.

5 Then let our songs abound,
   And every tear be dry;
   We're marching through Emmanuel's
   To fairer worlds on high.   [ground

Rev. ISAAC WATTS, 1707: verse 2, line 3, varied

NOTE—*The thought developed at some length in the original hymn is that the God who rules on high, "this awful God," is "ours," and will exert His powers "to carry us above."*

58 (BURG) 8. 7. 8. 7. Iambic

1 Our God, He is a God of might,
   His power is never failing;
   He safely leads us in the fight,
   'Gainst every foe prevailing.

2 Our God, He is a God of truth,
   His word remains unshaken;
   His justice and His righteousness
   Have every stronghold taken.

3 Our God, He is a God of love,
   His mercy is unending;
   He guards us all with tender care,
   Each day our souls defending.

4 Our God, He is a God of grace;
   Though sin our hearts hath hardened,
   His grace can wash away the stain,
   And heaven receive us, pardoned.

EMILY S. PERKINS, 1921

The Eternal God

59 COOLING C. M.

ALONZO J. ABBEY, 1858

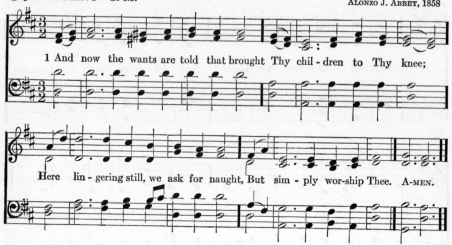

1 And now the wants are told that brought Thy chil-dren to Thy knee;
Here lin-gering still, we ask for naught, But sim-ply wor-ship Thee. A-MEN.

2 The hope of heaven's eternal days
   Absorbs not all the heart
That gives Thee glory, love, and praise,
   For being what Thou art.

3 For Thou art God, the One, the Same,
   O'er all things high and bright;
And round us, when we speak Thy Name,
   There spreads a heaven of light.

4 O wondrous peace, in thought to dwell
   On excellence divine;
To know that naught in man can tell
   How fair Thy beauties shine!

5 O Thou, above all blessing blest,
   O'er thanks exalted far,
Thy very greatness is a rest
   To weaklings as we are;

6 For when we feel the praise of Thee
   A task beyond our powers,
We say, "A perfect God is He,
   And He is fully ours."

Rev. WILLIAM BRIGHT, 1865

60 (MANOAH) C. M.

1 My God, how wonderful Thou art,
   Thy majesty how bright!
How beautiful Thy mercy-seat,
   In depths of burning light!

2 How dread are Thine eternal years,
   O everlasting Lord,
By prostrate spirits, day and night,
   Incessantly adored!

3 O how I fear Thee, living God,
   With deepest, tenderest fears;
And worship Thee with trembling hope
   And penitential tears.

4 Yet I may love Thee too, O Lord,
   Almighty as Thou art;
For Thou hast stooped to ask of me
   The love of my poor heart.

5 No earthly father loves like Thee,
   No mother half so mild
Bears and forbears, as Thou hast done
   With me, Thy sinful child.

6 Father of Jesus, love's Reward!
   What rapture will it be,
Prostrate before Thy throne to lie,
   And gaze and gaze on Thee.

Rev. FREDERICK W. FABER, 1848

God's Greatness

61 SERENITY C. M.

Arranged from WILLIAM V. WALLACE's "Ye winds that waft," 1836, by UZZIAH C. BURNAP

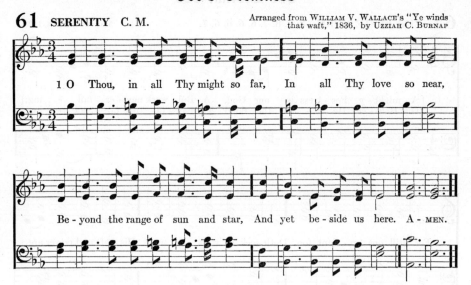

1 O Thou, in all Thy might so far, In all Thy love so near,

Be-yond the range of sun and star, And yet be-side us here. A - MEN.

2 What heart can comprehend Thy Name,
Or searching find Thee out
Who art within, a quickening Flame,
A Presence round about?

3 Yet though I know Thee but in part,
I ask not, Lord, for more;
Enough for me to know Thou art,
To love Thee and adore.

4 And dearer than all things I know
Is childlike faith to me,
That makes the darkest way I go
An open path to Thee.

Rev. FREDERICK L. HOSMER, 1876

MANOAH C. M.

Arranged from several sources by HENRY W. GREATOREX, 1851

1 My God, how won-der-ful Thou art, Thy maj-es-ty how bright!

How beau - ti - ful Thy mer - cy - seat, In depths of burn - ing light! A - MEN.

The Eternal God

62 EIN' FESTE BURG 8. 7. 8. 7. 6. 6. 6. 6. 7. MARTIN LUTHER, 1528

1 { A might-y For-tress is our God, A Bul-wark nev-er fail - ing;
Our Help-er He a-mid the flood Of mor-tal ills pre-vail - ing:}
For still our an-cient foe Doth seek to work us woe; His craft and power are
great; And armed with cru-el hate, On earth is not his e - qual. A-MEN.

EIN' FESTE BURG IST UNSER GOTT

2 Did we in our own strength confide,
  Our striving would be losing;
Were not the right man on our side,
  The man of God's own choosing:
Dost ask who that may be?
Christ Jesus, it is He;
Lord Sabaoth His Name,
From age to age the same,
  And He must win the battle.

3 And though this world, with devils filled,
  Should threaten to undo us;
We will not fear, for God hath willed
  His truth to triumph through us:

The prince of darkness grim,—
We tremble not for him;
His rage we can endure,
For lo! his doom is sure,
  One little word shall fell him.

4 That word above all earthly powers,
  No thanks to them, abideth;
The Spirit and the gifts are ours
  Through Him who with us sideth:
Let goods and kindred go,
This mortal life also;
The body they may kill;
God's truth abideth still,
  His kingdom is for ever.

MARTIN LUTHER, 1528. Translated by Rev. FREDERICK H. HEDGE, 1853

NOTE—*Heine called this hymn "The Marseillaise of the Reformation."*

63 ANGEL VOICES 8. 5. 8. 5. 8. 4. 3.

Sir Arthur Sullivan, 1872

1 An - gel voi - ces ev - er sing - ing Round Thy throne of light,

An - gel harps, for ev - er ring - ing, Rest not day nor night;

Thou-sands on - ly live to bless Thee, And con - fess Thee Lord of might. A-men.

Thou hast created all things, and for Thy pleasure they are and were created.—Rev. iv, 11

2 Thou who art beyond the farthest
  Mortal eye can scan,
Can it be that Thou regardest
  Songs of sinful man?
Can we feel that Thou art near us,
  And wilt hear us?
    Yea, we can.

3 Yea, we know Thy love rejoices
  O'er each work of Thine;
Thou didst ears and hands and voices
  For Thy praise combine;
Craftsman's art and music's measure
  For Thy pleasure
    Didst design.

4 Here, great God, today we offer
  Of Thine own to Thee;
And for Thine acceptance proffer,
  All unworthily,
Hearts and minds, and hands, and voices,
  In our choicest
    Melody.

5 Honor, glory, might and merit,
  Thine shall ever be,
Father, Son, and Holy Spirit,
  Blessèd Trinity:
Of the best that Thou hast given
  Earth and heaven
    Render Thee.

Rev. Francis Pott, 1861

Note—*The original title of this hymn is " For the Dedication of an Organ or for a Meeting of Choirs."*

The Eternal God

HOUGHTON 10. 10. 11. 11.

HENRY J. GAUNTLETT, 1861

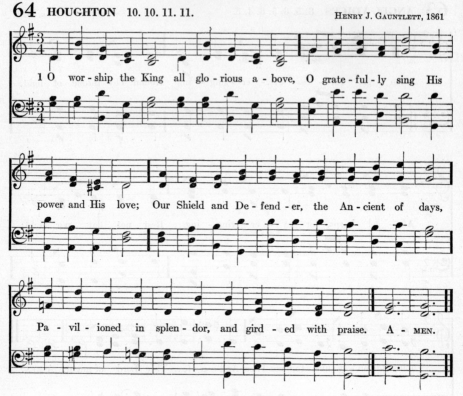

1 O wor-ship the King all glo-rious a-bove, O grate-ful-ly sing His
power and His love; Our Shield and De-fend-er, the An-cient of days,
Pa-vil-ioned in splen-dor, and gird-ed with praise. A-MEN.

Alternative tune, LYONS, No. 173

A PARAPHRASE OF PSALM CIV

2 O tell of His might, O sing of His grace,
Whose robe is the light, whose canopy space.
His chariots of wrath the deep thunder-clouds form,
And dark is His path on the wings of the storm.

3 The earth with its store of wonders untold,
Almighty, Thy power hath founded of old;
Hath stablished it fast by a changeless decree,
And round it hath cast, like a mantle, the sea.

4 Thy bountiful care what tongue can recite?
It breathes in the air; it shines in the light;
It streams from the hills; it descends to the plain;
And sweetly distils in the dew and the rain.

5 Frail children of dust, and feeble as frail,
In Thee do we trust, nor find Thee to fail;
Thy mercies how tender, how firm to the end,
Our Maker, Defender, Redeemer, and Friend!

Sir ROBERT GRANT, 1833

God's World

Thou who hast made Thy dwelling fair
With flowers below, above with starry lights,
And set Thine altars everywhere,—
Waiting for worshippers to come to Thee
In Thy great out-of-doors!
To Thee I turn, to Thee I make my prayer,
God of the open air.

From HENRY VAN DYKE'S "God of the Open Air," 1904

65 MAINZER L. M.

JOSEPH MAINZER, c. 1841

1 When the great sun sinks to his rest, His gold-en glo-ries thrill-ing me,

And voice-less long-ings stir my breast, Then teach me, Lord, to wor-ship Thee. A-MEN.

For a higher setting, see No. 110

The heavens are Thine, the earth also is Thine: as for the world and the fulness thereof,
Thou hast founded them.—Ps. lxxxix, 11

2 And when the stars—the daylight fled—
   In serried, shining ranks I see,
Filling the splendid vault o'erhead,
   Then teach me, Lord, to worship Thee.

3 If, roaming by the ocean's shore,
   The murmuring waves sing low to me,
Or thundering billows hoarsely roar,
   Then teach me, Lord, to worship Thee.

4 Or if in solemn forest shades
   The calm of nature steals o'er me,
And silence all my soul pervades,
   Then teach me, Lord, to worship Thee.

5 Not in the sacred shrines alone,
   Which chime their summons unto me,
Would I look upward to Thy throne,
   But everywhere would worship Thee.

Rev. MALTBIE D. BABCOCK; published in 1901

The Eternal God

66 **ELLACOMBE** 7. 6. 7. 6. D. XAV. LUD. HARTIG's *Vollständige Sammlung, c.* 1830

1 The heavens de - clare Thy glo - ry, The fir - ma - ment Thy power;

Day un - to day the sto - ry Re - peats from hour to hour;

Night un - to night re - ply - ing, Pro - claims in ev - ery land,

O Lord, with voice un - dy - ing, The won - ders of Thy hand. A-MEN.

A PARAPHRASE OF PSALM XIX

2 The sun with royal splendor
  Goes forth to chant Thy praise
And moonbeams soft and tender
  Their gentler anthem raise:
O'er every tribe and nation
  The music strange is poured;
The song of all creation
  To Thee, creation's Lord.

3 All heaven on high rejoices
  To do its Maker's will;
The stars with solemn voices
  Resound Thy praises still:
So let my whole behavior,
  Thoughts, words, and actions be,
O Lord, my Strength, my Saviour,
  One ceaseless song to Thee.

REV. THOMAS R. BIRKS, 1874

God's World

67 DEO GRATIAS Irregular

A. B. PONSONBY, 1913

1. The ships glide in at the har-bor's mouth, And the ships sail out to sea,
2. The har-vest waves in the breez-y morn, And the men go forth to reap;
3. The ships sail o-ver the har-bor bar A-way and a-way to sea;

And the wind that sweeps from the sun-ny south, It is sweet as sweet can be.
The full-ness comes to the tas-seled corn, Wheth-er we wake or sleep.
The ships sail in with the eve-ning star To the port where no tem-pests be.

There's a world of toil and a world of pains, There's a world of trou-ble and care,
And far on the hills by feet un-trod There are blossoms that scent the air,
The har-vests wave on the sum-mer hills, And the bands go forth to reap,

But O in a world where our Father reigns, There is glad-ness ev-ery-where.
For O in this world of our Father, God, There is beau-ty ev-ery-where.
And all is right, as our Father wills, Wheth-er we wake or sleep. A-MEN.

From *Worship and Song*, by Winchester and Conant:
Copyright, 1913, by The Pilgrim Press.

MRS. MARGARET E. SANGSTER, 1893

68 WIR PFLÜGEN 7. 6. 7. 6. D. with Refrain

JOHANN A. P. SCHULZ, 1800

1 We plough the fields, and scat-ter The good seed on the land, But it is fed and wa - tered By God's al-might - y hand; He sends the snow in win - ter, The warmth to swell the grain, The breez - es and the sun - shine, And soft re - fresh - ing rain.

REFRAIN

All good gifts a - round us Are sent from heaven a - bove; Then thank the Lord, O thank the Lord For all His love. A - MEN.

God's World

WIR PFLÜGEN UND WIR STREUEN

2 He only is the Maker
  Of all things near and far;
He paints the wayside flower
  He lights the evening star;
The winds and waves obey Him,
  By Him the birds are fed;
Much more to us, His children,
  He gives our daily bread.
    All good gifts, etc.

3 We thank Thee, then, O Father,
  For all things bright and good,
The seed-time and the harvest,
  Our life, our health, our food:
No gifts have we to offer
  For all Thy love imparts,
But that which Thou desirest,
  Our humble, thankful hearts.
    All good gifts, etc.

MATTHIAS CLAUDIUS, 1782. Translated by JANE M. CAMPBELL, 1861

69 LÜBECK 7. 7. 7. 7.   In FREYLINGHAUSEN's *Gesangbuch*, 1704

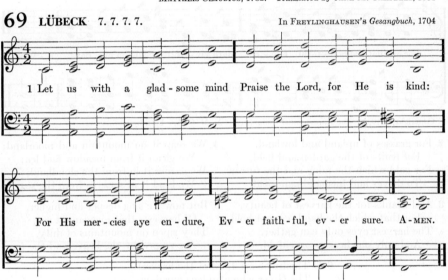

Alternative tune, INNOCENTS, No. 10

A PARAPHRASE OF PSALM CXXXVI

2 Let us blaze His Name abroad,
  For of gods He is the God:
    For His mercies aye endure,
    Ever faithful, ever sure.

3 He, with all-commanding might,
  Filled the new-made world with light:
    For His mercies aye endure,
    Ever faithful, ever sure.

4 He the golden-tressèd sun
  Caused all day his course to run:
    For His mercies aye endure,
    Ever faithful, ever sure.

5 And the moon to shine by night,
  'Mid her spangled sisters bright:
    For His mercies aye endure,
    Ever faithful, ever sure.

6 All things living He doth feed;
  His full hand supplies their need:
    For His mercies aye endure,
    Ever faithful, ever sure.

7 Let us therefore warble forth
  His high majesty and worth:
    For His mercies aye endure,
    Ever faithful, ever sure.

JOHN MILTON, 1624: the rhythm of some lines varied

NOTE—*The great poet printed at different times nineteen versions of various Psalms; the one of which the above verses are part was written, as he takes care to tell us, "at fifteen years old."*

The Eternal God

70 CALVERT 9.8.9.8.

ROBERT JERMAIN COLE, 1910

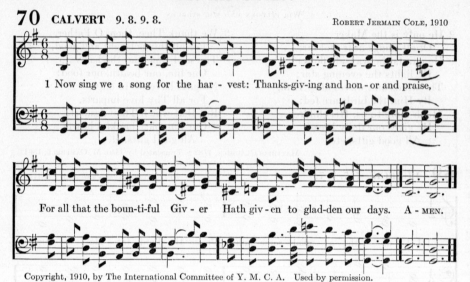

1 Now sing we a song for the har - vest: Thanks-giv-ing and hon - or and praise,

For all that the boun-ti-ful Giv - er Hath giv-en to glad-den our days. A - MEN.

Copyright, 1910, by The International Committee of Y. M. C. A. Used by permission.

2 For grasses of upland and lowland,
    For fruits of the garden and field,
For gold which the mine and the furrow
    To delver and husbandman yield.

3 And thanks for the harvest of beauty,
    For that which the hands cannot hold,
The harvest eyes only can gather,
    And only our hearts can enfold.

4 We reap it on mountain and moorland;
    We glean it from meadow and lea;
We garner it in from the cloudland;
    We bind it in sheaves from the sea.

5 But now we sing deeper and higher,
    Of harvests that eye cannot see;
They ripen on mountains of duty,
    Are reaped by the brave and the free.

6 O Thou who art Lord of the harvest,
    The Giver who gladdens our days,
Our hearts are for ever repeating
    Thanksgiving and honor and praise.

Arranged from Rev. JOHN W. CHADWICK, 1871

71 (LIFT UP YOUR HEADS) C. M.

1 The summer days are come again,
    With sun and clouds between,
And, fed alike by sun and rain,
    The trees grow broad and green.

2 The summer days are come again;
    Once more the glad earth yields
Her golden wealth of ripening grain,
    And breath of clover fields;

3 And deepening shade of summer woods,
    And glow of summer air,
And winging thoughts, and happy moods
    Of love and joy and prayer.

4 The summer days are come again;
    The birds are on the wing;
God's praises, in their loving strain,
    Unconsciously they sing.

5 We know who giveth all the good
    That doth our cup o'erbrim;
For summer joy in field and wood
    We lift our song to Him.

Arranged from Rev. SAMUEL LONGFELLOW, 1859

60

God's World

72 **TRENTHAM** S. M.

ROBERT JACKSON, 1894

1 This is my Fa-ther's world; I rest me in the thought Of rocks, and
2 This is my Fa-ther's world: He shines in all that's fair. In the rust-ling
3 This is my Fa-ther's world: O let me ne'er for-get That though the
4 This is my Fa-ther's world: The bat-tle is not done. Je-sus who
5 This is my Fa-ther's world: Why should my heart be sad? The Lord is

trees, of skies and seas: His hand the won-ders wrought.
grass I hear Him pass: He speaks to me ev-ery-where.
wrong seems oft so strong, God is the Ru-ler yet.
died shall be sat-is-fied, And earth and heaven be one.
King,— let the heav-ens ring: God reigns; let the earth be glad. A-MEN.

Rev. MALTBIE D. BABCOCK, published in 1901: verse 5, line 2, varied
Copyright, 1901, by Chas. Scribner's Sons.

LIFT UP YOUR HEADS C. M.

A German folk-song
arranged in *St. Alban's Tune Book*, 1866

1 The sum-mer days are come a-gain, With sun and clouds be-tween,

And, fed a-like by sun and rain, The trees grow broad and green. A-MEN.

The Eternal God

RUTH 6. 5. 6. 5. D.   SAMUEL SMITH, 1865

1 Sum-mer suns are glow-ing O-ver land and sea; Hap-py light is flow-ing, Boun-ti-ful and free; Ev-ery-thing re-joi-ces In the mel-low rays; All earth's thousand voi-ces Swell the psalm of praise. A-MEN.

Alternative tune, GOSHEN, No. 359

Truly the light is sweet, and a pleasant thing it is for the eyes to behold the sun.—ECCLES. xi, 7

2 God's free mercy streameth
  Over all the world,
And His banner gleameth,
  Everywhere unfurled:
Broad and deep and glorious
  As the heaven above,
Shines in might victorious
  His eternal love.

3 Lord, upon our blindness
  Thy pure radiance pour;
For Thy loving-kindness
  Make us love Thee more:
And when clouds are drifting
  Dark across our sky,
Then, the veil uplifting,
  Father, be Thou nigh.

4 We will never doubt Thee,
  Though Thou veil Thy light;
Life is dark without Thee,
  Death with Thee is bright.
Light of light, shine o'er us
  On our pilgrim way;
Go Thou still before us
  To the endless day.

Bishop W. WALSHAM HOW, 1871

74 ST. GEORGE'S, WINDSOR 7. 7. 7. 7. D. GEORGE J. ELVEY, 1858

1 Come, ye thank-ful peo-ple, come, Raise the song of har-vest-home:
All is safe-ly gath-ered in, Ere the win-ter storms be-gin;
God, our Ma-ker, doth pro-vide For our wants to be sup-plied:
Come to God's own tem-ple, come, Raise the song of har-vest-home. A-MEN.

They joy before Thee according to the joy in harvest.—ISA. ix, 3

2 All the world is God's own field,
Fruit unto His praise to yield;
Wheat and tares together sown,
Unto joy or sorrow grown:
First the blade, and then the ear,
Then the full corn shall appear:
Lord of harvest, grant that we
Wholesome grain and pure may be.

3 For the Lord our God shall come,
And shall take His harvest home;
From His field shall in that day
All offences purge away;

Give His angels charge at last
In the fire the tares to cast,
But the fruitful ears to store
In His garner evermore.

4 Even so, Lord, quickly come
To Thy final harvest-home;
Gather Thou Thy people in,
Free from sorrow, free from sin;
There for ever purified,
In Thy presence to abide:
Come, with all Thine angels, come,
Raise the glorious harvest-home.

Rev. HENRY ALFORD, Dean of Canterbury, 1844 (his text of 1867)

75 FOREST GREEN C. M. D.

An English traditional melody
arranged by R. VAUGHAN WILLIAMS, 1906

1 All beau-ti-ful the march of days, As sea-sons come and go;

The Hand that shaped the rose hath wrought The crys-tal of the snow;

Hath sent the hoar-y frost of heaven, The flow-ing wa-ters sealed,

And laid a si-lent love-li-ness On hill and wood and field. A-MEN.

Alternative tune, GABRIEL, No. 363

Has. thou entered into the treasures of the snow?—JOB xxxviii, 22

2 O'er white expanses sparkling pure
   The radiant morns unfold;
The solemn splendors of the night
   Burn brighter through the cold;
Life mounts in every throbbing vein,
   Love deepens round the hearth,
And clearer sounds the angel-hymn,
   "Good-will to men on earth."

3 O Thou from whose unfathomed law
   The year in beauty flows,
Thyself the vision passing by
   In crystal and in rose,
Day unto day doth utter speech,
   And night to night proclaim,
In ever-changing words of light,
   The wonder of Thy Name.

Mrs. FRANCES WHITMARSH WILE, 1912

God's Love

A Collect for Growth into God's Likeness

Eternal Love, who hast been our dwelling-place in all generations, and who makest us Thine own for ever: Draw us nearer to Thee day by day, and fill us wholly with Thyself; that living we may grow into Thy likeness more and more, and dying may behold Thee face to face; through Jesus Christ our Lord.   Amen.

76 WELLS   7. 7. 7. 7. 7. 7.   Adapted from DIMITRI BORTNIANSKI, 1825

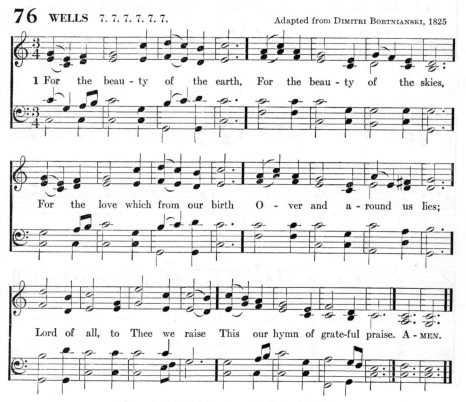

1 For the beau-ty of the earth, For the beau-ty of the skies,

For the love which from our birth O-ver and a-round us lies;

Lord of all, to Thee we raise This our hymn of grate-ful praise. A-MEN.

The earth is full of the goodness of the Lord.—Ps. xxxiii, 5

2 For the beauty of each hour
    Of the day and of the night,
Hill and vale, and tree and flower,
    Sun and moon, and stars of light;
Lord of all, to Thee we raise
This our hymn of grateful praise.

3 For the joy of ear and eye,
    For the heart and mind's delight,
For the mystic harmony
    Linking sense to sound and sight;
Lord of all, to Thee we raise
This our hymn of grateful praise.

4 For the joy of human love,
    Brother, sister, parent, child,
Friends on earth, and friends above,
    For all gentle thoughts and mild;
Lord of all, to Thee we raise
This our hymn of grateful praise.

5 For each perfect gift of Thine
    To our race so freely given,
Graces human and divine,
    Flowers of earth and buds of heaven;
Lord of all, to Thee we raise
This our hymn of grateful praise.

FOLLIOTT S. PIERPONT, 1864: each verse slightly varied
65

The Eternal God

THOMAS HASTINGS' setting of
"How calm and beautiful the morn," 1834

77 HASTINGS 8. 6. 8. 6. 8. 8.

1 I look to Thee in ev-ery need, And nev-er look in vain;

I feel Thy strong and ten-der love, And all is well a-gain: The

thought of Thee is might-ier far Than sin and pain and sor-row are. A-MEN.

They looked unto Him, and were lightened.—Ps. xxxiv, 5

2 Discouraged in the work of life,
　Disheartened by its load,
Shamed by its failures or its fears,
　I sink beside the road;
But let me only think of Thee,
And then new heart springs up in me.

3 Thy calmness bends serene above,
　My restlessness to still;
Around me flows Thy quickening life,
　To nerve my faltering will:
Thy presence fills my solitude;
Thy providence turns all to good.

4 Embosomed deep in Thy dear love,
　Held in Thy law, I stand;
Thy hand in all things I behold,
　And all things in Thy hand;
Thou leadest me by unsought ways,
And turn'st my mourning into praise.

Rev. SAMUEL LONGFELLOW, 1864

God's Love

78 ST. LEONARD C. M. D.

Henry Hiles, 1867

1 O gra - cious Fa - ther of man - kind, Our spir - its' Un - seen Friend,

High heav - en's Lord, our hearts' dear Guest, To Thee our prayers as - cend.

Thou dost not wait till hu - man speech Thy gifts di - vine im - plore;

Our dreams, our aims, our work, our lives Are prayers Thou lov - est more. A - MEN.

"A Hymn of Prayer"

2 Thou hearest these, the good and ill,
　Deep buried in each breast;
The secret thought, the hidden plan,
　Wrought out or unexpressed.
O cleanse our prayers from human dross,
　Attune our lives to Thee,
Until we labor for those gifts
　We ask on bended knee.

3 Our best is but Thyself in us,
　Our highest thought Thy will;
To hear Thy voice we need but love,
　And listen, and be still.

We would not bend Thy will to ours,
　But blend our wills with Thine;
Not beat with cries on heaven's doors,
　But live Thy life divine.

4 Thou seekest us in love and truth
　More than our minds seek Thee;
Through open gates Thy power flows in
　Like flood-tides from the sea.
No more we seek Thee from afar,
　Nor ask Thee for a sign,
Content to pray in life and love
　And toil, till all are Thine.

Rev. Henry H. Tweedy, 1926

Note—*This hymn, awarded first prize in a competition established by the "Homiletic Review" in 1925, is here printed by permission of the Editor.*

The Eternal God

HENRY BAKER, in the *Penny Post*, 1862, as "Hesperus:"
varied in James Pearce's *Hymn Music*, N. Y., 1872, as "Quebec"

1 Lord of all be - ing, throned a - far, Thy glo - ry flames from sun and star;

Cen - tre and soul of ev - ery sphere, Yet to each lov - ing heart how near! A - MEN.

"A SUN-DAY HYMN"

2 Sun of our life, Thy quickening ray
Sheds on our path the glow of day;
Star of our hope, Thy softened light
Cheers the long watches of the night.

3 Our midnight is Thy smile withdrawn;
Our noontide is Thy gracious dawn;
Our rainbow arch, Thy mercy's sign;
All, save the clouds of sin, are Thine.

4 Lord of all life, below, above,
Whose light is truth, whose warmth is love,
Before Thy ever-blazing throne
We ask no lustre of our own.

5 Grant us Thy truth to make us free,
And kindling hearts that burn for Thee;
Till all Thy living altars claim
One holy light, one heavenly flame.

OLIVER WENDELL HOLMES, 1859

NOTE—*This is the "Sun-day Hymn" at the close of Dr. Holmes' "The Professor at the Breakfast Table."*

LOUVAN L. M.

VIRGIL C. TAYLOR, 1847

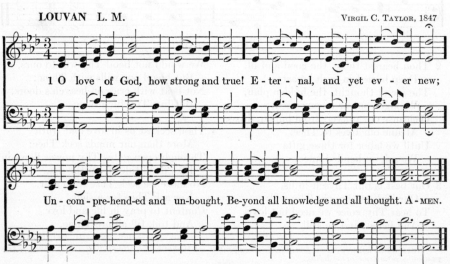

1 O love of God, how strong and true! E - ter - nal, and yet ev - er new;

Un - com - pre - hend - ed and un - bought, Be-yond all knowledge and all thought. A - MEN.

God's Love

80 LUFFENHAM L. M.

GEORGE A. MACFARREN, 1872

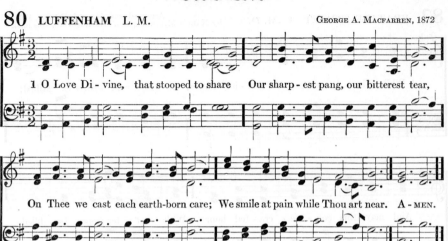

1 O Love Di - vine, that stooped to share Our sharp - est pang, our bitterest tear,

On Thee we cast each earth-born care; We smile at pain while Thou art near. A - MEN.

Alternative tune, QUEBEC, *opposite*

2 Though long the weary way we tread,
    And sorrow crown each lingering year,
No path we shun, no darkness dread,
    Our hearts still whispering, Thou art near.

3 When drooping pleasure turns to grief,
    And trembling faith is changed to fear,
The murmuring wind, the quivering leaf,
    Shall softly tell us, Thou art near.

4 On Thee we fling our burdening woe,
    O Love Divine, for ever dear;
Content to suffer while we know,
    Living and dying, Thou art near.

OLIVER WENDELL HOLMES, 1859

NOTE—*The hymn that Iris sang in Dr. Holmes' "The Professor at the Breakfast Table."*

81 (LOUVAN) L. M.

1 O love of God, how strong and true!
Eternal, and yet ever new;
Uncomprehended and unbought,
Beyond all knowledge and all thought.

2 O heavenly love, how precious still,
In days of weariness and ill,
In nights of pain and helplessness,
To heal, to comfort, and to bless!

3 O wide-embracing, wondrous love!
We read thee in the sky above,
We read thee in the earth below,
In seas that swell, and streams that flow.

4 We read thee best in Him who came
To bear for us the cross of shame;
Sent by the Father from on high,
Our life to live, our death to die.

5 We read thy power to bless and save,
E'en in the darkness of the grave;
Still more in resurrection light
We read the fulness of thy might.

6 O love of God, our shield and stay
Through all the perils of our way!
Eternal love, in thee we rest,
For ever safe, for ever blest.

REV. HORATIUS BONAR, 1861

82 **BRATTLE STREET** **C. M. D.**

Arranged from Ignaz J. Pleyel, 1791, by Nahum Mitchell, 1807: rearranged for this book

1 While Thee I seek, pro-tect-ing Power, Be my vain wish-es stilled;

And may this con-se-cra-ted hour With bet-ter hopes be filled.

2 Thy love the powers of thought be-stowed; To Thee my thoughts would soar;

Thy mer-cy o'er my life has flowed; That mer-cy I a-dore. A-men.

In the multitude of my thoughts within me Thy comforts delight my soul.—Ps. xciv, 19

3 In each event of life, how clear
   Thy ruling hand I see;
Each blessing to my soul more dear
   Because conferred by Thee.

4 In every joy that crowns my days,
   In every pain I bear,
My heart shall find delight in praise,
   Or seek relief in prayer.

5 When gladness wings my favored hour,
   Thy love my thoughts shall fill;
Resigned, when storms of sorrow lower,
   My soul shall meet Thy will.

6 My lifted eye, without a tear,
   The lowering storm shall see;
My steadfast heart shall know no fear;
   That heart will rest on Thee.

Helen M. Williams, 1786

God's Love

83 BELMONT C. M.

Arranged from WILLIAM GARDINER'S *Sacred Melodies*, 1812

1 Thou, Lord, art Love: and ev - ery- where Thy Name is bright - ly shown,

Be - neath, on earth, Thy foot-stool fair, A - bove, in heaven, Thy throne. A - MEN.

2 Thy word is love; in lines of gold
   There mercy prints its trace;
   In nature we Thy steps behold,
   The gospel shows Thy face.

3 Thy ways are love; though they transcend
   Our feeble range of sight,
   They wind, through darkness, to their end
   In everlasting light.

4 Thy thoughts are love; and Jesus is
   The living voice they find:

His love lights up the vast abyss
   Of the eternal Mind.

5 Thy chastisements are love; more deep
   They stamp the seal divine,
   And by a sweet compulsion keep
   Our spirits nearer Thine.

6 Thy heaven is the abode of Love:
   O blessed Lord, that we
   May there, when time's deep shades re-
   Be gathered home to Thee.   [move,

Rev. JAMES DRUMMOND BURNS, 1858

BEATITUDO C. M.

Rev. JOHN B. DYKES, 1875

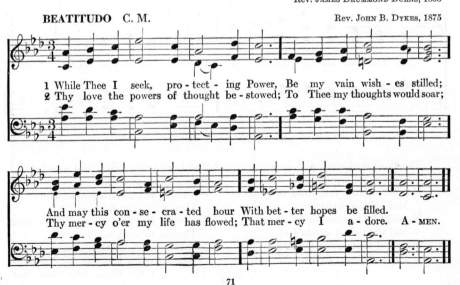

1 While Thee I seek, pro - tect - ing Power, Be my vain wish - es stilled;
2 Thy love the powers of thought be - stowed; To Thee my thoughts would soar;

And may this con - se - cra - ted hour With bet - ter hopes be filled.
Thy mer - cy o'er my life has flowed; That mer - cy I a - dore. A - MEN.

71

The Eternal God

84 **LAND OF REST** C. M. D.

RICHARD S. NEWMAN, 1879

1 The Lord is rich and mer - ci - ful, The Lord is ver - y kind;

O come to Him, come now to Him, With a be - liev - ing mind:

His com - forts, they shall strength-en thee, Like flow - ing wa - ters cool;

And He shall for thy spir - it be A foun - tain ev - er full. A - MEN.

Alternative tune, AMESBURY, No. 90

2 The Lord is glorious and strong,
　Our God is very high;
O trust in Him, trust now in Him,
　And have security:
He shall be to thee like the sea,
　And thou shalt surely feel
His wind that bloweth healthily
　Thy sicknesses to heal.

3 The Lord is wonderful and wise,
　As all the ages tell;
O learn of Him, learn now of Him,
　Then with thee it is well;
And with His light thou shalt be blest,
　Therein to work and live;
And He shall be to thee a rest
　When evening hours arrive.

Rev. THOMAS TOKE LYNCH, 1850

God's Love

85 SARDIS 8. 7. 8. 7.

Arranged from BEETHOVEN'S
"Romance for Violin," Opus 40, No. 1

1 God is Love; His mer-cy bright-ens All the path in which we rove;

Bliss He wakes, and woe He light-ens: God is Wis-dom, God is Love. A-MEN.

2 Chance and change are busy ever;
  Man decays, and ages move;
But His mercy waneth never:
  God is Wisdom, God is Love.

3 E'en the hour that darkest seemeth
  Will His changeless goodness prove;

From the mist His brightness streameth:
  God is Wisdom, God is Love.

4 He with earthly cares entwineth
  Hope and comfort from above;
Everywhere His glory shineth:
  God is Wisdom, God is Love.

Sir JOHN BOWRING, 1825

86 WAREHAM L. M.

WILLIAM KNAPP, 1738

1 My God, how end-less is Thy love! Thy gifts are ev-ery eve-ning new;

And morn-ing mer-cies from a-bove Gent-ly dis-til like ear-ly dew. A-MEN.

2 Thou spread'st the curtains of the night,
  Great Guardian of my sleeping hours:
Thy sovereign word restores the light,
  And quickens all my drowsy powers.

3 I yield my powers to Thy command,
  To Thee I consecrate my days;
Perpetual blessings from Thy hand
  Demand perpetual songs of praise.

Rev. ISAAC WATTS, 1709

A Collect for Trust

O God, our Heavenly Father, by whose appointment our ways of life proceed: We pray Thee so to confirm our trust in Thy providence, that, being saved alike from fear and from despondency, we may find pleasure in our tasks, contentment amidst our disappointments, and patience in any suffering. Give us a happy sense of all Thy blessings, and enable us to serve Thee with cheerful hearts: through Jesus Christ our Lord. Amen.

87 **WALDEN** C. M.

JAMES EDMUND JONES, 1906

1 The Lord's my Shep-herd, I'll not want; He makes me down to lie In pas-tures green, He lead-eth me The qui-et wa-ters by, The qui-et wa-ters by. A-MEN.

Used by permission

A PARAPHRASE OF PSALM XXIII

2 My soul He doth restore again;
    And me to walk doth make
Within the paths of righteousness,
    Ev'n for His own Name's sake.

3 Yea, though I walk in death's dark vale,
    Yet will I fear none ill;
For Thou art with me, and Thy rod
    And staff me comfort still.

4 My table Thou hast furnishèd
    In presence of my foes;
My head Thou dost with oil anoint,
    And my cup overflows.

5 Goodness and mercy all my life
    Shall surely follow me;
And in God's house for evermore
    My dwelling-place shall be.

The Scottish *Psalms of David in meter*, 1650; based on
Francis Rous, Sir William Mure, and others

NOTE—"*Walden*" *was originally set to Marie Corelli's version of this Psalm in her "God's Good Man," and named for the Rev. John Walden, the hero of that book.*

God's Guidance and Care

88 **ST. PETER** C. M.

ALEXANDER R. REINAGLE, 1836

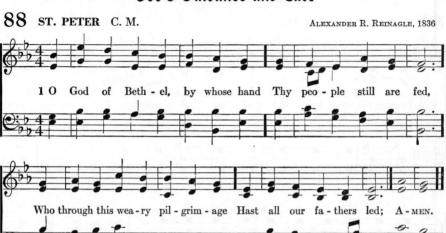

1 O God of Beth-el, by whose hand Thy peo-ple still are fed,

Who through this wea-ry pil-grim-age Hast all our fa-thers led; A-MEN.

2 Our vows, our prayers, we now present
Before Thy throne of grace;
God of our fathers, be the God
Of their succeeding race.

3 Through each perplexing path of life
Our wandering footsteps guide;
Give us each day our daily bread,
And raiment fit provide.

4 O spread Thy covering wings around
Till all our wanderings cease,
And at our Father's loved abode
Our souls arrive in peace.

5 Such blessings from Thy gracious hand
Our humble prayers implore;
And Thou shalt be our chosen God,
And portion evermore.

Verses 1–4, Rev. Philip Doddridge, 1737, recast by Rev. John Logan, 1781:
verse 1, line 1, varied, and verse 5 added, in Scottish *Translations and Paraphrases*, 1781

ST. PAUL C. M.

JAMES CHALMERS' *Collection*, 1748 or 1749

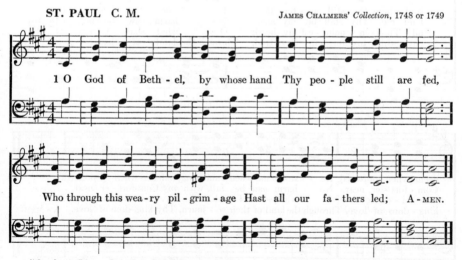

1 O God of Beth-el, by whose hand Thy peo-ple still are fed,

Who through this wea-ry pil-grim-age Hast all our fa-thers led; A-MEN.

"One hymn I love. It is that which, when sung to the tune of St. Paul's, makes men and women square them-selves and stand erect to sing, like an army that goes gladly to battle—'O God of Bethel.'"—Samuel R. Crockett.

The Eternal God

89 POLAND 11. 11. 11. 11.

THOMAS KOSCHAT, 1862

1 The Lord is my Shep - herd, nor want shall I know; I
2 Through the val - ley and shad - ow of death though I stray; Since
3 In the midst of af - flict - ion my ta - ble is spread; With
4 Let good - ness and mer - cy, my boun - ti - ful God, Still

feed in green pas - tures, safe fold - ed I rest; He lead - eth my
Thou art my Guard - ian, no e - vil I fear; Thy rod shall de -
bless - ings un - meas - ured my cup run - neth o'er; With per - fume and
fol - low my steps till I meet Thee a - bove; I seek by the

soul where the still wa - ters flow, Re - stores me when wandering, re -
fend me, Thy staff be my stay; No harm can be - fall, with my
oil Thou a - noint - est my head; O what shall I ask of Thy
path which my fore - fa - thers trod, Through the land of their so - journ, Thy

deems when oppressed, Re - stores me when wandering, redeems when op - pressed.
Com - fort - er near, No harm can be - fall, with my Com - fort - er near.
prov - i - dence more? O what shall I ask of Thy prov - i - dence more?
king - dom of love, Through the land of their so - journ, Thy king - dom of love. A - MEN.

JAMES MONTGOMERY'S version of PSALM XXIII, 1822

God's Guidance and Care

90 AMESBURY C. M. D.

Uzziah C. Burnap, in *The Hymnal*, 1895

1 I bow my fore-head to the dust, I veil mine eyes for shame,

And urge, in trem-bling self-dis-trust, A prayer with-out a claim.

No of-fering of mine own I have, Nor works my faith to prove;

I can but give the gifts He gave, And plead His love for love. A-MEN.

2 I dimly guess, from blessings known,
  Of greater out of sight;
And, with the chastened Psalmist, own
  His judgments too are right.
And if my heart and flesh are weak
  To bear an untried pain,
The bruisèd reed He will not break,
  But strengthen and sustain.

3 I know not what the future hath
  Of marvel or surprise,
Assured alone that life and death
  His mercy underlies.

And so beside the silent sea
  I wait the muffled oar:
No harm from Him can come to me
  On ocean or on shore.

4 I know not where His islands lift
  Their fronded palms in air;
I only know I cannot drift
  Beyond His love and care.
And Thou, O Lord, by whom are seen
  Thy creatures as they be,
Forgive me if too close I lean
  My human heart on Thee.

Arranged from John G. Whittier's "The Eternal Goodness," 1867

77

91 **LUX BENIGNA** 10. 4. 10. 4. 10. 10.   Rev. John B. Dykes, 1867

1 Lead, kind-ly Light, a-mid the en-cir-cling gloom, Lead Thou me on;
The night is dark, and I am far from home; Lead Thou me on:
Keep Thou my feet; I do not ask to see
The dis-tant scene,—one step en-nough for me. A-men.

In the daytime also He led them with a cloud, and all the night with a light of fire.—Ps. lxxviii, 14

2 I was not ever thus, nor prayed that Thou
  Shouldst lead me on;
I loved to choose and see my path; but now
  Lead Thou me on.
I loved the garish day, and, spite of fears,
Pride ruled my will: remember not past years.

3 So long Thy power hath blest me, sure it still
  Will lead me on
O'er moor and fen, o'er crag and torrent, till
  The night is gone;
And with the morn those angel faces smile,
Which I have loved long since, and lost awhile.

Rev. (later Cardinal) John H. Newman, 1833

God's Guidance and Care

92 **CAERSALEM** 8. 7. 8. 7. 4. 7.   ROBERT EDWARDS (1796–1862)

1 Guide me, O Thou Great Je-ho-vah, Pilgrim through this bar-ren land; I am
weak, but Thou art might-y, Hold me with Thy power-ful hand: Bread of heav-en,
Bread of heav-en, Bread of heav-en, Feed me till I want no more. A-MEN.

This God is our God for ever and ever: He will be our Guide even unto death.—Ps. xlviii, 14.

2 Open now the crystal fountain,
    Whence the healing stream doth flow;
Let the fire and cloudy pillar
    Lead me all my journey through:
        Strong Deliverer,
Be Thou still my Strength and Shield.

3 When I tread the verge of Jordan,
    Bid my anxious fears subside;
Death of deaths and hell's Destruction,
    Land me safe on Canaan's side:
        Songs of praises
I will ever give to Thee.

Rev. WILLIAM WILLIAMS in Welsh, 1745. Verse 1 translated by Rev. PETER WILLIAMS, 1771:
verses 2, 3, by Rev. WILLIAM WILLIAMS, c. 1772

NOTE—*This hymn may be sung to* REGENT SQUARE, *No. 50; but in the Welsh setting we hear the trumpeter sounding the clear call of faith and the tramp of the marching host.*

93 BISHOPGARTH 8. 7. 8. 7. D. Iambic   Sir Arthur Sullivan, 1897

1 Who trusts in God, a strong a-bode In heaven and earth pos-sess-es;

Who looks in love to Christ a-bove, No fear his heart op-press-es.

In Thee a-lone, dear Lord, we own Sweet hope and con-so-la-tion;

Our shield from foes, our balm for woes, Our great and sure sal-va-tion. A-MEN.

Alternative tune, CONSTANCE, No. 334

WER GOTT VERTRAUT, HAT WOHLGEBAUT

2 Though Satan's wrath beset our path,
  And worldly scorn assail us,
While Thou art near we will not fear,
  Thy strength shall never fail us:
Thy rod and staff shall keep us safe,
  And guide our steps for ever;
Nor shades of death, nor hell beneath,
  Our souls from Thee shall sever.

3 In all the strife of mortal life
  Our feet shall stand securely;
Temptation's hour shall lose its power,
  For Thou shalt guard us surely.
O God, renew, with heavenly dew,
  Our body, soul, and spirit,
Until we stand at Thy right hand,
  Through Jesus' saving merit.

Verse 1, Rev. JOACHIM MAGDEBURG, 1572; verses 2, 3, anonymous, 1597.
Translated by Rev. BENJ. H. KENNEDY, 1863: varied by Bishop W. WALSHAM HOW, 1864

NOTE—*Bishopgarth, one of the last of Sullivan's tunes, was written for Queen Victoria's Diamond Jubilee, 1897, and the profits of its sale (£202) were given to the Prince of Wales' Hospital Fund. "It is a tune," the composer wrote, "which I hope every one will be able to pick up quickly and sing heartily."*

94 NEUMARK 9. 8. 9. 8. 8. 8.

GEORG NEUMARK, 1657

1 If thou but suf-fer God to guide thee, And hope in Him through all thy ways,

He'll give thee strength, whate'er be-tide thee, And bear thee through the e - vil days:

Who trusts in God's un-chang-ing love Builds on the rock that naught can move. A - MEN.

WER NUR DEN LIEBEN GOTT LÄSST WALTEN

2 What can these anxious cares avail thee,
　These never-ceasing moans and sighs?
What can it help, if thou bewail thee
　O'er each dark moment as it flies?
Our cross and trials do but press
The heavier for our bitterness.

3 Only be still, and wait His leisure
　In cheerful hope, with heart content
To take whate'er thy Father's pleasure
　And all-deserving love hath sent;
Nor doubt our inmost wants are known
To Him who chose us for His own.

4 Sing, pray, and keep His ways unswerving,
　So do thine own part faithfully,
And trust His word,—though undeserving,
　Thou yet shalt find it true for thee
God never yet forsook at need
The soul that trusted Him indeed.

GEORG NEUMARK, 1641.
Translated by CATHERINE WINKWORTH, 1855, 1863

The Eternal God

95 HE LEADETH ME L. M. D.

WILLIAM B. BRADBURY, 1864

1 He lead-eth me: O bless-ed thought! O words with heaven-ly com-fort fraught!

What-e'er I do, wher-e'er I be, Still 'tis God's hand that lead-eth me.

REFRAIN

He lead-eth me, He lead-eth me; By His own hand He lead-eth me:

His faith-ful fol-lower I would be, For by His hand He lead-eth me. A-MEN.

2 Sometimes 'mid scenes of deepest gloom,
Sometimes where Eden's bowers bloom,
By waters calm, o'er troubled sea,—
Still 'tis His hand that leadeth me.—REF.

3 Lord, I would clasp Thy hand in mine,
Nor ever murmur nor repine;
Content, whatever lot I see,
Since 'tis my God that leadeth me.—REF.

4 And when my task on earth is done,
When, by Thy grace, the victory's won,
E'en death's cold wave I will not flee,
Since God through Jordan leadeth me.—REF.

Rev. JOSEPH H. GILMORE, 1862

NOTE—*The hymn was written in four 6-line verses by Mr. Gilmore after an evening meeting at the First Baptist Church, Philadelphia, where he had lectured on "The Lord is my Shepherd . . . He leadeth me." The last two lines were added to each verse by the composer to make a refrain.*

82

God's Guidance and Care

ZENNOR 10. 10. 10. 10. 6. 6.

FREDERICK C. MAKER (1844–

1 He leads us on by paths we did not know; Up - ward He leads us, though our steps be slow; Though oft we faint and *Unison*

fal - ter on the way, Though storms and dark - ness oft ob - scure the day, *Harmony*

Yet, when the clouds are gone, We know He leads us on. A - MEN.

I will lead them in paths that thy love not known.—Isa. xlii, 16

2 He leads us on through all the unquiet years;
Past all our dreamland hopes, and doubts, and fears
He guides our steps; through all the tangled maze
Of losses, sorrows, and o'erclouded days
   We know His will is done,
   And still He leads us on.

3 And soon or late the rugged field of strife
Shall catch the sunlight that transfigures life;
The heart shall win the discipline of pain,
And know the struggle has not been in vain;
   Its doubts and fears shall cease,
   And Christ will bring it peace.

Verses 1 and 2 by HIRAM O. WILEY, 1865: Verse 3 written for this book

The Eternal God

97 **DOLOMITE CHANT** 6. 6. 6. 6.

An Austrian melody
harmonized by JOSEPH T. COOPER, 1877

1 Not so in haste, my heart; Have faith in God and wait; Al-though He lin-ger long, He nev-er comes too late........... A - MEN.

For a lower setting, see No. 379

2 He never comes too late,
   He knoweth what is best;
Vex not thyself in vain;
   Until He cometh, rest.

3 Until He cometh, rest,
   Nor grudge the hours that roll;

The feet that wait for God
   Are soonest at the goal;

4 Are soonest at the goal
   That is not gained by speed;
Then hold thee still, my heart,
   For I shall wait His lead.

BRADFORD TORREY, 1875

98 **NAOMI** C. M.

Arranged from HANS G. NÄGELI, by LOWELL MASON, 1836

1 Fa-ther, what-e'er of earth-ly bliss Thy sov-ereign will de-nies,
Ac-cept-ed at Thy throne of grace, Let this pe-ti-tion rise: A-MEN.

2 Give me a calm, a thankful heart,
   From every murmur free;
The blessings of Thy grace impart,
   And make me live to Thee.

3 Let the sweet hope that Thou art mine
   My life and death attend;
Thy presence through my journey shine,
   And crown my journey's end.

ANNE STEELE, 1760: varied by Rev. A. M. TOPLADY, 1776

99 CONCORD 6. 6. 6. 6. D.

James C. Knox

1 Thy way, not mine, O Lord, How - ev - er dark it be:

Lead me by Thine own hand, Choose out the path for me.

Smooth let it be or rough, It will be still the best;

Wind - ing or straight, it leads Right on - ward to Thy rest. A - MEN.

Make Thy way straight before my face.—Ps. v, 8.

2 I dare not choose my lot;
   I would not, if I might;
 Choose Thou for me, my God:
   So shall I walk aright.
 Take Thou my cup, and it
   With joy or sorrow fill,
 As best to Thee may seem;
   Choose Thou my good and ill.

3 Choose Thou for me my friends,
   My sickness or my health;
 Choose Thou my cares for me,
   My poverty or wealth.
 Not mine, not mine the choice,
   In things or great or small;
 Be Thou my guide, my strength,
   My wisdom, and my all.

Rev. Horatius Bonar, 1859

Note—*This setting stands apart from those more familiar, as an interpretation of Bonar's hymn, in its using the accents of the music to strengthen the logical stresses of the words.*

The Eternal God

100 **CHRIST CHURCH** 8. 8. 8. 4.

Rev. Edward S. Medley,
composed 1868, published 1909

1 O God, not on-ly in dis-tress, In pain and want and wea-ri-ness,

Organ Ped.

Thy ten-der Spir-it stoops to bless, Thy will is done. A-MEN.

2 But oftener on the wings of peace
And girt about with tenderness,
Thou comest, and all troubles cease,—
Thy will is done.

3 In all that nature hath supplied,
In flowers along the country side,
In morning light, in eventide,
Thy will is done.

4 In youthful days, when joys increase,
In light, in hope, in happiness,
In quiet times of trustful peace,
Thy will is done.

5 Thy will is pure, O Lord, and just;
And we, frail creatures of the dust,
Through good or ill, can only trust
Thy will is done.

Frederick Smith, c. 1870

SHELTERING WING L. M.

Sir Joseph Barnby, 1883

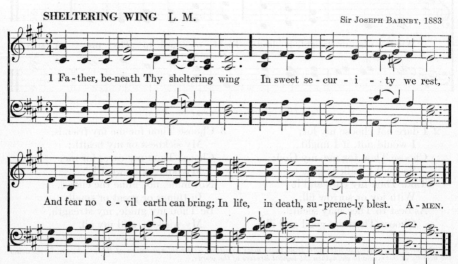

1 Fa-ther, be-neath Thy sheltering wing In sweet se-cur-i-ty we rest,

And fear no e-vil earth can bring; In life, in death, su-preme-ly blest. A-MEN.

86

101 MY SHEPHERD 5. 6. 6. 4. 6. 6. 6. 4.

A Thuringian Folk-song
arranged by JOHN B. CRAMER

1 Thou art my Shep-herd, Car-ing in ev-ery need, Watch-ing Thy flock to feed, Trust-ing Thee still. In the green pas-tures low, Where liv-ing wa-ters flow, Safe by Thy side I go, Fear-ing no ill. A-MEN.

A PARAPHRASE OF PSALM XXIII

2 Or if my way lie
Where darkening shadows nigh
My soul would terrify
With sudden chill,—
Yet I am not afraid;
While softly on my head
Thy tender hand is laid,
I fear no ill.

3 Goodness and mercy
Ever shall follow me,
Till by Thy grace I see
Thy holy hill;
Lord, in that home with Thee,
Joyful eternally,
Folded Thy flock shall be,
Safe from all ill.

Miss M. E. THALHEIMER, 1867, and Mrs. M. SCOTT-HAYCROFT, 1904

102 (SHELTERING WING) L. M.

1 Father, beneath Thy sheltering wing
In sweet security we rest,
And fear no evil earth can bring;
In life, in death, supremely blest.

2 For life is good, whose tidal flow
The motions of Thy will obeys;
And death is good, that makes us know
The life divine which all things sways.

3 And good it is to bear the cross,
And so Thy perfect peace to win;
And nought is ill, nor brings us loss,
Nor works us harm, save only sin.

4 Redeemed from this, we ask no more,
But trust the love that saves to guide;
Thy grace that yields so rich a store,
Will grant us all we need beside.

WILLIAM H. BURLEIGH, 1864

Our Lord Jesus Christ
Christmas

A Collect for Christmas Eve

Lord Jesus, for whose sake all motherhood is holy, and since whose coming the little children are first in the kingdom of Thy Father: Come to every household and family that loves Thee on this Christmas Eve. Speak comforting things to the heart of every mother, and take the little children into Thine arms, O Christ. Let every Christmas gift be a reminder of Thee, and let Thy Name be spoken softly in every home. Lord Jesus, hear; Lord Jesus, come; and light this home with Christmas love. Amen.

103 BARTON 7. 7. 7. 7. 6. 4.

Rev. REGINALD F. DALE, 1881

1 "No room" with-in the dwell-ing For Him whose love ex-cell-ing

Toward those who nev-er sought Him, To earth from heav-en brought Him,

Who count-ed not the cost To seek the lost. A - MEN.

There was no room for them in the inn.—ST. LUKE ii, 7.

2 "No room"; so to the manger
They bore the kingly Stranger;
But angel hosts attended,
And angel voices blended,
  While on His Mother's breast
  He lay at rest.

3 "No room": O Babe so tender
To Thee our hearts we render,
Not meet for Thy possessing,
Yet make them by Thy blessing
  A home wherein to dwell,
  Emmanuel.

Rev. ROBERT H. BAYNES, 1881

Christmas

104 ST. LOUIS   8. 6. 8. 6. 7. 6. 8. 6.   LEWIS H. REDNER, 1868

1 O lit - tle town of Beth - le - hem, How still we see thee lie;

A - bove thy deep and dream - less sleep The si - lent stars go by:

Yet in thy dark streets shi - neth The ev - er - last - ing Light;

The hopes and fears of all the years Are met in thee to - night. A - MEN.

2 For Christ is born of Mary;
    And gathered all above,
While mortals sleep, the angels keep
    Their watch of wondering love.
O morning stars, together
    Proclaim the holy birth;
And praises sing to God the King,
    And peace to men on earth.

3 How silently, how silently,
    The wondrous gift is given!
So God imparts to human hearts
    The blessings of His heaven.

No ear may hear His coming,
    But in this world of sin,
Where meek souls will receive Him still,
    The dear Christ enters in.

4 O holy Child of Bethlehem,
    Descend to us, we pray;
Cast out our sin, and enter in,
    Be born is us today.
We hear the Christmas angels
    The great glad tidings tell;
O come to us, abide with us,
    Our Lord Emmanuel.

Bishop PHILLIPS BROOKS, 1868

NOTE—*This carol was written for the Christmas Sunday School service of the Church of the Holy Trinity, Philadelphia,*

89

Our Lord Jesus Christ

A Collect for Christmas Day

O God, our Heavenly Father, who dost call to our remembrance the birthday of Thy
Son, our Saviour Jesus Christ: Give us grace to keep this festival with pure faith and
holy love; that while we join our voices with theirs who sang Glory to God in the Highest,
we may not forget to spread abroad also the gospel of Thy peace and good will towards
men: through Jesus Christ our Lord.   Amen.

105 ANTIOCH C. M.

LOWELL MASON, 1830

1 Joy to the world! the Lord is come: Let earth re-ceive her King;
Let ev-ery heart pre-pare Him room, And heaven and na-ture sing, And
heaven and na-ture sing, And heaven, and heaven and na-ture sing. A-MEN.

Alternative tune, NATIVITY, No. 167

2 Joy to the earth! the Saviour reigns:
　Let men their songs employ;
While fields and floods, rocks, hills, and
　Repeat the sounding joy.　　[plains

3 No more let sins and sorrows grow,
　Nor thorns infest the ground;
He comes to make His blessings flow
　Far as the curse is found.

4 He rules the world with truth and grace,
　And makes the nations prove
The glories of His righteousness,
　And wonders of His love.

Rev. ISAAC WATTS, 1719

NOTE—*The tune was printed as "Arranged from Händel;" but such a source has not been identified.*

Christtmas

106 CHRISTMAS MORN 7. 6. 7. 6. D.

EDWARD J. HOPKINS, 1881

1 The sky can still re-mem-ber The ear-liest Chris-tmas morn,

When in the cold De-cem-ber The Sav-iour Christ was born.

No star un-folds its glo-ry, No trum-pet wind is blown,

But tells the Christ-mas sto-ry In mu-sic of its own. A-MEN.

2 O never-failing splendor!
   O never-silent song!
Still keep the green earth tender,
   Still keep the gray earth strong,
Still keep the brave earth dreaming
   Of deeds that shall be done,
While children's lives come streaming
   Like sunbeams from the sun.

3 O angels sweet and splendid,
   Throng in our hearts and sing
The wonders which attended
   The coming of the King;
Till we too, boldly pressing
   Where once the shepherds trod,
Climb Bethlehem's Hill of Blessing,
   And find the Son of God.

Bishop PHILLIPS BROOKS (1835–1893)

107 SHACKELFORD C. M. D.

FREDERICK H. CHEESWRIGHT, c. 1889

1 While shep-herds watched their flocks by night, All seat-ed on the ground,

The an-gel of the Lord came down, And glo-ry shone a-round.

2 "Fear not," said he,— for might-y dread Had seized their trou-bled mind,—

"Glad ti-dings of great joy I bring To you and all man-kind." A-MEN.

Alternative tune, CHRISTMAS, No. 372

3 "To you, in David's town, this day
   Is born of David's line
A Saviour, who is Christ the Lord;
   And this shall be the sign:

4 "The heavenly Babe you there shall find
   To human view displayed,
All meanly wrapt in swathing bands,
   And in a manger laid."

5 Thus spake the seraph, and forthwith
   Appeared a shining throng
Of angels praising God, and thus
   Addressed their joyful song:

6 "All glory be to God on high,
   And to the earth be peace:
Good-will henceforth from heaven to men
   Begin, and never cease."

NAHUM TATE, 1702

Christmas

108 BETHLEHEM ROAD 8. 7. 8. 7. 8. 7. Iambic Rev. CALVIN W. LAUFER, 1925

1 A King might miss the guid-ing star, A Wise Man's foot might stum-ble;

For Beth-le-hem is ver-y far From all ex-cept the hum-ble.

'Tis Christmas Day! 'Tis Christmas Day! And Christmas hearts are hum-ble. A-MEN.

"A CAROL OF CHRISTMAS AT BETHLEHEM"

2 Some pilgrims seek a hallowed shrine;
 Some soldiers march to danger;
Some travellers seek an inn—its sign,
 "The Baby in a Manger."
  When Christ was born on Christmas morn,
  They laid him in a manger.

3 There is no palace in that place,
 Nor any seat of learning,
No hill-top vision of God's face,
 No altar candles burning.
  O come and see our Christmas tree,
  And Christmas candles burning.

4 But he who gets to Bethlehem
 Shall hear the oxen lowing;
And, if he humbly kneel with them,
 May catch far trumpets blowing.
  From far away, on Christmas Day,
  May hear God's trumpets blowing.

Rev. LOUIS F. BENSON, 1921

93

109 IRBY 8. 7. 8. 7. 8. 8.   HENRY J. GAUNTLETT, 1849

To be sung in unison

1. {Once in roy - al Da - vid's cit - y Stood a
   {Where a moth - er laid her Ba - by In a
   low - ly cat - tle - shed,}
   man - ger for His bed:} Ma - ry was that moth - er mild,
   Je - sus Christ her lit - tle Child. A - MEN.

2 He came down to earth from heaven
    Who is God and Lord of all,
And His shelter was a stable,
    And His cradle was a stall:
With the poor, the mean, and lowly,
Lived on earth our Saviour Holy.

3 And, through all His wondrous childhood
    He would honor and obey,
Love and watch the lowly maiden
    In whose gentle arms He lay:
Christian children all must be
Mild, obedient, good as He.

5 And our eyes at last shall see Him,
 Through His own redeeming love;
For that Child so dear and gentle
 Is our Lord in heaven above
And He leads His children on
 To the place where He is gone.

6 Not in that poor lowly stable,
 With the oxen standing by,
We shall see Him, but in heaven,
 Set at God's right hand on high;
When like stars His children crowned
All in white shall wait around.

Mrs. CECIL F. ALEXANDER, 1848

110 MAINZER L. M.

JOSEPH MAINZER, c. 1841

1 I heard the bells on Christ-mas day Their old fa-mil-iar car-ols play,

And wild and sweet The words re-peat Of peace on earth, good-will to men; A-MEN.

For a lower setting, see No. 65

"CHRISTMAS BELLS"

2 And thought how, as the day had come,
The belfries of all Christendom
 Had rolled along
 The unbroken song
Of peace on earth, good-will to men:

3 Till, ringing, singing on its way,
The world revolved from night to day,
 A voice, a chime,
 A chant sublime
Of peace on earth, good-will to men.

4 And in despair I bowed my head;
"There is no peace on earth," I said;
 "For hate is strong,
 And mocks the song
Of peace on earth, good-will to men."

5 Then pealed the bells more loud and deep:
"God is not dead; nor doth He sleep!
 The wrong shall fail,
 The right prevail,
With peace on earth, good-will to men."

HENRY W. LONGFELLOW, 1864

NOTE—*The lyric was written on a Christmas Day while the Civil War was yet in progress, and the poet's "despair" is explained by the two verses here omitted, which tell how the wind from the South seemed to bring the thundering of the cannon:*

"And with the sound
The carols drowned
Of peace on earth, good-will to men."

111 STILLE NACHT 6. 6. 8. 8. 6. 6.

Franz Grüber, 1818

1 Si - lent night, ho - ly night, All is dark, save a light
2 Peace-ful night, ho - li - est night, Dark - ness flies, all is light,
3 Si - lent night, ho - li - est night, Child of heaven! O how bright

Yon - der where they sweet vi - gil keep O'er the Babe, who in si - lent sleep,
Shep-herds hear the an - gels sing: "Al - le - lu - ia! hail the King,
Thou didst smile on us when Thou wast born; Blest in - deed was that hap - py morn,

Rests in heav - en - ly peace, Rests in heav - en - ly peace.
Christ the Sav - iour is here, Je - sus the Sav - iour is here."
Full of heav - en - ly joy, Full of heav - en - ly joy. A - men.

Rev. Joseph Mohr, 1818;
the translation compiled from several sources

112 (PUER NOBIS NASCITUR) L. M.

Gelobet seist Du, Jesus Christ

1 All praise to Thee, Eternal Lord,
Clothed in a garb of flesh and blood;
Choosing a manger for Thy throne,
While worlds on worlds are Thine alone.

2 Once did the skies before Thee bow;
A Virgin's arms contain Thee now:
Angels who did in Thee rejoice
Now listen for Thine infant voice.

3 A little Child, Thou art our Guest,
That weary ones in Thee may rest;
Forlorn and lowly is Thy birth,
That we may rise to heaven from earth.

4 Thou comest in the darksome night
To make us children of the light,
To make us, in the realms divine,
Like Thine own angels round Thee shine.

5 All this for us Thy love hath done;
By this to Thee our love is won:
For this we tune our cheerful lays,
And shout our thanks in ceaseless praise.

Martin Luther, 1524.   The translation (anonymous) in *Sabbath Hymn Book*, 1858

113 **BRETAGNE** 7. 7. 7.

An old Breton melody
harmonized by Edward Shippen Barnes, 1926

Slowly

1 On the birth-day of the Lord An-gels sang with

one ac-cord, *"In ex-cel-sis glo-ri-a."* A-men.

In Excelsis Gloria

2 Tidings true an angel told
Certain shepherds in the wold:—
In excelsis gloria!

3 Tidings great and full of glee,
Christ and His nativity:—
In excelsis gloria!

4 Born is our Emmanuel
As proclaimed by Gabriel:—
In excelsis gloria!

5 His the laud and victory,
Angels sang, and so sing we:–
"In excelsis gloria!"

6 Let the present company
Raise the voice of melody:—
"In excelsis gloria!"

Arranged for this book from traditional carols

PUER NOBIS NASCITUR L. M.

Composed or adapted by Michael Praetorius, 1609
harmonized by George R. Woodward, 1904

1 All praise to Thee, E-ter-nal Lord, Clothed in a garb of flesh and blood;

Choos-ing a man-ger for Thy throne, While worlds on worlds are Thine a-lone. A-men.

Alternative tune, canonbury, No. 7

97

114 MENDELSSOHN 7. 7. 7. 7. D. with Refrain

Arranged from MENDELSSOHN's
Festgesang, 1840, by WILLIAM H. CUMMINGS, 1850

1 Hark! the her - ald an - gels sing, "Glo - ry to the new - born King;
Peace on earth, and mer - cy mild, God and sin - ners rec - on - ciled!"
Joy - ful, all ye na - tions, rise, Join the tri - umph of the skies;
With the an - gel - ic host pro - claim, "Christ is born in Beth - le - hem!"

REFRAIN

Hark! the her - ald an - gels sing, "Glo - ry to the new-born King." A - MEN.

2 Christ, by highest heaven adored;
Christ, the Everlasting Lord!
Late in time behold Him come,
Offspring of the Virgin's womb:
Veiled in flesh the Godhead see;
Hail the Incarnate Deity,
Pleased as man with men to dwell,
Jesus, our Emmanuel.—REF.

3 Hail, the heaven-born Prince of Peace!
Hail, the Sun of Righteousness!
Light and life to all He brings,
Risen with healing in His wings.
Mild He lays His glory by,
Born that man no more may die,
Born to raise the sons of earth,
Born to give them second birth.—REF.

Rev. CHARLES WESLEY, 1739; altered by G. WHITEFIELD, 1753, M. MADAN, 1760,
Supplement to New Version, c. 1782, and J. KEMPTHORNE, 1810

Christmas

115 THERE'S A SONG 6. 6. 6. 6. 12. 12. GEORGE F. ROOT, 1879

1 There's a song in the air! There's a star in the sky! There's a
moth-er's deep prayer And a ba-by's low cry! And the star rains its fire while the
beau-ti-ful sing, For the man-ger of Beth-le-hem cra-dles a King. A - MEN.

2 There's a tumult of joy
  O'er the wonderful birth!
For the Virgin's sweet Boy
  Is the Lord of the Earth.
Ay! the star rains its fire and the beautiful sing,
For the manger of Bethlehem cradles a King.

3 In the light of that star
  Lie the ages impearled;
And that song from afar
  Has swept over the world:
Every hearth is aflame, and the beautiful sing
In the homes of the nations that Jesus is King.

4 We rejoice in the light,
  And we echo the song
That comes down through the night
  From the heavenly throng;
Ay! we shout to the lovely evangel they bring,
And we greet in His cradle our Saviour and King.

JOSIAH G. HOLLAND, 1871

99

116 THE FIRST NOËL Irregular

A traditional melody in
W. SANDYS' *Christmas Carols*, 1833

1 The first No - el the an - gel did say Was to cer - tain poor
2 They look - ed up and saw a star Shi - ning in the
3 And by the light of that same star, Three wise - men
4 This star drew nigh to the north - west, O'er Beth - le -
5 Then en - tered in those wise men three, Full rev - er - ent -
6 Then let us all with one ac - cord Sing prais - es

1 shep-herds in fields as they lay; In fields where they lay keep - ing their
2 east, be - yond them far, And to the earth it gave great
3 came from coun - try far; To seek for a King was their in -
4 hem it took its rest, And there it did both stop and
5 ly up - on their knee, And of - fered there, in His pres -
6 to our heaven - ly Lord, That hath made heaven and earth of

1 sheep, On a cold win - ter's night that was so deep.
2 light, And so it con - tin - ued both day and night.
3 tent, And to fol - low the star wher - ev - er it went.
4 stay, Right o - ver the place where Je - sus lay.
5 ence, Their gold, and myrrh, and frank - in - cense.
6 naught, And with His blood man - kind hath bought.

Christmas

No - el, No - el, No - el, No - el, Born is the King of Is - ra - el. A - MEN.

NOTE—The French word "Noël," now again becoming familiar, signifies "Christmas" or "Christmas Carol." In English Christmas poetry it sometimes means "news" or "glad tidings," and sometimes "Christmas" itself. The words also are traditional.

117 STELLA 8. 6. 6. 8. 6. 6.

HORATIO W. PARKER, 1893

1 All my heart this night re - joi - ces, As I hear, far and near,

Sweet - est an - gel voi - ces; "Christ is born," their choirs are sing - ing,

Till the air ev - ery - where Now with joy is ring - ing. A - MEN.

FRÖHLICH SOLL MEIN HERZE SPRINGEN

2 Hark! a voice from yonder manger,
　　Soft and sweet, doth entreat:
　　　"Flee from woe and danger;
　Brethren, come; from all doth grieve you
　You are freed; all you need
　　I will surely give you."

3 Come, then, let us hasten yonder:
　　Here let all, great and small,
　　　Kneel in awe and wonder;

Love Him who with love is yearning,
　　Hail the Star that from far
　　　Bright with hope is burning.

4 Blessèd Saviour, let me find Thee!
　　Keep Thou me close to Thee,
　　　Cast me not behind Thee:
Life of life, my heart Thou stillest,
　Calm I rest on Thy breast,
　　All this void Thou fillest.

Rev. PAUL GERHARDT, 1656.　Translated by CATHERINE WINKWORTH, 1858

118 ADESTE FIDELES Irregular

In J. F. WADE'S *Cantus diversi*, 1751

1 O come, all ye faith-ful, Joy-ful and tri-umph-ant, O come ye, O
2 God of ... God, ... Light ... of ... Light; ... Born of a
3 Sing, choirs of an - gels; Sing in ex - ul - ta - tion, Sing, all ye
4 Yea, Lord, we greet Thee, Born this hap - py morn - ing: Je - sus, to

come ye to Beth - le - hem; Come and be - hold Him
Vir - gin, made ver - y Man: Ver - y .... God, Be -
cit - i - zens of heaven a - bove; Glo - ry to God .....
Thee ...... be glo - ry given; Word of the Fa - ther,

Born the King of an - gels;
got - ten, not cre - at - ed: O come, let us a - dore Him, O come, let us a -
In .... the ... high - est;
Late in flesh ap - pear-ing:

dore Him, O come, let us a - dore Him, Christ the Lord. A - MEN.

An anonymous 17th or 18th century Latin hymn;
translated by Rev. FREDERICK OAKLEY and slightly varied

NOTE—*For the Christmas gospel of world peace, see* "*It came upon the midnight clear,*" *No. 278.*

The Epiphany

O God who didst manifest Thy Son unto the Gentiles by the shining of a star; Have compassion upon any of the children of men who are yet walking in the darkness of sin. Lead them by Thy Holy Spirit to Him who is the light of the world, that walking in His light they may at length attain to the light of everlasting life: through Jesus Christ our Lord. Amen.

119 DIX 7. 7. 7. 7. 7. 7.　　Arranged from CONRAD KOCHER's "Treuer Heiland," 1838

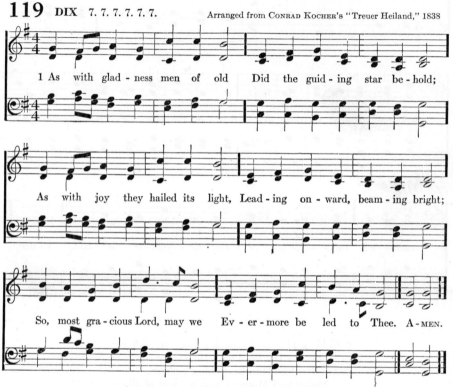

1 As with glad-ness men of old Did the guid-ing star be-hold;

As with joy they hailed its light, Lead-ing on-ward, beam-ing bright;

So, most gra-cious Lord, may we Ev-er-more be led to Thee. A-MEN.

2 As with joyful steps they sped
To that lowly manger-bed,
There to bend the knee before
Him whom heaven and earth adore;
So may we with willing feet
Ever seek Thy mercy-seat.

3 As they offered gifts most rare
At that manger rude and bare;
So may we with holy joy,
Pure, and free from sin's alloy,
All our costliest treasures bring,
Christ, to Thee, our heavenly King.

4 Holy Jesus, every day
Keep us in the narrow way;
And, when earthly things are past,
Bring our ransomed souls at last
Where they need no star to guide
Where no clouds Thy glory hide.

5 In the heavenly country bright
Need they no created light;
Thou its Light, its Joy, its Crown,
Thou its Sun which goes not down;
There for ever may we sing
Alleluias to our King.

WILLIAM C. DIX, 1861

NOTE—*The Epiphany (January 6th) commemorates the visit of the Magi, and, as prophetic of the homage of the nations to Christ, has long been regarded as especially a missionary occasion.*

120 SANTA LAURA 11. 10. 11. 10.

WILLIAM A. BARRETT, 1865

1 Bright-est and best of the sons of the morn-ing, Dawn on our dark-ness and lend us thine aid; Star of the east, the ho - ri - zon a - dorn - ing, Guide where our in - fant· Re - deem - er is laid. A - MEN.

Alternative tune, WESLEY, No. 295

2 Cold on His cradle the dewdrops are shining;
　　Low lies His head with the beasts of the stall:
　Angels adore Him in slumber reclining
　　Maker and Monarch and Saviour of all.

3 Say, shall we yield Him, in costly devotion,
　　Odors of Edom and offerings divine,
　Gems of the mountain and pearls of the ocean,
　　Myrrh from the forest, or gold from the mine?

4 Vainly we offer each ample oblation;
　　Vainly with gifts would His favor secure:
　Richer by far is the heart's adoration;
　　Dearer to God are the prayers of the poor.

5 Brightest and best of the sons of the morning,
　　Dawn on our darkness, and lend us thine aid;
　Star of the east, the horizon adorning,
　　Guide where our infant Redeemer is laid.

Bishop REGINALD HEBER, 1811

104

The Epiphany

121 THREE KINGS 8. 8. 8. 6. with Refrain E. W. KELLOGG, 1862

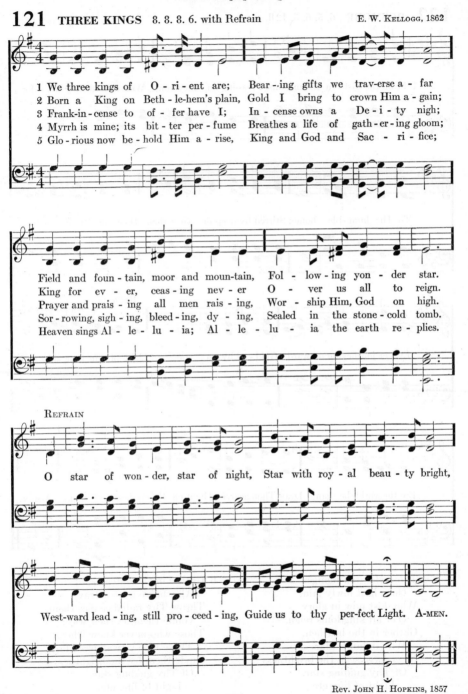

1 We three kings of O - ri - ent are; Bear - ing gifts we trav-erse a - far
2 Born a King on Beth - le-hem's plain, Gold I bring to crown Him a - gain;
3 Frank-in - cense to of - fer have I; In - cense owns a De - i - ty nigh;
4 Myrrh is mine; its bit - ter per - fume Breathes a life of gath - er - ing gloom;
5 Glo - rious now be - hold Him a - rise, King and God and Sac - ri - fice;

Field and foun - tain, moor and moun-tain, Fol - low-ing yon - der star.
King for ev - er, ceas - ing nev - er O - ver us all to reign.
Prayer and prais - ing all men rais - ing, Wor - ship Him, God on high.
Sor - rowing, sigh - ing, bleed-ing, dy - ing, Sealed in the stone - cold tomb.
Heaven sings Al - le - lu - ia; Al - le - lu - ia the earth re - plies.

REFRAIN

O star of won - der, star of night, Star with roy - al beau - ty bright,

West-ward lead - ing, still pro - ceed - ing, Guide us to thy per-fect Light. A-MEN.

Rev. JOHN H. HOPKINS, 1857

122 ROSMORE 6. 5. 6. 5. 12 ll.

HENRY G. TREMBATH, 1893

1 From the east-ern moun-tains, Press-ing on, they come, Wise men in their wis - dom,

To His hum - ble home; Stirred by deep de - vo - tion, Hast - ing from a - far,

Ev - er journeying on-ward, Guid - ed by a star. Light of life that shi - neth

REFRAIN

Ere the worlds be - gan, Draw Thou near, and light-en Ev-ery heart of man. A-MEN.

2 Thou who in a manger
  Once hast lowly lain,
Who dost now in glory
  O'er all kingdoms reign,
Gather in the heathen,
  Who in lands afar
Ne'er have seen the brightness
  Of Thy guiding star.
    Light of life, etc.

3 Gather in the outcasts,
  All who've gone astray,
Throw Thy radiance o'er them,
  Guide them on their way:
Those who never knew Thee,
  Those who've wandered far,
Guide them by the brightness
  Of Thy guiding star.
    Light of life, etc.

4 Onward through the darkness
  Of the lonely night,
Shining still before them
  With Thy kindly light,
Guide them, Jew and Gentile,
  Homeward from afar,
Young and old together,
  By Thy guiding star.
    .Light of life, etc.

5 Until every nation,
  Whether bond or free,
'Neath Thy starlit banner,
  Jesus, follows Thee
O'er the distant mountains
  To that heavenly home,
Where nor sin nor sorrow
  Evermore shall come.
  Light of life, etc.

Rev. GODFREY THRING, 1873

123 STUTTGART 8. 7. 8. 7.   Adapted from a melody in *Psalmodia Sacra*, GOTHA, 1715

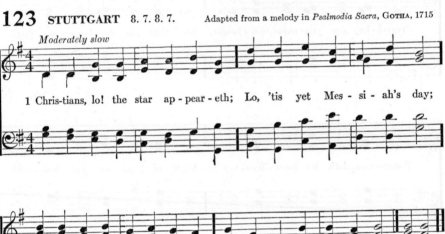

1 Chris-tians, lo! the star ap-pear-eth; Lo, 'tis yet Mes-si-ah's day;

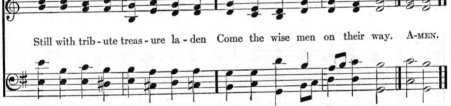

Still with trib-ute treas-ure la-den Come the wise men on their way. A-MEN.

2 Where a life is spent in service,
    Walking where the Master trod,
  There is scattered myrrh most fragrant
    For the blessèd Christ of God.

3 Whoso bears his brother's burden,
    Whoso shares another's woe,
  Brings his frankincense to Jesus
    With the men of long ago.

4 When we soothe earth's weary children,
    Tending best the least of them,
  'Tis the Lord Himself we worship,
    Bringing gold to Bethlehem.

5 Christians, lo! the star appeareth,
    Leading still the ancient way;
  Christians, onward with your treasure;
    It is still Messiah's day.

Rev. JAMES A. BLAISDELL, 1900

124 WATCHMAN 7. 7. 7. 7. D.

LOWELL MASON, 1830

1 Watch-man, tell us of the night, What its signs of prom-ise are:

Travel-ler, o'er yon moun-tain's height, See that glo-ry-beam-ing star!

Watch-man, doth its beau-teous ray Aught of hope or joy fore-tell?

Travel-ler, yes, it brings the day, Prom-ised day of Is-ra-el. A - MEN.

He calleth to me out of Seir, Watchman, what of the night? Watchman, what of the night?—ISA. xxi, 11

2 Watchman, tell us of the night;
　Higher yet that star ascends:
　Traveller, blessedness and light,
　　Peace and truth, its course portends.
　Watchman, will its beams alone
　　Gild the spot that gave them birth?
　Traveller, ages are its own;
　　And it bursts o'er all the earth.

3 Watchman, tell us of the night,
　For the morning seems to dawn:
　Traveller, darkness takes its flight;
　　Doubt and terror are withdrawn.
　Watchman, let thy wanderings cease;
　　Hie thee to thy quiet home.
　Traveller, lo, the Prince of Peace,
　　Lo, the Son of God is come!

Sir JOHN BOWRING, 1825

Christ's Life on Earth

A Collect for Grace to Follow Christ

O God, who didst give Thy Son to be born of woman and to number His sinless years: We pray Thee that the light of Christ may shine anew upon these paths which once were trodden by His blessed feet, and may enfold our daily lives within the beauty of His holiness and the fellowship of His peace. We ask it in His Name. Amen.

125 NAZARETH 8. 8. 8. 8. 8. 8.

A Swiss melody, arranged in *Crown of Jesus Music*, 1864

1 Ye fair green hills of Gal - i - lee, That gir - dle qui - et Naz-a-reth,

What glo - rious vis-ion did ye see Of Him who con-quered sin and death;

When o'er your flow-ered slopes He trod, And grew in grace with man and God? A-MEN.

2 We saw no glory crown His head
　　As childhood ripened into youth;
　No angels on His errands sped;
　　He wrought no sign save meekness, truth;
　While duty marked each step He trod,
　And love to man, and love to God.

3 Jesus, my Saviour, Master, King,
　　Who didst for me the burden bear,
　While saints in heaven Thy glory sing,
　　Let me on earth Thy likeness wear;
　Mine be the path Thy feet have trod,
　Of love to man, and love to God.

Rev. EUSTACE R. CONDER, 1887: with four lines varied

126 BETHLEHEM C. M. D.　　　　　Sir Joseph Barnby, 1895

1 O sing a song of Beth-le-hem, Of shep-herds watch-ing there,

And of the news that came to them From an-gels in the air:

The light that shone on Beth-le-hem Fills all the world to-day;

Of Je-sus' birth and peace on earth The an-gels sing al-way. A-men.

2 O sing a song of Nazareth,
　Of sunny days of joy,
O sing of fragrant flowers' breath,
　And of the sinless Boy:
For now the flowers of Nazareth
　In every heart may grow;
Now spreads the fame of His dear Name
　On all the winds that blow.

3 O sing a song of Galilee,
　Of lake and woods and hill,
Of Him who walked upon the sea
　And bade its waves be still:

For though, like waves on Galilee,
　Dark seas of trouble roll,
When faith has heard the Master's word,
　Falls peace upon the soul.

4 O sing a song of Calvary,
　Its glory and dismay;
Of Him who hung upon the tree
　And took our sins away:
For He who died on Calvary
　Is risen from the grave,
And Christ our Lord, by heaven adored,
　Is mighty now to save.

Rev. Louis F. Benson, 1899

127 SCENES THAT ARE BRIGHTEST 11. 11. 11. 11. Arranged from WILLIAM V. WALLACE, 1845

1 Blest land of Ju - de - a! thrice hal-lowed of song; Where the ho - liest of mem - o - ries pil - grim - like throng; In the shade of thy palms, by the shores of thy sea, On the hills of thy beau - ty, my heart is with thee. A-MEN.

2 Blue sea of the hills! in my spirit I hear
Thy waters, Gennesaret, chime on my ear;
Where the Lowly and Just with the people sat down,
And thy spray on the dust of His sandals was thrown.

3 O here with His flock the sad Wanderer came;
These hills He toiled over in grief are the same;
The founts where He drank by the wayside still flow,
And the same airs are blowing which breathed on His brow.

4 And what if my feet may not tread where He trod,
Nor my ears hear the dashing of Galilee's flood,
Nor my eyes see the cross which He bowed Him to bear,
Nor my knees press Gethsemane's garden of prayer,—

5 Yet, Loved of the Father, Thy Spirit is near
To the meek and the lowly and penitent here;
And the voice of Thy love is the same even now
As at Bethany's tomb or on Olivet's brow.

JOHN G. WHITTIER, 1837

128 REST 8. 6. 8. 8. 6.

FREDERICK C. MAKER, 1887

1 Dear Lord and Fa - ther of man-kind, For - give our fool - ish ways;

Re - clothe us in our right - ful mind, In pur - er lives Thy

serv - ice find, In deep - er rev - erence, praise. A - MEN.

For a higher setting, see No. 227

2 In simple trust like theirs who heard,
   Beside the Syrian sea,
   The gracious calling of the Lord,
   Let us, like them, without a word
   Rise up and follow Thee.

3 O Sabbath rest by Galilee!
   O calm of hills above,
   Where Jesus knelt to share with Thee
   The silence of eternity
   Interpreted by love!

4 With that deep hush subduing all
   Our words and works that drown
   The tender whisper of Thy call,
   As noiseless let Thy blessing fall
   As fell Thy manna down.

5 Drop Thy still dews of quietness,
   Till all our strivings cease:
   Take from our souls the strain and stress,
   And let our ordered lives confess
   The beauty of Thy peace.

Abridged from JOHN G. WHITTIER's "The Brewing of Soma," 1872

129 CUSHMAN 11. 10. 11. 10.

Rev. Herbert B. Turner, 1905

1 We would see Je - sus, lo! His star is shi - ning A - bove the sta - ble while the an - gels sing; There in a man - ger, on the hay re - cli - ning, Haste, let us lay our gifts be - fore the King. A - MEN.

Copyright, 1905, by H. B. Turner

Sir, we would see Jesus.—St. John xii, 21

2 We would see Jesus, Mary's Son most holy,
  Light of the village life from day to day;
Shining revealed through every task most lowly,
  The Christ of God, the Life, the Truth, the Way.

3 We would see Jesus, on the mountain teaching,
  With all the listening people gathered round;
While birds and flowers and sky above are preaching
  The blessedness which simple trust has found.

4 We would see Jesus, in His work of healing,
  At eventide before the sun was set;
Divine and human, in His deep revealing
  Of God and man in loving service met.

5 We would see Jesus, in the early morning,
  Still as of old He calleth, "Follow Me";
Let us arise, all meaner service scorning:
  Lord, we are Thine, we give ourselves to Thee.

Rev. J. Edgar Park, 1913

(From *Worship and Song* by Winchester and Conant; copyright, 1913, by The Pilgrim Press. Used by permission.)

130 MARGARET Irregular   Rev. T. Richard Matthews, 1876

1 Thou didst leave Thy throne and Thy king-ly crown When Thou
cam-est to earth for me, But in Beth-lehem's home was there
found no room For Thy ho-ly na-tiv-i-ty: O
come to my heart, Lord Je-sus! There is room in my heart for Thee. A-men.

2 Heaven's arches rang when the angels sang,
  Proclaiming Thy royal degree;
But of lowly birth didst Thou come to earth,
  And in great humility:
O come to my heart, Lord Jesus!
There is room in my heart for Thee.

3 The foxes found rest, and the birds their nest,
  In the shade of the forest tree;
But Thy couch was the sod, O Thou Son of God,
  In the desert of Galilee:
O come to my heart, Lord Jesus!
There is room in my heart for Thee.

4 Thou camest, O Lord, with the living word
  That should set Thy people free;
But with mocking scorn, and with crown of thorn,
  They bore Thee to Calvary:
O come to my heart, Lord Jesus!
  Thy cross is my only plea.

5 When heaven's arches shall ring, and her choirs shall sing,
  At Thy coming to victory,
Let Thy voice call me home, saying, "Yet there is room,
  There is room at My side for thee."
And my heart shall rejoice, Lord Jesus,
  When Thou comest and callest for me.

EMILY E. S. ELLIOTT, 1864

131 ARMSTRONG 7. 7. 5. 7. 7. 5.

GEORGE W. CHADWICK, 1888

1 When the Lord of love was here, Hap-py hearts to Him were dear,
Though His heart was sad; Worn and lone-ly for our sake,
Yet He turned a-side to make All the wea-ry glad. A-MEN.

2 Meek and lowly were His ways,
  From His loving grew His praise,
    From His giving, prayer:
  All the outcasts thronged to hear,
  All the sorrowful drew near
    To enjoy His care.

3 When He walked the fields, He drew
  From the flowers, and birds, and dew,
    Parables of God;
  For within His heart of love
  All the soul of man did move,
    God had His abode.

4 Lord, be ours Thy power to keep
  In the very heart of grief,
    And in trial, love.
  In our meekness to be wise,
  And through sorrow to arise
    To our God above.

5 Fill us with Thy deep desire
  All the sinful to inspire,
    With the Father's life:
  Free us from the cares that press
  On the heart of worldliness,
    From the fret and strife.

REV. STOPFORD BROOKE, 1881

132 BISHOPTHORPE C. M.

In EDWARD MILLER'S
The Psalms of David for Parish Churches, 1790

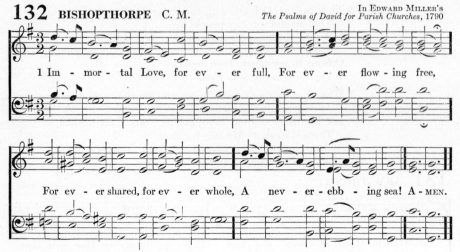

1 Im - mor - tal Love, for ev - er full, For ev - er flow - ing free,

For ev - er shared, for ev - er whole, A nev - er - ebb - ing sea! A - MEN.

2 Our outward lips confess the Name
  All other names above;
  Love only knoweth whence it came,
  And comprehendeth love.

3 We may not climb the heavenly steeps
  To bring the Lord Christ down:
  In vain we search the lowest deeps,
  For Him no depths can drown.

4 But warm, sweet, tender, even yet
  A present help is He;
  And faith has still its Olivet,
  And love its Galilee.

5 The healing of His seamless dress
  Is by our beds of pain;
  We touch Him in life's throng and press,
  And we are whole again.

6 Through Him the first fond prayers are said
  Our lips of childhood frame,
  The last low whispers of our dead
  Are burdened with His Name.

7 Our Lord, and Master of us all,
  Whate'er our name or sign,
  We own Thy sway, we hear Thy call,
  We test our lives by Thine.

Arranged from JOHN G. WHITTIER'S "Our Master," 1866

SERENITY C. M.

Arranged from WILLIAM V. WALLACE'S
"Ye winds that waft," 1836, by UZZIAH C. BURNAP

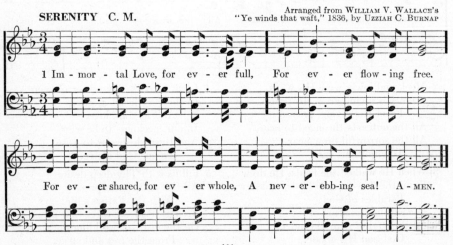

1 Im - mor - tal Love, for ev - er full, For ev - er flow - ing free.

For ev - er shared, for ev - er whole, A nev - er - ebb - ing sea! A - MEN.

133 **WALSALL** C. M.   In John Chetham's *A Book of Psalmody*, 1718

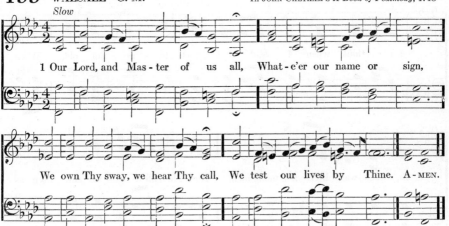

Slow

1 Our Lord, and Mas-ter of us all, What-e'er our name or sign,

We own Thy sway, we hear Thy call, We test our lives by Thine. A-men.

2 Thou judgest us; Thy purity
  Doth all our lusts condemn;
The love that draws us nearer Thee
  Is hot with wrath to them.

3 Yet, weak and blinded though we be,
  Thou dost our service own;
We bring our varying gifts to Thee,
  And Thou rejectest none.

4 To Thee our full humanity,
  Its joys and pains, belong;
The wrong of man to man on Thee
  Inflicts a deeper wrong.

5 Who hates, hates Thee; who loves, becomes
  Therein to Thee allied;
All sweet accords of hearts and homes
  In Thee are multiplied.

6 Apart from Thee all gain is loss,
  All labor vainly done;
The solemn shadow of Thy cross
  Is better than the sun.

7 Our Friend, our Brother, and our Lord,
  What may Thy service be?
Nor name, nor form, nor ritual word,
  But simply following Thee.

Arranged from John G. Whittier's "Our Master," 1866

FAITH C. M.   Rev. John B. Dykes, 1867

1 Our Lord, and Mas-ter of us all, What-e'er our name or sign,

We own Thy sway, we hear Thy call, We test our lives by Thine. A-men.

Our Lord Jesus Christ

134 **SWEET STORY** 11. 8. 12. 9.

A folk song, arranged by
WILLIAM B. BRADBURY, 1859

1 I think when I read that sweet sto-ry of old, When Je-sus was here a-mong men, How He called lit-tle chil-dren as lambs to His fold, I should like to have been with them then. A-MEN.

2 I wish that His hands had been placed on my head,
    That His arm had been thrown around me,
  And that I might have seen His kind look when He said,
    "Let the little ones come unto Me."

3 Yet still to His footstool in prayer I may go,
    And ask for a share in His love;
  And if I now earnestly seek Him below,
    I shall see Him and hear Him above.

4 But thousands and thousands who wander and fall
    Never heard of that heavenly home;
  I should like them to know there is room for them all,
    And that Jesus has bid them to come.

5 I long for the joy of that glorious time,
    The sweetest and brightest and best,
  When the dear little children of every clime
    Shall crowd to His arms and be blest.

MRS. JEMIMA LUKE, 1841

NOTE—*Most of this famous hymn was written by Mrs. Luke (then Miss Thompson) on the back of an envelope while travelling in a stage-coach. It was sung by the Sunday school in the chapel on her father's estate, near Bath, England, and by him copied and sent to the S. S. Teachers' Magazine. "But for my father's intervention the hymn would in all probability never have been preserved."*

135 LEIGHTON S. M.

HENRY W. GREATOREX, 1849

1 Thou say'st, "Take up thy cross, O man, and fol-low Me"; The night is black, the feet are slack, Yet we would fol - low Thee. A - MEN.

2 But, O dear Lord, we cry,
  That we Thy face could see!
Thy blessèd face one moment's space—
  Then might we follow Thee!

3 Dim tracts of time divide
  Those golden days from me;
Thy voice comes strange o'er years of change,
  How can I follow Thee?

4 Comes faint and far Thy voice
  From vales of Galilee;
Thy vision fades in ancient shades;
  How should we follow Thee?

5 O heavy cross—of faith
  In what we cannot see!
As once of yore Thyself restore,
  And help to follow Thee.

6 If not as once Thou cam'st
  In true humanity,
Come yet as Guest within the breast
  That burns to follow Thee.

7 Within our heart of hearts
  In nearest nearness be:
Set up Thy throne within Thine own:
  Go, Lord: we follow Thee.

FRANCIS T. PALGRAVE, 1865

MARSHALL S. M.

REV. G. JARVIS GEER, 1870

1 Thou say'st, "Take up thy cross, O man, and fol - low Me"; The night is black, the feet are slack, Yet we would fol - low Thee. A - MEN.

Our Lord: The Entry into Jerusalem

A Collect for Palm Sunday

Forgive, O God, the sins of all who cry Hosanna to Thy Son in the hour of His triumph and forsake Him in the hour of His passion. And grant unto Thy servants so to receive Him in humble hearts that we may be numbered at the last with the great multitude of all peoples and tongues, who stand before the throne in white robes and with palms in their hands, and ascribe their salvation to Thee and unto the Lamb which taketh away the sins of the world. Amen.

136 ST. DROSTANE L. M.

Rev. JOHN B. DYKES, 1862

1 Ride on! ride on in ma-jes-ty! Hark! all the tribes Ho-san-na cry; Thine hum-ble beast pur-sues his road With palms and scat-tered gar-ments strowed. A-MEN.

Alternative tune, PARK STREET, No. 292

2 Ride on! ride on in majesty!
In lowly pomp ride on to die:
O Christ, Thy triumphs now begin
O'er captive death and conquered sin.

3 Ride on! ride on in majesty!
The wingèd squadrons of the sky
Look down with sad and wondering eyes
To see the approaching sacrifice.

4 Ride on! ride on in majesty!
Thy last and fiercest strife is nigh;
The Father on His sapphire throne
Expects His own Anointed Son.

5 Ride on! ride on in majesty!
In lowly pomp ride on to die;
Bow Thy meek head to mortal pain,
Then take, O God, Thy power, and reign.

Rev. HENRY H. MILMAN, 1827: verse 1, line 3, varied

The Entry into Jerusalem

137 ST. THEODULPH 7. 6. 7. 6. D. MELCHIOR TESCHNER, 1615

May be sung in unison

1 All glo-ry, laud, and hon - or To Thee, Re - deem - er, King,

To whom the lips of chil - dren Made sweet ho - san - nas ring.

Thou art the King of Is - rael, Thou Da - vid's roy - al Son,

Who in the Lord's Name com - est, The King and Bless - ed One. A - MEN.

GLORIA LAUS ET HONOR

2 The company of angels
  Are praising Thee on high,
And mortal men, and all things
  Created, make reply.
The people of the Hebrews
  With palms before Thee went;
Our praise and prayer and anthems
  Before Thee we present.

3 To Thee, before Thy passion,
  They sang their hymns of praise;
To Thee, now high exalted,
  Our melody we raise.
Thou didst accept their praises;
  Accept the prayers we bring,
Who in all good delightest,
  Thou good and gracious King.

THEODULPH OF ORLEANS, c. 820. Translated by Rev. JOHN M. NEALE, 1854:
as varied in *Hymns ancient and modern*, 1861

121

A Collect on the Passion

Most gracious God, who gavest Thy Son to suffer and die for our redemption: Hallow these songs that follow Him in devout remembrance of His cross and grave; that we who sing may be drawn into the fellowship of His sufferings and may abide always in the spirit of His sacrifice. In whose Name we pray. Amen.

138 LANIER Irregular   Peter C. Lutkin, 1905

1 In - to the woods my Mas - ter went, Clean for - spent, for - spent;
2 Out of the woods my Mas - ter went, And He was well con - tent;

In - to the woods my Mas - ter came, For-spent with love and shame. But the
Out of the woods my Mas - ter came, Con - tent with death and shame. When

ol - ives they were not blind to Him, The lit - tle gray leaves were kind to Him,
death and shame would woo Him last, From un - der the trees they drew Him last,

The thorn - tree had a mind to Him, When in - to the woods He came.
'Twas on a tree they slew Him last, When out of the woods He came. A - MEN.

Sidney Lanier, 1880

The Passion

139 HAVEN 7. 7. 7. 7. EDWIN H. LEMARE, Senior, 1889

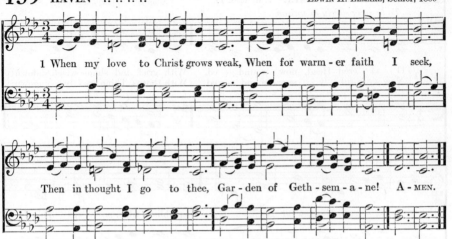

1 When my love to Christ grows weak, When for warm-er faith I seek,

Then in thought I go to thee, Gar-den of Geth-sem-a-ne! A-MEN.

2 There I walk amidst the shades,
While the lingering twilight fades,
Meet my Saviour, friendless, lone,
See Him weep, and hear Him groan.

3 There I watch the agony
That He underwent for me;
And with pitying love confess,
Ne'er was sorrow like to His.

4 When my love for Christ grows weak,
When for stronger faith I seek,
Hill of Calvary! I go
To thy scenes of fear and woe.

5 There with trembling awe I see
Jesus tortured on the tree,
Hear the scoffers' savage cries,
While for them, for me, He dies.

6 Yes, for me He toiled and bled,
Bowed in death His gracious head;
And to Him my soul shall give
Love and reverence while I live.

Rev. JOHN R. WREFORD, 1837

140 (HAVEN) 7. 7. 7. 7.

1 Never further than Thy cross,
Never higher than Thy feet!
Here earth's precious things seem dross,
Here earth's bitter things grow sweet.

2 Gazing thus, our sin we see,
Learn Thy love while gazing thus;
Sin, which laid the cross on Thee,
Love, which bore the cross for us.

3 Here we learn to serve and give,
And, obedient, self deny;
Here we gather love to live,
Here we gather faith to die.

4 Pressing onward as we can,
Still to this our hearts shall tend;
Where our earliest hopes began,
There our last aspirings end;

5 Till amid the hosts of light,
We in Thee redeemed, complete,
Through Thy cross made pure and white,
Cast our crowns before Thy feet.

Mrs. ELIZABETH R. CHARLES, 1860

Our Lord Jesus Christ

141 **PASSION CHORALE** 7. 6. 7. 6. D.
Melody by H. L. HASSLER, 1564–1612
Adapted and harmonized by J. S. BACH

To be sung slowly in unison

1 {O sa - cred Head, now wound - ed, With grief and shame weighed down;
Now scorn-ful - ly sur - round - ed With thorns, Thine on - ly crown;}

O sa - cred Head, what glo - ry, What bliss till now was Thine!

Yet, though de - spised and go - ry, I joy to call Thee mine. A-MEN.

O HAUPT VOLL BLUT UND WUNDEN

2 O noblest Brow and dearest,
In other days the world
All feared when Thou appearedst;
What shame on Thee is hurled!
How art Thou pale with anguish,
With sore abuse and scorn;
How does that visage languish
Which once was bright as morn!

3 What Thou, my Lord, hast suffered
Was all for sinners' gain:
Mine, mine was the transgression,
But Thine the deadly pain.
Lo, here I fall, my Saviour!
'Tis I deserve Thy place;
Look on me with Thy favor,
Vouchsafe to me Thy grace.

4 What language shall I borrow
To thank Thee, dearest Friend,
For this Thy dying sorrow,
Thy pity without end?
O make me Thine for ever;
And should I fainting be,
Lord, let me never, never
Outlive my love to Thee.

Ascribed to BERNARD OF CLAIRVAUX (1091–1153)
Translated (into German) by Rev. PAUL GERHARDT, 1656
Translated (from the German) by Rev. JAMES W. ALEXANDER, 1830
124

142 MEIRIONYDD 7. 6. 7. 6. D.

A Welsh hymn melody

In moderate time

1 O Je - sus, we a - dore Thee, Up - on the cross, our King!

We bow our hearts be - fore Thee, Thy gra - cious Name we sing.

That Name hath brought sal - va - tion, That Name in life our stay,

Our peace, our con - so - la - tion, When life shall fade a - way. A-MEN.

2 Yet doth the world disdain Thee,
　Still passing by the cross:
Lord, may our hearts retain Thee;
　All else we count but loss.
Ah, Lord, our sins arraigned Thee,
　And nailed Thee to the tree:
Our pride, O Lord, disdained Thee;
　Yet deign our Hope to be.

3 O glorious King, we bless Thee,
　No longer pass Thee by;
O Jesus, we confess Thee
　The Son enthroned on high.
Lord, grant to us remission;
　Life through Thy death restore;
Yea, grant us the fruition
　Of life for evermore.

Rev. ARTHUR T. RUSSELL, 1851

143 RATHBUN 8. 7. 8. 7.

ITHAMAR CONKEY, 1851

1 In the cross of Christ I glo-ry, Tower-ing o'er the wrecks of time;

All the light of sa-cred sto-ry Gath-ers round its head sub-lime. A-MEN.

God forbid that I should glory, save in the cross of our Lord Jesus Christ.—GAL. vi, 14.

2 When the woes of life o'ertake me,
　Hopes deceive, and fears annoy,
Never shall the cross forsake me:
　Lo! it glows with peace and joy.

3 When the sun of bliss is beaming
　Light and love upon my way,
From the cross the radiance streaming
　Adds more lustre to the day.

4 Bane and blessing, pain and pleasure,
　By the cross are sanctified;
Peace is there that knows no measure,
　Joys that through all time abide.

5 In the cross of Christ I glory,
　Towering o'er the wrecks of time;
All the light of sacred story
　Gathers round its head sublime.

Sir JOHN BOWRING, 1825

HOLYROOD 7. 7. 7. 7.

MASSAH M. WARNER, 1898

1 It is fin-ished: o'er that Brow Creeps the shad-ow ev-en now.

One with us to life's last breath, Je-sus shares the cup of death. A-MEN.

144 MEDITATION C. M.

JOHN H. GOWER, 1890

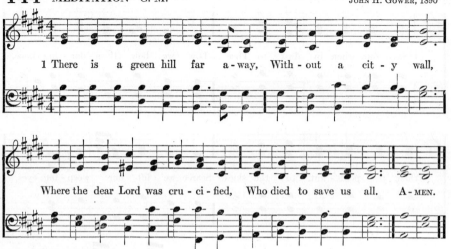

1 There is a green hill far a-way, With-out a cit-y wall,

Where the dear Lord was cru-ci-fied, Who died to save us all. A-MEN.

Copyright by John H. Gower.

2 We may not know, we cannot tell,
　What pains He had to bear;
　But we believe it was for us
　He hung and suffered there.

3 He died that we might be forgiven,
　He died to make us good,
　That we might go at last to heaven,
　Saved by His precious blood.

4 There was no other good enough
　To pay the price of sin;
　He only could unlock the gate
　Of heaven, and let us in.

5 O dearly, dearly has He loved,
　And we must love Him too,
　And trust in His redeeming blood,
　And try His works to do.

Mrs. CECIL F. ALEXANDER, 1848

NOTE—*These verses first appeared in her "Hymns for Little Children," 1848*

145 (HOLYROOD) 7. 7. 7. 7.

It is finished.—ST. JOHN xix, 30

1 It is finished: o'er that Brow
　Creeps the shadow even now.
　One with us to life's last breath,
　Jesus shares the cup of death.

2 Through the gloaming long ago
　Prophets saw Messiah's woe.
　Now their visions are fulfilled,
　And that lonely Heart is stilled.

3 "Lo! I come to do Thy will,"
　Rings the old evangel still.
　"It is finished!" says the Son,
　When the Father's will is done.

4 They who followed to the cross,
　Mindful only of their loss,
　Bow their stricken heads and say,
　"It is finished: come away."

5 "It is finished!" As the cry
　Echoes from the hills on high,
　They who sang on Christmas Day
　Fold their sinless hands and pray.

6 Take that piercèd Body down;
　Now unbind the thorny crown;
　Lay that Head on earth's cold breast;
　It is finished: Jesus, rest.

Rev. LOUIS F. BENSON, 1897, 1917

146 BLUMENTHAL 7. 7. 7. 7. D.

Arranged from JACQUES BLUMENTHAL, 1847

1 Sav - iour, when in dust to Thee Low we bow the a - dor - ing knee,
When, re - pent - ant, to the skies Scarce we lift our weep - ing eyes,
O by all Thy pains and woe Suf - fered once for man be - low,—
Bend - ing from Thy throne on high, Hear our sol - emn lit - an - y. A - MEN.

2 By the sacred griefs that wept
O'er the grave where Lazarus slept,
By the boding tears that flowed
Over Salem's loved abode,
By the anguished sigh that told
Treachery lurked within Thy fold,—
From Thy seat above the sky
Hear our solemn litany.

3 By Thine hour of dire despair,
By Thine agony of prayer,
By the cross, the nail, the thorn,
Piercing spear, and torturing scorn,

By the gloom that veiled the skies
O'er the dreadful sacrifice,—
Listen to our humble cry,
Hear our solemn litany.

4 By Thy deep expiring groan,
By the sad sepulchral stone,
By the vault whose dark abode
Held in vain the rising God,—
O from earth to heaven restored,
Mighty, re-ascended Lord,
Listen, listen to the cry
Of our solemn litany.

Sir ROBERT GRANT, 1815 (his text of 1839)

147 ROCKINGHAM L. M.

Adapted by EDWARD MILLER
in his *Psalms of David*, 1790

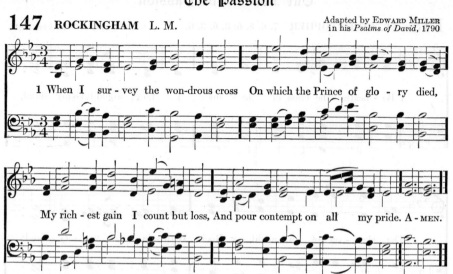

1 When I sur-vey the won-drous cross On which the Prince of glo-ry died,

My rich-est gain I count but loss, And pour contempt on all my pride. A-MEN.

2 Forbid it, Lord, that I should boast,
Save in the death of Christ my God:
All the vain things that charm me most,
I sacrifice them to His blood.

3 See, from His head, His hands, His feet,
Sorrow and love flow mingled down:
Did e'er such love and sorrow meet,
Or thorns compose so rich a crown?

4 Were the whole realm of nature mine,
That were a present far too small;
Love so amazing, so divine,
Demands my soul, my life, my all.

REV. ISAAC WATTS, 1707 (his text of 1709)

SPANISH HYMN 7. 7. 7. 7. D.

"The Spanish Hymn, arranged for the Musical Fund
Society," by BENJAMIN CARR, Philadelphia, 1826

FINE

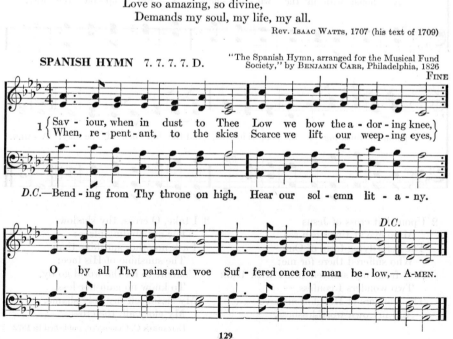

1 {Sav-iour, when in dust to Thee Low we bow the a-dor-ing knee,}
{When, re-pent-ant, to the skies Scarce we lift our weep-ing eyes,}

D.C.—Bend-ing from Thy throne on high, Hear our sol-emn lit-a-ny.

O by all Thy pains and woe Suf-fered once for man be-low,— A-MEN.

148 ST. CHRISTOPHER 7. 6. 8. 6. 8. 6. 8. 6. FREDERICK C. MAKER, 1881

1 Be - neath the cross of Je - sus I fain would take my stand,

The shad - ow of a might - y Rock With - in a wea - ry land;

A home with-in the wil - der - ness, A rest up - on the way,

From the burn-ing of the noon-tide heat, And the bur - den of the day. A - MEN.

2 Upon that cross of Jesus
  Mine eye at times can see
The very dying form of One
  Who suffered there for me:
And from my smitten heart with tears
  Two wonders I confess,—
The wonders of His glorious love
  And my own worthlessness.

3 I take, O cross, thy shadow
  For my abiding-place:
I ask no other sunshine than
  The sunshine of His face;
Content to let the world go by,
  To know no gain nor loss,
My sinful self my only shame,
  My glory all, the cross.

ELIZABETH C. CLEPHANE, published in 1872

Easter

149 NEWCASTLE 6. 6. 8. 8. 6.

HENRY L. MORLEY, 1875

1 We praise Thee, we bless Thee, O Sav - iour risen to - day!

Thou who didst drain the bit - ter cup, Thou who Thy life didst

of - fer up, To take our sins a - way. A - MEN.

2 We praise Thee, we bless Thee,
  O Lord of death and life!
We follow where Thy feet have gone,
Through deepest night to fairest dawn,
  To peace through stubborn strife.

3 [*We praise Thee, we bless Thee,
  Even when our hearts are riven!
Thou art anear the dying bed,
Thy hand beneath the fainting head,
  And Thou Thyself art heaven.]

4 We praise Thee, we bless Thee,
  With every pulse and breath.
Ours is the never-ending hymn
That saints began in ages dim,
  Thou Conqueror of death!

5 We praise Thee, we bless Thee,
  This happy Easter Day.
Through earth and skies the chorus rings,
O Lord of lords and King of kings,
  Who takes our sins away!

MRS. MARGARET E. SANGSTER, 1897

* This verse may be reserved for occasional use.

Our Lord Jesus Christ

150 JOWETT   11. 11. 11. 11. 11. 11. (or 6. 5. 12 ll.)   FRANK L. SEALY, 1911

1 God hath sent His an - gels to the earth a - gain, Bring-ing joy - ful ti - dings
to the sons of men; They who first at Christmas thronged the heaven-ly way
Now be - side the tomb - door sit on East - er Day.

REFRAIN

An - gels, sing His tri - umph as you sang His birth: "Christ: the Lord, is risen. Peace, good-will on earth." A - MEN.

Behold, angels came and ministered unto Him.—ST. MATT. iv, 11

2 In the dreadful desert, where the Lord was tried,
  There the faithful angels gathered at His side;
  And when in the garden, grief and pain and care
  Bowed Him down with anguish, they were with Him there.
  Angels, sing His triumph as you sang His birth:
  "Christ the Lord is risen.   Peace, good-will on earth."

3 Yet the Christ they honor is the same Christ still,
  Who, in light and darkness, did His Father's will;
  And the tomb deserted shineth like the sky,
  Since He passed out from it into victory.
      Angels, sing His triumph as you sang His birth:
      "Christ the Lord is risen. Peace, good-will on earth."

4 God has still His angels, helping, at His word,
  All His faithful children, like their faithful Lord;
  Soothing them in sorrow, arming them in strife,
  Opening wide the tomb-doors, leading into life.
      Angels, sing His triumph as you sang His birth:
      "Christ the Lord is risen. Peace, good-will on earth."

Bishop PHILLIPS BROOKS, 1877

151 HOLY CROSS C. M.

Adapted from THOMAS HASTINGS, 1831
in S. SMITH's Selection of Psalm and Hymn Tunes, 1865

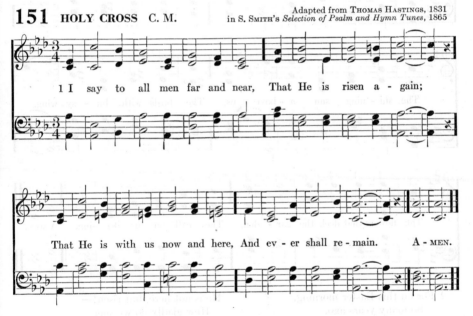

1 I say to all men far and near, That He is risen a - gain;

That He is with us now and here, And ev - er shall re - main. A - MEN.

ICH SAG' ES JEDEM, DASS ER LEBT

2 And what I say, let each this morn
    Go tell it to his friend,
  That soon in every place shall dawn
    His kingdom without end.

3 Now first to souls who thus awake
    Seems earth a fatherland;
  A new and endless life they take
    With rapture from His hand.

4 The fears of death and of the grave
    Are whelmed beneath the sea,
  And every heart, now light and brave,
    May face the things to be.

5 The way of darkness that He trod
    To heaven at last shall come,
  And he who hearkens to His word
    Shall reach His Father's home.

G. F. P. VON HARDENBERG, 1802:
translated by CATHERINE WINKWORTH, 1858

152 LANCASHIRE 7. 6. 7. 6. D.

HENRY SMART, 1836

1 O come, let us be joy - ful This glo - rious Eas - ter Day;

For, "Je - sus Christ is ris - en!" All voi - ces seem to say.

The shi - ning sun a - bove us, The birds with bu - sy wing,

The flowers that deck the gar - den, They call on us to sing. A-MEN.

2 For on this Easter morning,
  So many years ago,
Our Saviour rose victorious,
  And conquered death the foe.
As night drew near to sunrise
  The stone was rolled away:
No bars could bind the captive
  Who there in darkness lay.

3 So, when His friends came seeking,
  They found an empty grave.
Bright angels told the story
  Of how He came to save.

He is not here, but risen!—
  How gladly do we sing
Our Easter hymns of praises
  To Christ our risen King.

4 This gladsome Easter Sunday
  Our happy songs ascend;
We know He loves to hear us,
  He is the children's Friend.
With flowers and birds and sunshine
  We join in music gay:
For, "Jesus Christ is risen!"
  All voices seem to say.

HERBERT G. SMITH, 1911

153 ROTTERDAM 7. 6. 7. 6. D. BERTHOLD TOURS, 1875

1 The day of res - ur - rec - tion! Earth, tell it out a - broad;

The Pass - o - ver of glad - ness, The Pass - o - ver of God.

From death to life e - ter - nal, From this world to the sky,

Our Christ hath brought us o - ver With hymns of vic - to - ry. A - MEN.

Jesus met them, saying, All hail.—ST. MATT. xxviii, 9

2 Our hearts be pure from evil,
  That we may see aright
The Lord in rays eternal
  Of resurrection-light;
And, listening to His accents,
  May hear, so calm and plain,
His own "All hail!" and hearing,
  May raise the victor-strain.

3 Now let the heavens be joyful,
  Let earth her song begin;
Let the round world keep triumph,
  And all that is therein;
Invisible and visible,
  Their notes let all things blend,
For Christ the Lord hath risen,
  Our Joy that hath no end.

From the Greek of JOHN OF DAMASCUS (8th cent.),
by Rev. JOHN M. NEALE, 1862: the first line varied

NOTE—*John of Damascus, author of this and the next hymn, is regarded as the last but one of the Fathers of the Greek Church, and by Dr. Neale, as the greatest of her poets. Dr. Neale's version begins, "'Tis the Day of Resur-rection."*

154 ST. KEVIN   7. 6. 7. 6. D. Trochaic   Sir ARTHUR SULLIVAN, 1872

Stately

1 Come, ye faith-ful, raise the strain Of tri-umph-ant glad-ness:
God hath brought His Is-ra-el In-to joy from sad-ness;
Loosed from Pha-raoh's bit-ter yoke Ja-cob's sons and daugh-ters;
Led them with un-moist-ened foot Through the Red Sea wa-ters. A-MEN.

2 'Tis the spring of souls to-day:
　Christ hath burst His prison,
And from three days' sleep in death
　As a sun hath risen;
All the winter of our sins,
　Long and dark, is flying
From His light, to whom we give
　Laud and praise undying.

3 Now the Queen of seasons, bright
　With the day of splendor,
With the royal feast of feasts,
　Comes its joy to render;

Comes to glad Jerusalem,
　Who with true affection
Welcomes in unwearied strains
　Jesus' resurrection.

4 Neither might the gates of death,
　Nor the tomb's dark portal,
Nor the watchers, nor the seal,
　Hold Thee as a mortal:
But to-day amidst the Twelve
　Thou didst stand, bestowing
That Thy peace, which evermore
　Passeth human knowing.

From the Greek of JOHN OF DAMASCUS (8th cent.),
by Rev. JOHN M. NEALE, 1859

Easter

155 HERMAS 6. 5. 6. 5. 12 ll. FRANCES R. HAVERGAL, 1871

1 "Wel-come, hap-py morn-ing!" Age to age shall say: Hell to - day is van-quished;

Heaven is won to - day. Lo! the Dead is liv - ing, God for ev - er - more!

REFRAIN

Him, their true Cre - a - tor, All His works a - dore. "Wel-come, hap-py morn-ing!"

Age to age shall say: Hell to - day is vanquished, Heaven is won to - day. A - MEN.

SALVE, FESTA DIES, TOTO VENERABILIS ÆVO

2 Earth with joy confesses,
　Clothing for her spring,
All good gifts returned with
　Her returning King:
Bloom in every meadow.
　Leaves on every bough,
Speak His sorrows ended,
　Hail His triumph now.—REF.

3 Thou, of life the Author,
　Death didst undergo,
Tread the path of darkness,
　Saving strength to show;

Come then, True and Faithful,
　Now fulfil Thy word,
'Tis Thine own third morning;
　Rise, O buried Lord.—REF.

4 Loose the souls long-prisoned,
　Bound with Satan's chain;
All that now is fallen
　Raise to life again;
Show Thy face in brightness,
　Bid the nations see;
Bring again our daylight;
　Day returns with Thee.—REF.

VENANTIUS H. C. FORTUNATUS (c. 530–609):
arranged and translated by Rev. JOHN ELLERTON, 1868

137

Our Lord Jesus Christe

156 NAAMAN 10. 10. 10. 10. Dactylic

Arranged from the quartet "Honor and Glory" in Sir MICHAEL COSTA'S *Naaman*, 1866

1 Bless - ing and hon - or and glo - ry and power, Wis - dom and
rich - es and strength ev - er - more, Give ye to Him who our
bat - tle hath won, Whose are the king-dom, the crown, and the throne. A-MEN.

Worthy is the Lamb that was slain to receive power, and riches, and wisdom, and strength, and honor, and glory and blessing.—REV. v, 12

2 Past are the darkness, the storm, and the war;
Come is the radiance that sparkled afar;
Breaketh the gleam of the day without end;
Riseth the sun that shall never descend.

3 Ever ascendeth the song and the joy,
Ever descendeth the love from on high,
Blessing and honor and glory and praise,
This is the theme of the hymns that we raise.

4 Life of all life, and true Light of all light,
Star of the dawning, unchangingly bright,
Sun of the Salem, whose lamp is the Lamb,
Theme of the ever-new, ever-glad psalm!

5 Give we the glory and praise to the Lamb,
Take we the robe and the harp and the palm,
Sing we the song of the Lamb that was slain,
Dying in weakness, but rising to reign.

Arranged from Rev. HORATIUS BONAR, 1866

138

Easter

157 **EASTER FLOWERS** 7. 7. 7. 6. with Refrain   G. Waring Stebbins, 1913

To be sung in unison

1 Eas - ter flowers are bloom - ing bright, Eas - ter skies pour ra - diant light,

Christ our Lord is risen in might, Glo - ry in the high - est!

Refrain

Al - le - lu - ia! Al - le - lu - ia! Christ our Lord is

risen in might, Al - le - lu - ia! A - men.

Copyright, 1913, by Benjamin Shepard

2 Angels carolled this sweet lay,
When in manger rude He lay;
Now once more cast grief away,
Glory in the highest!—ref.

3 He, then born to grief and pain,
Now to glory born again,
Calleth forth our gladdest strain,
Glory in the highest!—ref.

4 As He riseth, rise we too,
Tune we heart and voice anew,
Offering homage glad and true,
Glory in the highest!—ref.

Mary A. Nicholson, 1875

139

158 SPES CELESTIS C. M. D.

W. A. SMITH, 1879

1 Now morn-ing lifts her dew-y veil, With new-born bless-ings crowned;

O haste we then her light to hail In courts of ho-ly ground:

But Christ hath spread a fair-er morn, From dark-ness ris-ing free,

And, in His glo-rious light new-born, We lift the ju-bi-lee. A-MEN.

AD TEMPLA NOS RURSUS VOCAT

2 When from the swaddling-bands of night
Sprang forth the world so fair,
All-radiant in her robes of light,
O what a power was there!
But when our God who gave His Son
A guilty world to spare,
Awoke to life the guiltless One,
O what a love was there!

3 When fresh from the Eternal's hand
The earth in beauty stood,
All decked with light at His command
He saw, and called it good:

But yet a goodlier world it lay
In the Creator's sight
When Jesus took its sins away
And washed its robes of light.

4 Still, when the lights of rising morn
The shades of night have riven,
We may descry, by fancy borne,
The golden domes of heaven:
But now that our eternal Sun
Hath spread His beams abroad,
In Him we see the Holy One,
And mount at once to God.

CHARLES COFFIN (Latin), 1736.
The translation (by Rev. ISAAC WILLIAMS, 1834) recast for this book
140

159   **EASTER HYMN**   7. 7. 7. 7. with Alleluias   *Lyra Davidica*, 1708

1 Jesus Christ is risen today, Alleluia!
Our triumphant holy day, Alleluia!
Who did once, upon the cross, Alleluia!
Suffer to redeem our loss. Alleluia! A-MEN.

2 Hymns of praise then let us sing
Unto Christ our heavenly King,
Who endured the cross and grave,
Sinners to redeem and save.
    Alleluia!

3 But the pains which He endured
Our salvation have procured;
Now above the sky He's King,
Where the angels ever sing.
    Alleluia!

4 Sing we to our God above
Praise eternal as His love;
Praise Him, all ye heavenly host,
Father, Son, and Holy Ghost.
    Alleluia!

As arranged in ARNOLD's *Compleat Psalmodist*, 1749;
and varied in *Supplement to New Version*, c. 1816: the doxology added

Our Lord Jesus Christ

160 **SANCTUARY** 8. 7. 8. 7. D.   Rev. John B. Dykes, 1871

1 Al - le - lu - ia! Al - le - lu - ia! Hearts to heaven and voi - ces raise;

Sing to God a hymn of glad - ness, Sing to God a hymn of praise:

He who on the cross a Vic - tim For the world's sal - va - tion bled,

Je - sus Christ, the King of Glo - ry, Now is ris - en from the dead. A - MEN.

Now is Christ risen from the dead, and become the firstfruits of them that slept.—1 Cor. xv, 20

2 Christ is risen, Christ the first-fruits
  Of the holy harvest-field,
Which will all its full abundance
  At His second coming yield:
Then the golden ears of harvest
  Will their heads before Him wave,
Ripened by His glorious sunshine
  From the furrows of the grave.

3 Christ is risen; we are risen.
  Shed upon us heavenly grace,
Rain and dew and gleams of glory
  From the brightness of Thy face;

That we, Lord, with hearts in heaven,
  Here on earth may fruitful be,
And by angel-hands be gathered,
  And be ever safe with Thee.

4 Alleluia! Alleluia!
  Glory be to God on high;
To the Father, and the Saviour
  Who has gained the victory;
Glory to the Holy Spirit,
  Fount of love and sanctity;
Alleluia! Alleluia!
  To the Triune Majesty.

Bishop Christopher Wordsworth, 1862

161 **PALESTRINA** 8. 8. 8. with Alleluias

Adapted from a Gloria Patri, by
G. P. DA PALESTRINA, 1591;
by W. H. MONK, 1861

Al - le - lu - ia! Al - le - lu - ia! Al - le - lu - ia!

1 The strife is o'er, the bat - tle done; The vic - to - ry of life is won;

The song of tri - umph has be - gun. Al - le - lu - ia! A - MEN.

FINITA JAM SUNT PRAELIA

2 The powers of death have done their worst,
  But Christ their legions hath dispersed:
  Let shouts of holy joy outburst.
      Alleluia!

3 The three sad days have quickly sped,
  He rises glorious from the dead:
  All glory to our risen Head!
      Alleluia!

4 He closed the yawning gates of hell;
  The bars from heaven's high portals fell:
  Let hymns of praise His triumphs tell.
      Alleluia!

5 Lord, by the stripes which wounded Thee,
  From death's dread sting Thy servants free,
  That we may live and sing to Thee,
      Alleluia!

An anonymous Latin hymn, translated by Rev. FRANCIS POTT, 1861

162 UNIVERSITY COLLEGE 7. 7. 7. 7.

HENRY J. GAUNTLETT, 1852

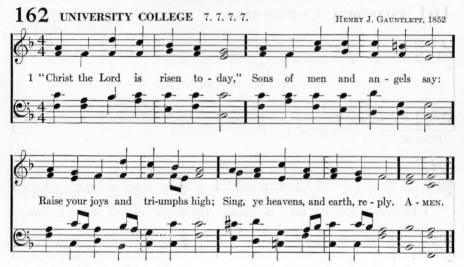

1 "Christ the Lord is risen to-day," Sons of men and an-gels say:

Raise your joys and tri-umphs high; Sing, ye heavens, and earth, re-ply. A-MEN.

2 Lives again our glorious King:
Where, O death, is now thy sting?
Once He died, our souls to save:
Where thy victory, O grave?

3 Love's redeeming work is done,
Fought the fight, the battle won;
Death in vain forbids Him rise;
Christ has opened Paradise.

4 Soar we now where Christ has led,
Following our exalted Head:
Made like Him, like Him we rise;
Ours the cross, the grave, the skies.

5 King of glory, Soul of bliss,
Everlasting life is this,
Thee to know, Thy power to prove,
Thus to sing, and thus to love.

Rev. CHARLES WESLEY, 1739: verse 2, line 3, varied

MONKLAND 7. 7. 7. 7.

Arranged by JOHN B. WILKES
for *Hymns ancient and modern*, 1861

1 "Christ the Lord is risen to-day," Sons of men and an-gels say:

Raise your joys and tri-umphs high; Sing, ye heavens, and earth, re-ply. A-MEN.

Christ Ascended

A Collect for Heavenly-Mindedness

O God, Eternal King, who hast exalted Thy Son with great triumph unto Thy throne and kingdom; Grant that while He reigneth with Thee in heaven we may not bow down to the things of earth, but that our hearts may there be lifted up whither our Lord and Saviour is gone before, and that our lives may be submitted to His holy governance. Amen.

163 ASCENSION 7. 7. 7. 7. with Alleluias   WILLIAM H. MONK, 1861

1 Hail the day that sees Him rise; Al - - - le - lu - - - ia!

To His throne a - bove the skies; Al - - - le - lu - ia!

Christ, a - while to mor - tals given, Al - - - le - lu - - ia!

Re - as - cends His na - tive heaven. Al - - le - lu - ia! A - MEN.

2 There for Him high triumph waits;
Lift your heads, eternal gates;
He hath conquered death and sin;
Take the King of glory in.

3 Lo! the heaven its Lord receives,
Yet He loves the earth He leaves
Though returning to His throne,
Still He calls mankind His own.

4 Still for us He intercedes,
His prevailing death He pleads,
Near Himself prepares our place,
He the first-fruits of our race.

5 Lord, though parted from our sight
Far above the starry height,
Grant our hearts may thither rise,
Seeking Thee above the skies.

REV. CHARLES WESLEY, 1739: revised in *Hymns ancient and modern*, 1861

145

164 CORONATION C. M.

OLIVER HOLDEN, 1793

1 All hail the power of Je-sus' Name! Let an-gels pros-trate fall;

Bring forth the roy-al di-a-dem, To crown Him Lord of all;

Bring forth the roy-al di-a-dem, To crown Him Lord of all. A-MEN.

2 Crown Him, ye martyred saints who now
   Beneath God's altar call
Unbind the thorns that pierced His brow
   And crown Him Lord of all.

3 Ye souls new-born of nobler race
   Than perished in man's fall,
Hail Him who saves you by His grace,
   And crown Him Lord of all.

4 Sinners, whose love can ne'er forget
   Your rescue from sin's thrall,
Go, spread your trophies at His feet,
   And crown Him Lord of all.

5 Let every kindred, every tribe
   And nation, great or small,
To Him all majesty ascribe,
   And crown Him Lord of all.

6 O that with yonder sacred throng
   We at His feet may fall;
   We'll join the everlasting song,
   And crown Him Lord of all.

Arranged from Rev. EDWARD PERRONET, 1779–80:

NOTE—"*All hail!*" *was the angelic salutation of the risen Lord (St. Matt. xxviii: 9), and the original hymn of eight verses was entitled, "On the Resurrection." It has from the first been subject to alteration in the effort to avoid its peculiar phraseology without impairing its unapproached fervor and fine refrain. Of the present version, the 2nd & 3rd verses were recast, and the 4th altered, for the present book. The 5th verse was recast, and the 6th added, by Rev. John Rippon in 1787; the former of which is here varied.*

146

Christ Ascended

(*Second Tune*)

LAUS TIBI, CHRISTE C. M. D.

Gerard F. Cobb (1838–1904)

1 All hail the power of Je - sus' Name! Let an - gels pros - trate fall;

Bring forth the roy - al di - a - dem, To crown Him Lord of all.

2 Crown Him, ye mar - tyred saints who now Be - neath God's al - tar call;

Un-bind the thorns that pierced His brow, And crown Him Lord of all. A - MEN.

Note by the Composer—*To be sung, not smoothly, but with rhythm well marked, in the manner of a March.*

147

165 ORTONVILLE C. M.

THOMAS HASTINGS, 1837

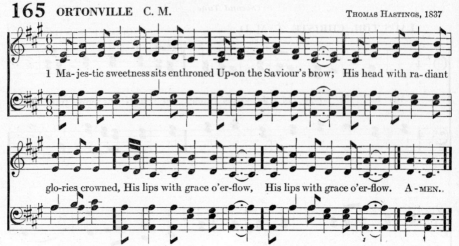

1 Ma-jes-tic sweetness sits enthroned Up-on the Saviour's brow; His head with ra-diant glo-ries crowned, His lips with grace o'er-flow, His lips with grace o'er-flow. A-MEN.

2 No mortal can with Him compare,
Among the sons of men;
Fairer is He than all the fair
That fill the heavenly train.

3 He saw me plunged in deep distress,
He flew to my relief;
For me He bore the shameful cross,
And carried all my grief.

4 To Him I owe my life and breath,
And all the joys I have;
He makes me triumph over death,
And saves me from the grave.

5 To heaven, the place of His abode,
He brings my weary feet;
Shows me the glories of my God,
And makes my joys complete.

6 Since from His bounty I receive
Such proofs of love divine,
Had I a thousand hearts to give,
Lord, they should all be Thine.

Rev. SAMUEL STENNETT, 1787: the second line varied

NATIVITY C. M.

HENRY LAHEE, 1855

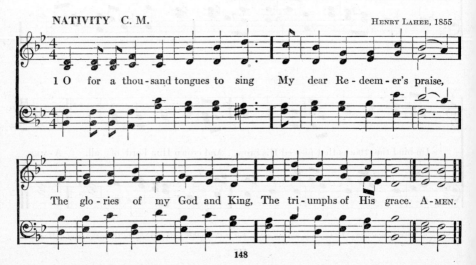

1 O for a thou-sand tongues to sing My dear Re-deem-er's praise, The glo-ries of my God and King, The tri-umphs of His grace. A-MEN.

166 SCHÖNSTER HERR JESU 5. 6. 8. 5. 5. 8.

A Silesian folk-song: in
Schleischen Volkslieder, Leipzig, 1842

1 Fair - est Lord Je - sus, Ru - ler of all na - ture,
O Thou of God and man the Son; Thee will I cher - ish,
Thee will I hon - or, Thou, my soul's Glo - ry, Joy, and Crown. A - men.

SCHÖNSTER HERR JESU

2 Fair are the meadows,
Fairer still the woodlands,
Robed in the blooming garb of spring:
Jesus is fairer, Jesus is purer,
Who makes the woeful heart to sing.

3 Fair is the sunshine,
Fairer still the moonlight,
And all the twinkling, starry host:
Jesus shines brighter, Jesus shines purer,
Than all the angels heaven can boast.

An anonymous 17th century German hymn.
The translation anonymous, 1850

167 (NATIVITY) C. M.

1 O for a thousand tongues to sing
My dear Redeemer's praise,
The glories of my God and King,
The triumphs of His grace!

2 Jesus—the Name that charms our fears,
That bids our sorrows cease;
'Tis music in the sinner's ears,
'Tis life, and health, and peace.

3 He breaks the power of reigning sin,
He sets the prisoner free;
His blood can make the foulest clean;
His blood availed for me.

4 He speaks;—and, listening to His voice,
New life the dead receive,
The mournful broken hearts rejoice,
The humble poor believe.

5 Hear Him, ye deaf; His praise, ye dumb,
Your loosened tongues employ;
Ye blind, behold your Saviour come;
And leap, ye lame, for joy!

6 My gracious Master and my God,
Assist me to proclaim
And spread through all the earth abroad
The honors of Thy Name.

Rev. CHARLES WESLEY, 1739: verse 3, line 1, varied

149

168 **HARWELL** 8. 7. 8. 7. 7. 7. with Refrain   LOWELL MASON, 1840

1 Hark! ten thou-sand harps and voi-ces Sound the note of praise a-bove;

Je-sus reigns and heaven re-joi-ces; Je-sus reigns, the God of love:

See, He sits on yon-der throne; Je-sus rules the world a-lone.

REFRAIN

Al-le-lu-ia! Al-le-lu-ia! Al-le-lu-ia! A-men. A-MEN.

And I heard the voice of harpers harping with their harps.—REV. xiv, 2

2 King of glory, reign for ever,
  Thine an everlasting crown;
Nothing from Thy love shall sever
  Those whom Thou hast made Thine own:
Happy objects of Thy grace,
Destined to behold Thy face.—REF.

3 Saviour, hasten Thine appearing;
  Bring, O bring the glorious day,
When, the awful summons hearing,
  Heaven and earth shall pass away:
Then, with golden harps, we'll sing,
"Glory, glory to our King!"—REF.

Rev. THOMAS KELLY, 1806

Christ Ascended

169 LAUDES DOMINI 6. 6. 6. 6. 6. 6.   Sir JOSEPH BARNBY, 1868

1 When morn-ing gilds the skies, My heart a-wak-ing cries,

May Je-sus Christ be praised! A-like at work and prayer,

To Je-sus I re-pair; May Je-sus Christ be praised! A-MEN.

BEIM FRÜHEN MORGENLICHT

2 When sleep her balm denies,
  My silent spirit sighs,
    May Jesus Christ be praised!
  When evil thoughts molest,
  With this I shield my breast,
    May Jesus Christ be praised!

3 The night becomes as day,
  When from the heart we say,
    May Jesus Christ be praised!
  The powers of darkness fear,
  When this sweet chant they hear,
    May Jesus Christ be praised!

4 In heaven's eternal bliss
  The loveliest strain is this,
    May Jesus Christ be praised!
  Let earth, and sea, and sky
  From depth to height reply,
    May Jesus Christ be praised!

5 Be this, while life is mine,
  My canticle divine,
    May Jesus Christ be praised!
  Be this the eternal song,
  Through all the ages on,
    May Jesus Christ be praised!

Anonymous (c. 1800).   Translated by Rev. EDWARD CASWALL, 1853, 1858

170 MORLEY 6. 5. 6. 5. D.

THOMAS MORLEY, 1867

1 At the Name of Je - sus Ev - ery knee shall bow, Ev-ery tongue con - fess Him

King of glo - ry now. 'Tis the Fa-ther's pleas - ure We should call Him Lord,

Who from the be - gin - ning Was the might - y Word. A - MEN.

That at the Name of Jesus every knee should bow. — PHIL. ii, 10

2 At His voice creation
  Sprang at once to sight,
All the angel faces,
  All the hosts of light,
Thrones and dominations,
  Stars upon their way,
All the heavenly orders
  In their great array.

3 Humbled for a season,
  To receive a Name
From the lips of sinners
  Unto whom He came,
Faithfully He bore it
  Spotless to the last,
Brought it back victorious,
  When from death He passed.

4 In your hearts enthrone Him;
  There let Him subdue
All that is not holy,
  All that is not true:
Crown Him as your Captain
  In temptation's hour:
Let His will enfold you
  In its light and power.

5 Brothers, this Lord Jesus
  Shall return again,
With His Father's glory,
  With His angel train;
For all wreaths of empire
  Meet upon His brow,
And our hearts confess Him
  King of glory now.

CAROLINE M. NOEL, 1870: verse 3, line 4 varied

152

Christ Ascended

171 PAPWORTH 6. 5. 6. 5. D.   EDWARD J. HOPKINS 1870

1 Sav - iour, bless - ed Sav - iour, Lis - ten while we sing; Hearts and voi - ces rais - ing Prais - es to our King: All we have we of - fer, All we hope to be, Bod - y, soul, and spir - it, All we yield to Thee. A-MEN.

2 Nearer, ever nearer,
    Christ, we draw to Thee,
Deep in adoration
    Bending low the knee:
Thou for our redemption
    Cam'st on earth to die;
Thou, that we might follow,
    Hast gone up on high.

3 Great, and ever greater,
    Are Thy mercies here;
True and everlasting
    Are the glories there,
Where no pain nor sorrow,
    Toil nor care, is known,
Where the angel legions
    Circle round Thy throne.

4 Onward, ever onward,
    Journeying o'er the road
Worn by saints before us,
    Journeying on to God;
Leaving all behind us,
    May we hasten on,
Backward never looking
    Till the prize is won.

5 Higher then, and higher,
    Bear the ransomed soul,
Earthly toils forgotten,
    Saviour, to its goal;
Where, in joys unthought of,
    Saints with angels sing,
Never weary, raising
    Praises to their King.

REV. GODFREY THRING, 1862; as revised by him in 1882

172 AUTUMN 8. 7. 8. 7. D.

Adapted from Psalm xlii in the Genevan Psalter, 1551

1 Christ, a - bove all glo - ry seat - ed, King tri - um - phant, strong to save,

Dy - ing, Thou hast death de - feat - ed, Bur - ied, Thou hast spoiled the grave.

2 Thou art gone where now is giv - en What no mor - tal might could gain,

On the e - ter - nal throne of heav - en In Thy Fa - ther's power to reign. A-MEN.

Alternative tune, AUSTRIAN HYMN, No. 207

AETERNE REX ALTISSIME

3 There Thy kingdoms all adore Thee,
  Heaven above and earth below;
While the depths of hell before Thee
  Trembling and amazèd bow.

4 We, O Lord, with hearts adoring,
  Follow Thee beyond the sky:
Hear our prayers Thy grace imploring,
  Lift our souls to Thee on high;

5 So when Thou again in glory
  On the clouds of heaven shalt shine,
We Thy flock may stand before Thee,
  Owned for evermore as Thine.

6 Hail! all hail! In Thee confiding,
  Jesus, Thee shall all adore,
In Thy Father's might abiding
  With one Spirit evermore.

An anonymous 6th or 7th century Latin hymn.
Translated by Bishop JAMES R. WOODFORD, 1852

Christ Ascended

173 **LYONS** 10. 10. 11. 11.   Arranged from MICHAEL HAYDN (1737–1806)

1 Ye serv-ants of God, your Mas-ter pro-claim, And pub-lish a-broad His
won-der-ful Name; The Name, all-vic-to-rious, of Je-sus ex-tol;
His king-dom is glo-rious, and rules o-ver all. A-MEN.

Praise, O ye servants of the Lord, praise the Name of the Lord.—Ps. cxiii, 1

2 God ruleth on high, almighty to save;
  And still He is nigh—His presence we have:
  The great congregation His triumph shall sing,
  Ascribing salvation to Jesus, our King.

3 Salvation to God, who sits on the throne!
  Let all cry aloud, and honor the Son:
  The praises of Jesus the angels proclaim,
  Fall down on their faces and worship the Lamb.

4 Then let us adore, and give Him His right,
  All glory and power, and wisdom and might,
  All honor and blessing, with angels above,
  And thanks never ceasing, and infinite love.

REV. CHARLES WESLEY, 1744: verse 3, line 3, varied

174 CORONÆ 8. 7. 8. 7. 4. 7.

WILLIAM H. MONK, 1871

1 Look, ye saints; the sight is glo-rious: See the Man of Sor-rows now;

From the fight re-turned vic-to-rious, Ev-ery knee to Him shall bow:

Crown Him! Crown Him! Crowns be-come the Vic-tor's brow. A-MEN.

We see Jesus—crowned with glory and honor.—HEB. ii, 9

2 Crown the Saviour, angels, crown Him;
   Rich the trophies Jesus brings;
   In the seat of power enthrone Him,
   While the vault of heaven rings:
   Crown Him! Crown Him!
   Crown the Saviour King of kings.

3 Sinners in derision crowned Him,
   Mocking thus the Saviour's claim;
   Saints and angels crowd around Him,

Own His title, praise His Name:
   Crown Him! Crown Him!
   Spread abroad the Victor's fame.

4 Hark, those bursts of acclamation!
   Hark, those loud triumphant chords!
   Jesus takes the highest station;
   O what joy the sight affords:
   Crown Him! Crown Him!
   King of kings, and Lord of lords.
   Rev. THOMAS KELLY, 1809

LOOK, YE SAINTS 8. 7. 8. 7. D.

An English melody:
arranged by GEORGE C. STEBBINS, 1878

1 { Look, ye saints; the sight is glo-rious: See the Man of Sor-rows now;
    From the fight re-turned vic-to-rious, Ev-ery knee to Him shall bow: }

Christ Ascended

Crown Him! Crown Him! Crown Him! Crown Him! Crowns be - come the Vic - tor's brow.

Crown Him! Crown Him! Crown Him! Crown Him! Crowns be - come the Vic - tor's brow. A-MEN.

By permission of Hope Publishing Co.

175 SWEDEN L. M.

HENRY HILES, 1868

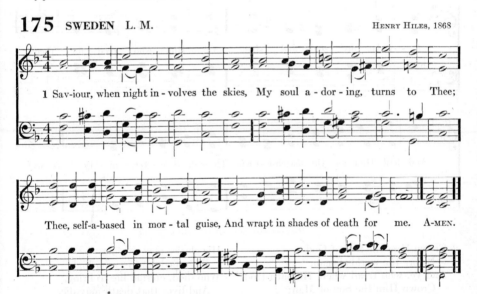

1 Sav-iour, when night in - volves the skies, My soul a - dor - ing, turns to Thee;

Thee, self-a-based in mor - tal guise, And wrapt in shades of death for me. A-MEN.

2 On Thee my waking raptures dwell,
  When crimson gleams the east adorn,
Thee, Victor of the grave and hell,
  Thee, Source of life's eternal morn.

3 When noon her throne in light arrays,
  To Thee my soul triumphant springs;
Thee, throned in glory's endless blaze,
  Thee, Lord of lords and King of kings.

4 O'er earth when shades of evening steal,
  To death and Thee my thoughts I give;
To death, whose power I soon shall feel,
  To Thee, with whom I trust to live.

Rev. THOMAS GISBORNE, 1803; verse 2, line 1, varied

176 DIADEMATA S. M. D.

Sir George J. Elvey 1868

1 Crown Him with ma - ny crowns, The Lamb up - on His throne;

Hark! how the heaven - ly an - them drowns All mu - sic but its own:

A - wake, my soul, and sing Of Him who died for thee,

And hail Him as thy match-less King Through all e - ter - ni - ty. A - MEN.

And on His head were many crowns.—Rev. xix, 12

2 Crown Him the Son of God
  Before the worlds began,
And ye, who tread where He hath trod,
  Crown Him the Son of Man;
Who every grief hath known
  That wrings the human breast,
And takes and bears them for His own,
  That all in Him may rest.

3 Crown Him the Lord of life,
  Who triumphed o'er the grave,
And rose victorious in the strife
  For those He came to save;

His glories now we sing
  Who died, and rose on high,
Who died, eternal life to bring,
  And lives that death may die.

4 Crown Him the Lord of heaven,
  Enthroned in worlds above;
Crown Him the King, to whom is given
  The wondrous name of Love.
Crown Him with many crowns,
  As thrones before Him fall,
Crown Him, ye kings, with many crowns,
  For He is King of all.

Verse 1 is by Rev. Matthew Bridges, 1851:
the remainder by Rev. Godfrey Thring, 1882

The Second Coming

Preserve us, O God, from the love of this present world, that we may await with patient hope the day of the Lord, and abide in Him; and that when He shall appear we may have confidence and not be ashamed before Him at His coming: through Jesus Christ our Lord and Saviour. Amen.

177 WOODLAND 8. 6. 8. 8. 6.

NATHANIEL D. GOULD, 1832

1 Re - turn, dear Lord, to those who look With ea - ger eyes that yearn For Thee a - mong the gar - den flowers; Af - ter the dark and lone - ly hours As morn - ing light re - turn. A - MEN.

Alternative tune, REST, No. 128

2 Return to those who wander far,
  With lamps that dimly burn,
Along the troubled road of thought,
Where doubt and conflict come unsought,—
  With inward joy return.

3 Return to those on whom the yoke
  Of life is hard and stern;
Renew the hope within their breast,
Draw them to Thee and give them rest:
  O Friend of Man, return.

4 Return to this war-weary world,
  And help us all to learn
The secret of victorious life,
The love that triumphs over strife,—
  O Prince of Peace, return.

5 Jesus, we ask not now that day
  When all men shall discern
Thy coming with the angelic host;
To-day, to all who need Thee most,
  In silent ways return!

REV. HENRY VAN DYKE, 1922

178 MOUNT HOLYOKE 15. 15. 15. 15.

M. L. WOSTENHOLM, 1910

1 There's a light up-on the moun-tains, and the day is at the spring,

When our eyes shall see the beau-ty and the glo - ry of the King:

Wea-ry was our heart with wait-ing, and the night-watch seemed so long,

But His tri-umph-day is break-ing, and we hail it with a song. A-MEN.

Org.

Go ye out to meet Him.—ST. MATT. xxv, 6

2 In the fading of the starlight we may see the coming morn;
   And the lights of men are paling in the splendors of the dawn:
   For the eastern skies are glowing as with light of hidden fire,
   And the hearts of men are stirring with the throbs of deep desire.

3 There's a hush of expectation, and a quiet in the air,
   And the breath of God is moving in the fervent breath of prayer;
   For the suffering, dying Jesus is the Christ upon the throne,
   And the travail of our spirits is the travail of His own.

4 He is breaking down the barriers, He is casting up the way;
He is calling for His angels to build up the gates of day:
But His angels here are human, not the shining hosts above;
For the drum-beats of His army are the heart-beats of our love.

5 Hark! we hear a distant music, and it comes with fuller swell;
'Tis the triumph-song of Jesus, of our King, Emmanuel!
Go ye forth with joy to meet Him! and, my soul, be swift to bring
All thy sweetest and thy dearest for the triumph of our King!

HENRY BURTON, 1910

179 HAPPY LAND 6. 4. 6. 4. 6. 7. 6. 4.   In R. A. SMITH's *Select Melodies*, 1827

1 Hark! 'tis the watchman's cry, Wake, breth-ren, wake! Je - sus Him-self is nigh;
Wake, breth-ren, wake! Sleep is for sons of night; Ye are chil-dren of the light;
Yours is the glo - ry bright; Wake, breth - ren, wake! A - MEN.

Now it is high time to awake out of sleep.—ROM. xiii, 11

2 Call to each wakening band,
Watch, brethren, watch!
Clear is our Lord's command,
Watch, brethren, watch!
Be ye as men that wait
Always at their Master's gate,
E'en though He tarry late;
Watch, brethren, watch!

3 Hear we the Shepherd's voice,
Pray, brethren, pray!
Would ye His heart rejoice,
Pray, brethren, pray!

Sin calls for ceaseless fear,
Weakness needs the Strong One near,
Long as ye struggle here,
Pray, brethren, pray!

4 Sound now the final chord,
Praise, brethren, praise!
Thrice holy is the Lord,
Praise, brethren, praise!
What more befits the tongues
Soon to join the angels' songs?
While heaven the note prolongs
Praise, brethren, praise!

In the *Revival Magazine*, Nov. 19, 1859

180 ALFORD 7. 6. 8. 6. D.　　　　　Rev. John B. Dykes, 1875

1 Ten thou - sand times ten thou - sand In spark - ling rai - ment bright

The ar - mies of the ran - somed saints Throng up the steeps of light:

'Tis fin - ished, all is fin - ished, Their fight with death and sin:

Fling o - pen wide the gold - en gates, And let the vic - tors in. A-MEN.

The coming of our Lord Jesus Christ, and our gathering together unto Him.—2 Thess. ii, 1

For a lower setting, see No. 350

2 What rush of alleluias
　Fills all the earth and sky!
What ringing of a thousand harps
　Bespeaks the triumph nigh!
O day, for which creation
　And all its tribes were made;
O joy, for all its former woes
　A thousand fold repaid!

3 O then what raptured greetings
　On Canaan's happy shore;
What knitting severed friendships up
　Where partings are no more!

Then eyes with joy shall sparkle,
　That brimmed with tears of late;
Not then are orphans fatherless,
　Nor widows desolate.

4 Bring near Thy great salvation,
　Thou Lamb for sinners slain;
Fill up the roll of Thine elect,
　Then take Thy power, and reign:
Appear, Desire of nations,
　Thine exiles long for home;
Show in the heaven Thy promised sign;
　Thou Prince and Saviour, come.

Rev. Henry Alford, 1867
with the rhythm of one line revised

The Second Coming

181 **SWISS MELODY** 11.10.11.10. From L. DIETSCH's *Recueil de Cantiques*, Paris, 1851

1 Hark what a sound, and too di-vine for hear-ing, Stirs on the earth and trem-bles in the air! Is it the thun-der of the Lord's ap-pear-ing? Is it the mu-sic of His people's prayer? A-MEN.

2 Surely He cometh, and a thousand voices
   Shout to the saints and to the deaf are dumb;
  Surely He cometh, and the earth rejoices,
   Glad in His coming who hath sworn, "I come."

3 This hath He done and shall we not adore Him?
   This shall He do and can we still despair?
  Come let us quickly fling ourselves before Him,
   Cast at His feet the burthen of our care,

4 Flash from our eyes the glow of our thanksgiving,
   Glad and regretful, confident and calm,
  Then thro' all life and what is after living
   Thrill to the tireless music of a psalm.

5 Thro' life, thro' death, thro' sorrow and thro' sinning,
   He shall suffice me, for He hath sufficed;
  Christ is the end, for Christ was the beginning,
   Christ the beginning, for the end is Christ.

The closing stanzas of FREDERIC W. H. MYERS' *Saint Paul*, 1867:
with the rhythm of one line revised

Our Lord Jesus Christ

182 **VENI EMMANUEL** 8. 8. 8. 8. 8. 8.

Adapted by Thomas Helmore, 1854, from a "French missal"

1 O come, O come, Em - man - u - el, And ran - som cap - tive Is - ra - el;

That waits in low - ly ex - ile here, Un - til the Son of God ap - pear.

Re-joice! Re-joice! Em - man - u - el Shall come to thee, O Is - ra - el! A-men.

Alternative tune, MELITA, No. 398

VENI, VENI, EMMANUEL

2 O come, Thou Branch of Jesse's stem,
Unto Thine own, and rescue them:
From sin's dark depths Thy people save,
And give them victory o'er the grave.
Rejoice! Rejoice! Emmanuel
Shall come to thee, O Israel.

3 O come, Thou bright and morning Star,
And bring us comfort from afar;
Dispel the shadows of the night,
And turn our darkness into light.
Rejoice! Rejoice! Emmanuel
Shall come to thee, O Israel.

4 O come, Thou Lord of David's key;
The gate of heaven unfolds to Thee;
Make safe for us the heavenward road,
And bar the way to death's abode.
Rejoice! Rejoice! Emmanuel
Shall come to thee, O Israel.

5 O come, O come, Thou Lord of might
Who to Thy tribes from Sinai's height
In olden time didst give the law
In cloud and majesty and awe.
Rejoice! Rejoice! Emmanuel
Shall come to thee, O Israel.

An 18th century paraphrase of five of the seven ancient Antiphons sung at Vespers in Advent: the translation compiled for this Book

164

The Second Coming

183 HELMSLEY 8. 7. 8. 7. 4. 7.

THOMAS OLIVERS in WESLEY's *Select Hymns*, 1765;
varied in MADAN's *Collection*, 1769

1 { Lo! He comes, with clouds de - scend - ing,
  { Thou - sand thou - sand saints at - tend - ing
Once for fa - vored sin - ners slain; }
Swell the tri - umph of His train: }
Al - - le - lu - ia! Al - - le - lu - ia! Al - le -
lu - ia! God ap - pears on earth to reign. A-MEN.

Alternative tune, CORONÆ, No. 174

2 Every eye shall now behold Him,
  Robed in dreadful majesty;
Those who set at naught and sold Him,
  Pierced, and nailed Him to the Tree,
  Deeply wailing,
Shall the true Messiah see.

3 Now Redemption, long expected,
  See in solemn pomp appear!
All His saints, by man rejected,
  Now shall meet Him in the air:
  Alleluia!
See the day of God appear!

4 Yea, Amen! let all adore Thee,
  High on Thine eternal throne;
Saviour, take the power and glory,
  Claim the kingdom for Thine own.
  O come quickly;
Alleluia! come, Lord, come.

Verses 1, 2, 4, by Rev. CHARLES WESLEY, 1758;
verse 3, by Rev. JOHN CENNICK. 1752

165

The Holy Spirit

A Collect to the Holy Spirit

Spirit of God, whose very Name, The Comforter, maketh melody above the noises and confusions of our life: Fulfill Thy gentle ministries to these waiting hearts, that with reverent assurance we may take that Name upon our lips, and speak to Thee and one another in the comfortable words of holy song. Amen.

184 VENI SANCTE SPIRITUS 7. 7. 7. D. Composed by SAMUEL WEBBE; first printed in *An Essay on the Church Plain Chant*, 1782

1 Ho - ly Spir - it, come a - way; Spare from heaven a sin - gle ray Of the glo - ry that is Thine. Fa - ther of the poor, come low, Riv - er of God's boun - ty, flow, Light of hearts, en - light - en mine. A - MEN.

VENI SANCTE SPIRITUS

2 Comforter of men, the best,
  In our souls the welcome Guest
    Sweet Refreshment on the way!
  While we labor, our Repose,
  Like a cooling wind that blows,
    And our sorrow's only Stay!

3 Blessèd Light, Thyself impart
  To the fastness of the heart
    Trusting Thee and penitent.
  Didst Thy power forsake us, then
  There were nothing left in men,
    Nothing that is innocent.

4 Cleanse the life from every stain,
  Make dry places bloom again,
    All our wounded hopes renew:
  Bend the stubborn will to Thee,
  Till love's frosted stream runs free,
    Till our fickle faith rings true.

5 All whose hearts believe in Thee,
  All the lives that cleave to Thee,
    With Thy sevenfold grace defend:
  Make us worthy Thy reward,
  Crown Thy full salvation, Lord,
    With the joy that has no end.

An anonymous Latin Sequence of the 13th century: translated for this book

185 **KIRBY BEDON** 6. 6. 4. 6. 6. 6. 4. EDWARD BUNNETT, 1887

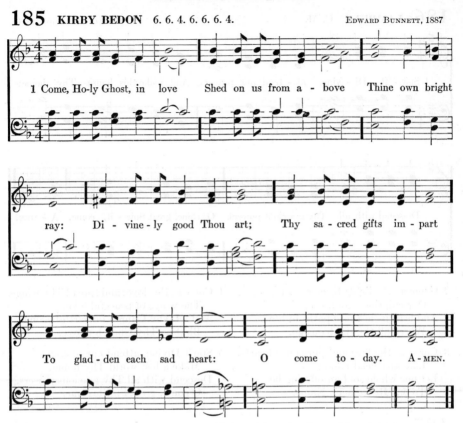

1 Come, Ho-ly Ghost, in love Shed on us from a - bove Thine own bright ray: Di - vine - ly good Thou art; Thy sa - cred gifts im - part To glad - den each sad heart: O come to - day. A - MEN.

VENI SANCTE SPIRITUS

2 Come, tenderest Friend and best,
Our most delightful Guest,
  With soothing power:
Rest, which the weary know;
Shade, 'mid the noontide glow;
Peace, when deep griefs o'erflow,—
  Cheer us this hour.

3 Come, Light serene, and still
Our inmost bosoms fill;
  Dwell in each breast:
We know no dawn but Thine;
Send forth Thy beams divine
On our dark souls to shine,
  And make us blest.

4 Exalt our low desires;
Extinguish passion's fires;
  Heal every wound:
Our stubborn spirits bend,
Our icy coldness end,
Our devious steps attend,
  While heavenward bound.

5 Come, all the faithful bless:
Let all who Christ confess
  His praise employ;
Give virtue's rich reward;
Victorious death accord,
And, with our glorious Lord,
  Eternal joy.

An anonymous Latin Sequence of the 13th century:
paraphrased by Rev. RAY PALMER, 1858

NOTE—*No. 184 is a close rendering in the original metre, and No. 185 is a paraphrase, of the hymn known in the Middle Ages as "The Golden Sequence," and called by Archbishop Trench "The loveliest of all the hymns in the whole circle of Latin sacred poetry."*

186 LAMBETH C. M.

WILLIAM SCHULTHES, 1871

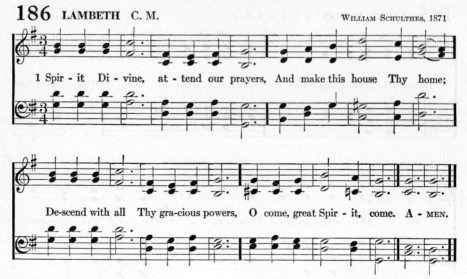

1 Spir - it Di - vine, at - tend our prayers, And make this house Thy home;

De-scend with all Thy gra-cious powers, O come, great Spir - it, come. A - MEN.

2 Come as the light; to us reveal
　Our emptiness and woe;
And lead us in those paths of life
　Where all the righteous go.

3 Come as the fire; and purge our hearts,
　Like sacrificial flame:
Let our whole soul an offering be
　To our Redeemer's Name.

4 Come as the dove; and spread Thy wings,
　The wings of peaceful love;
And let Thy Church on earth become
　Blest as Thy Church above.

5 Spirit Divine, attend our prayers;
　Make a lost world Thy home;
Descend with all Thy gracious powers,
　O come, great Spirit, come.

Rev. ANDREW REED, 1829

187 (LAMBETH or ST. AGNES) C. M.

Be of good cheer, I have overcome the world.—ST. JOHN, xvi, 33

1 Thy victory is in the heart,
　Thy kingdom is within;
When outward pride and pomp depart,
　Thy glory doth begin.

2 Thine army, ever in the field,
　Is led by love and light;

Thy followers fall but never yield,
　Triumphant in the right.

3 O King most meek and wonderful,
　Grant us among Thy host,
To follow Thee, to fight for Thee,
　Knights of the Holy Ghost.

Rev. HENRY VAN DYKE, 1922

188 (HERMON) C. M.

1 Thy home is with the humble, Lord;
　The simplest are the best;
Thy lodging is in child-like hearts;
　Thou makest there Thy rest.

2 Dear Comforter, eternal Love,
　If Thou wilt stay with me,

Of lowly thoughts and simple ways
　I'll build a house for Thee.

3 Who made this beating heart of mine
　But Thou, my heavenly Guest?
Let no one have it, then, but Thee,
　And let it be Thy rest.

Arranged from Rev. FREDERICK W. FABER'S
"Sweetness in Prayer," 1849

Invocation and Praise

189 **ST. AGNES** C. M.   Rev. John B. Dykes, 1866

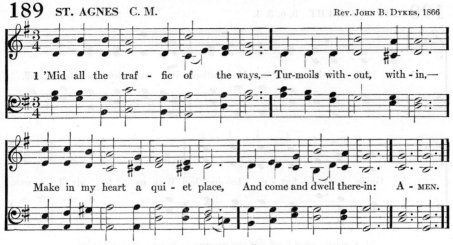

1 'Mid all the traf - fic of the ways,— Tur-moils with-out, with - in,—

Make in my heart a qui - et place, And come and dwell there-in: A - men.

"Sanctuary"

2—A little shrine of quietness,
    All sacred to Thyself,
Where Thou shalt all my soul possess,
    And I may find myself:

3—A little shelter from life's stress,
    Where I may lay me prone,
And bare my soul in loneliness,
    And know as I am known:

4—A solitude where I can think,
    A haven of retreat,
Where of Thy red wine I may drink,
    And of Thy white bread eat:

5—A little place of mystic grace,
    Of self and sin swept bare,
Where I may look upon Thy face,
    And talk with Thee in prayer.

6 Come!— occupy my silent place,
    And make Thy dwelling there!
More grace is wrought in quietness
    Than any is aware.

John Oxenham, 1917

From *The Vision Splendid:* copyright, 1917, by George H. Doran Co.

HERMON C. M.   Lowell Mason, 1832

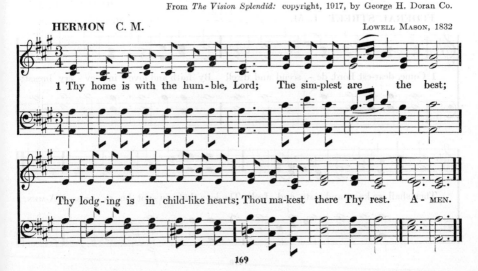

1 Thy home is with the hum - ble, Lord; The sim-plest are the best;

Thy lodg-ing is in child-like hearts; Thou ma-kest there Thy rest. A - men.

169

190 ST. CUTHBERT 8. 6. 8. 4.

Rev. John B. Dykes, 1861

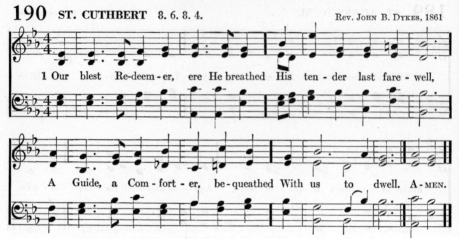

1 Our blest Re-deem-er, ere He breathed His ten-der last fare-well,

A Guide, a Com-fort-er, be-queathed With us to dwell. A-men.

The Comforter, whom I will send unto you from the Father.—St. John, xv, 26

2 He came in semblance of a dove,
　　With sheltering wings outspread,
　The holy balm of peace and love
　　On earth to shed.

3 He came sweet influence to impart,
　　A gracious, willing Guest,
　While He can find one humble heart
　　Wherein to rest.

4 And His that gentle voice we hear,
　　Soft as the breath of even,
　That checks each thought, that calms
　　And speaks of heaven. [each fear,

5 And every virtue we possess,
　　And every victory won,
　And every thought of holiness,
　　Are His alone.

6 Spirit of purity and grace,
　　Our weakness, pitying, see:
　O make our hearts Thy dwelling-place,
　　And worthier Thee.

Harriet Auber, 1829

FEDERAL STREET L. M.

Henry K. Oliver, 1832

1 Come, dear-est Lord, de-scend and dwell By faith and love in ev-ery breast;

Then shall we know and taste and feel The joys that can-not be ex-pressed. A-men.

191 ST. WYSTAN 6. 5. 6. 5.   Rev. LORD J. THEOBALD BUTLER, 1881

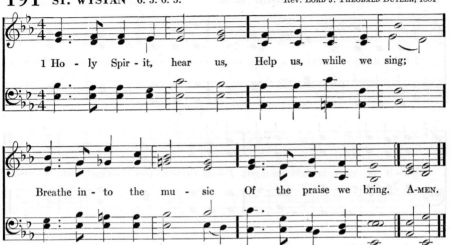

1 Ho - ly Spir - it, hear us, Help us, while we sing;

Breathe in - to the mu - sic Of the praise we bring. A-MEN.

2 Holy Spirit, teach us
    Some new truth to-day;
    Nearer come, and prompt us
    When we kneel to pray.

3 Holy Spirit, aid us
    While Thy Book we read;
    Gild its hallowed pages
    With the light we need.

4 Holy Spirit, give us
    Each a lowly mind;
    Make us more like Jesus,
    Brave, and pure, and kind.

5 Holy Spirit, brighten
    Every hour of toil;
    And our times of leisure
    Let no folly spoil.

6 Holy Spirit, keep us
    Safe from sins that lie
    Hidden by some pleasure
    From our careless eye.

7 Holy Spirit, help us
    Daily by Thy might
    What is wrong to conquer,
    And to choose the right.

WILLIAM H. PARKER, 1880: recast for this book.

192 (FEDERAL STREET) L. M.

1 Come, dearest Lord, descend and dwell
    By faith and love in every breast;
    Then shall we know and taste and feel
    The joys that cannot be expressed.

2 Come, fill our hearts with inward strength;
    Make our enlargèd souls possess
    And learn the height, and breadth, and length
    Of Thine unmeasurable grace.

3 Now to the God whose power can do
    More than our thoughts or wishes know,
    Be everlasting honors done
    By all the Church, through Christ His Son.

Rev. ISAAC WATTS, 1709

193 MATER MISERICORDIÆ L. M.

Sir Alfred S. Scott-Gatty, 1899; as
arranged for *The Hymnal revised*, 1911

1 Spir-it Di-vine, Cre-a-tor, come; Dwell in our kin-dred souls at home:

Spir-it of grace, in light ar-rayed, Fill all the tem-ples Thou hast made. A-MEN.

VENI CREATOR SPIRITUS

2 Comforter! Still we name that Name;
Gift that from God the Highest came,
Fountain of life, its fire of love,
And its true hallowing from above.

3 Thou givest faith its sevenfold dower;
Thine is God's finger-touch of power;
Promise of God, expected long,
Wakening silent tongues to song.

4 Bathe every sense in heaven's glow;
Bring heaven's love to hearts below;
And, when our mortal flesh proves frail,
Let Thine immortal strength prevail.

5 Drive all our foemen far away;
Grant us Thy gift of peace to-day;
Then lead us on! If Thou wilt guide,
Ill shall not come, nor fear abide.

6 Show us the Father, Holy One;
Make us through Thee to know the Son:
Spirit Divine, for evermore
Thee will we trust and Thee adore.

Of unknown authorship, perhaps of the 9th
century: translated for this book.

NOTE—*By common consent, a place is accorded the "Veni Creator" given to no other hymn. It is the most often used of all the hymns of the Latin-speaking church; the only one of them retained in use (in translation) by the Reformed Churches of both England and Scotland; and the only metrical hymn in the Book of Common Prayer; where it is appointed to be sung at every ordination.*

194 (CHARITY) 7. 7. 7. 5.

And now abideth faith, hope, charity, these three: but the greatest of these is charity.—1 COR., xiii, 13

1 Gracious Spirit, Holy Ghost,
Taught by Thee we covet most,
Of Thy gifts at Pentecost,
Holy, heavenly love.

2 Faith, that mountains could remove,
Tongues of earth or heaven above,
Knowledge—all things—empty prove,
Without heavenly love.

3 Love is kind, and suffers long;
Love is meek, and thinks no wrong;
Love than death itself more strong;
Therefore, give us love.

4 Prophecy will fade away,
Melting in the light of day;
Love will ever with us stay;
Therefore, give us love.

5 Faith will vanish into sight;
Hope be emptied in delight;
Love in heaven will shine more bright;
Therefore, give us love.

6 From the overshadowing
Of Thy gold and silver wing,
Shed on us who to Thee sing
Holy, heavenly love.

Bishop CHRISTOPHER WORDSWORTH, 1862

195 **MERCY** 7. 7. 7. 7.

Arranged from Louis M. Gottschalk's
"La dernière Espérance," 1854

1 Ho - ly Spir - it, Truth Di - vine, Dawn up - on this soul of mine;

Word of God, and in - ward Light, Wake my spir - it, clear my sight. A - MEN

2 Holy Spirit, Love Divine,
Glow within this heart of mine;
Kindle every high desire;
Perish self in Thy pure fire!

3 Holy Spirit, Power Divine,
Fill and nerve this will of mine;
By Thee may I strongly live,
Bravely bear, and nobly strive.

4 Holy Spirit, Right Divine,
King within my conscience reign;

Be my Law, and I shall be
Firmly bound, for ever free.

5 Holy Spirit, Peace Divine,
Still this restless heart of mine;
Speak to calm this tossing sea,
Stayed in Thy tranquillity.

6 Holy Spirit, Joy Divine,
Gladden Thou this heart of mine;
In the desert ways I sing,
"Spring, O Well, for ever spring."

Rev. Samuel Longfellow, 1864

CHARITY 7. 7. 7. 5.

Sir John Stainer, 1868

1 Gra - cious Spir - it, Ho - ly Ghost, Taught by Thee, we cov - et most,

Voices in unison

Of Thy gifts at Pen - te - cost, Ho - ly, heaven - ly love. A - MEN.

196 MORECAMBE 10. 10. 10. 10.

FREDERICK C. ATKINSON'S setting of
"Abide with me," c. 1870

1 Spir - it of God, de - scend up - on my heart; Wean it from earth; through all its puls - es move; Stoop to my weak - ness, might - y as Thou art, And make me love Thee as I ought to love. A - MEN.

2 I ask no dream, no prophet-ecstasies,
   No sudden rending of the veil of clay,
No angel-visitant, no opening skies;
   But take the dimness of my soul away.

3 Hast Thou not bid us love Thee, God and King?
   All, all Thine own, soul, heart, and strength, and mind;
I see Thy cross—there teach my heart to cling:
   O let me seek Thee, and O let me find.

4 Teach me to feel that Thou art always nigh;
   Teach me the struggles of the soul to bear,
To check the rising doubt, the rebel sigh;
   Teach me the patience of unanswered prayer.

5 Teach me to love Thee as Thine angels love,
   One holy passion filling all my frame;
The baptism of the heaven-descended Dove,
   My heart an altar, and Thy love the flame.

REV. GEORGE CROLY, 1854

Inspiration of the Holy Scriptures

A Collect for Enlightenment

Incline Thine ear, O God, unto these our songs, wherein our hearts respond to the great truths Thou hast revealed unto us in Holy Scripture; and grant us the enlightenment of Thy Spirit that we may come into a fuller understanding of Thy word and be enabled to worship Thee in spirit and in truth: through Jesus Christ our Lord. Amen.

197 BREAD OF LIFE 6. 4. 6. 4. D.

WILLIAM F. SHERWIN, 1877

1 Break Thou the bread of life, Dear Lord, to me, As Thou didst break the loaves Be-side the sea; Be-yond the sa-cred page I seek Thee, Lord; My spir-it pants for Thee, O liv-ing Word. A-MEN.

And He . . . took the five loaves, and the two fishes, and looking up to heaven, He blessed, and brake, and gave the loaves to His disciples.—ST. MATT. xiv, 19

2 Bless Thou the truth, dear Lord,
    To me—to me—
As Thou didst bless the bread
    By Galilee;
Then shall all bondage cease,
    All fetters fall;
And I shall find my peace,
    My All in all.

MARY A. LATHBURY, 1877

NOTE—*Miss Lathbury's hymns, this and Nos. 24 and 212, are closely associated with the services in the amphi theatre of the Chautauqua Assembly, for which they were written.*

198 **ADESTE FIDELES** 11. 11. 11. 11. In J. F. WADE's *Cantus Diversi*, 1751

1 How firm a foun-da-tion, ye saints of the Lord, Is laid for your faith in His ex-cel-lent word! What more can He say than to you He hath said,— You who un-to Je-sus for ref-uge have fled? You who un-to Je-sus for ref-uge have fled? A-MEN.

The foundation of God standeth sure.—2 TIM. ii, 19

2 "Fear not, I am with thee, O be not dismayed;
I, I am thy God, and will still give thee aid;
I'll strengthen thee, help thee, and cause thee to stand,
Upheld by My righteous, omnipotent hand.

3 "When through the deep waters I call thee to go,
The rivers of woe shall not thee overflow;
For I will be with thee thy troubles to bless,
And sanctify to thee thy deepest distress.

Inspiration of the Holy Scriptures

4 "When through fiery trials thy pathway shall lie,
My grace, all-sufficient, shall be thy supply;
The flame shall not hurt thee; I only design
Thy dross to consume, and thy gold to refine.

5 "The soul that on Jesus hath leaned for repose,
I will not, I will not desert to his foes;
That soul, though all hell should endeavor to shake,
I'll never, no, never, no, never forsake."

Signed "K," in Rippon's Selection, 1787

199 NOX PRÆCESSIT C. M.

J. Baptiste Calkin, 1875

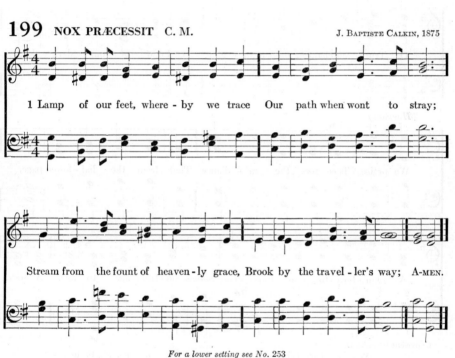

1 Lamp of our feet, where - by we trace Our path when wont to stray;

Stream from the fount of heaven - ly grace, Brook by the travel - ler's way; A-men.

For a lower setting see No. 253

Alternative tune, ST. AGNES, No. 186

2 Bread of our souls, whereon we feed;
　True manna from on high;
Our guide and chart, wherein we read
　Of realms beyond the sky;

3 Pillar of fire, through watches dark,
　Or radiant cloud by day;
When waves would whelm our tossing bark,
　Our anchor and our stay;

4 Word of the ever-living God,
　Will of His glorious Son:—
Without thee how could earth be trod, .
　Or heaven itself be won?

5 Lord, grant us all aright to learn
　The wisdom it imparts;
And to its heavenly teaching turn,
　With simple, childlike hearts.

Bernard Barton, the "Quaker Poet," 1836:
the last verse varied

200 NEILSON 7. 6. 7. 6. D. JOHN H. GOWER, 1894

Voices in unison

1 O Word of God In - car - nate, O Wis - dom from on high,

O Truth un-changed, un - chan - ging, O Light of our dark sky;

Harmony

We praise Thee for the ra - diance That from the hal - lowed page,

A lan - tern to our foot - steps, Shines on from age to age. A - MEN.

Copyright by John H. Gower

Ye shine as lights in the world; holding forth the word of life.—PHIL. ii, 15, 16

2 The Church from her dear Master
　Received the gift divine,
And still that light she lifteth
　O'er all the earth to shine.
It is the golden casket
　Where gems of truth are stored;
It is the heaven-drawn picture
　Of Christ, the living Word.

3 It floateth like a banner
　Before God's host unfurled;
It shineth like a beacon
　Above the darkling world.

It is the chart and compass
　That o'er life's surging sea,
'Mid mists and rocks and quicksands,
　Still guides, O Christ, to Thee.

4 O make Thy Church, dear Saviour,
　A lamp of purest gold,
To bear before the nations
　Thy true light, as of old.
O teach Thy wandering pilgrims
　By this their path to trace,
Till, clouds and darkness ended,
　They see Thee face to face.

Bishop W. WALSHAM HOW, 1867

The Church and its Fellowship

201 AURELIA 7. 6. 7. 6. D. Samuel S. Wesley's setting of "Jerusalem the Golden," 1864

1 The Church's one Foun - da - tion Is Je - sus Christ her Lord;

She is His new cre - a - tion By wa - ter and the word:

From heaven He came and sought her To be His ho - ly Bride;

With His own blood He bought her, And for her life He died. A - MEN.

2 Elect from every nation,
   Yet one o'er all the earth,
Her charter of salvation
   One Lord, one faith, one birth;
One holy Name she blesses,
   Partakes one holy food,
And to one hope she presses,
   With every grace endued.

3 Though with a scornful wonder
   Men see her sore oppressed,
By schisms rent asunder,
   By heresies distressed,

Yet saints their watch are keeping,
   Their cry goes up, "How long?"
And soon the night of weeping
   Shall be the morn of song.

4 'Mid toil and tribulation,
   And tumult of her war,
She waits the consummation
   Of peace for evermore;
Till with the vision glorious
   Her longing eyes are blest,
And the great Church victorious
   Shall be the Church at rest.

Rev. Samuel J. Stone, 1866

179

The Church and its Fellowship

202 LYNTON C. M.

A. J. JAMOUNEAU, 1904

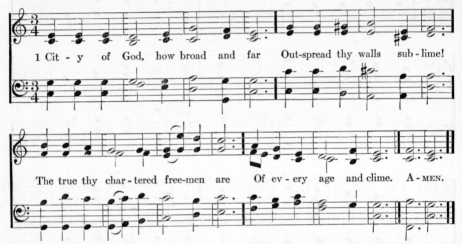

1 Cit - y of God, how broad and far Out-spread thy walls sub - lime!
The true thy char - tered free-men are Of ev - ery age and clime. A - MEN.

2 One holy Church, one army strong,
  One steadfast high intent,
One working band, one harvest-song,
  One King Omnipotent!

3 How purely hath thy speech come down
  From man's primeval youth;
How grandly hath thine empire grown
  Of freedom, love, and truth!

4 How gleam thy watchfires through the [night
  With never-fainting ray!
How rise thy towers, serene and bright,
  To meet the dawning day!

5 In vain the surge's angry shock,
  In vain the drifting sands:
Unharmed upon the eternal Rock
  The eternal city stands.

REV. SAMUEL JOHNSON, 1860

203 (NATIVITY) C. M.

1 Come let us join with faithful souls
  Our song of faith to sing,
One brotherhood in heart are we,
  And one our Lord and King.

2 Faithful are all who love the truth
  And dare the truth to tell,
Who steadfast stand at God's right hand,
  And strive to serve Him well.

3 And faithful are the gentle hearts
  To whom the power is given
Of every hearth to make a home,
  Of every home a heaven.

4 O mighty host! no tongue can tell
  The numbers of its throng;
No words can sound the music vast
  Of its grand battle-song.

5 From step to step it wins its way
  Against a world of sin;
Part of the battle-field is won,
  And part is yet to win.

6 O Lord of Hosts, our faith renew,
  And grant us, in Thy love,
To sing the songs of victory
  With faithful souls above.

REV. WILLIAM G. TARRANT, 1892

204 DUNDEE C. M.

In the Scottish Psalter of 1615

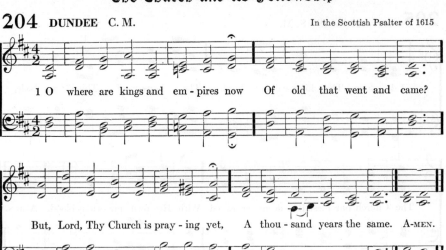

1 O where are kings and em - pires now Of old that went and came?

But, Lord, Thy Church is pray - ing yet, A thou - sand years the same. A-MEN.

2 We mark her goodly battlements,
   And her foundations strong;
   We hear within the solemn voice
   Of her unending song.

3 For not like kingdoms of the world
   Thy holy Church, O God;
   Though earthquake shocks are threaten-
   And tempests are abroad;   [ing her,

4 Unshaken as eternal hills,
   Immovable she stands,
   A mountain that shall fill the earth,
   A house not made by hands.

Arranged from Bishop A. CLEVELAND COXE's "Chelsea," 1839

NATIVITY C. M.

HENRY LAHEE, 1855

1 Come, let us join with faith - ful souls Our song of faith to sing;

One broth - er - hood in heart are we, And one our Lord and King. A - MEN.

205 ST. THOMAS S. M.

Aaron Williams, 1763

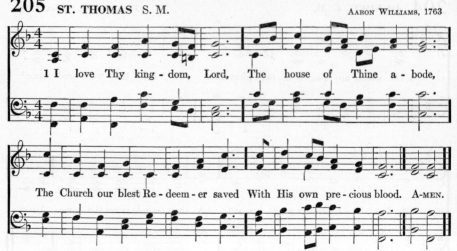

1 I love Thy king - dom, Lord, The house of Thine a - bode, The Church our blest Re - deem - er saved With His own pre - cious blood. A-men.

2 I love Thy Church, O God:
   Her walls before Thee stand,
   Dear as the apple of Thine eye,
   And graven on Thy hand.

3 For her my tears shall fall,
   For her my prayers ascend;
   To her my cares and toils be given,
   Till toils and cares shall end.

4 Beyond my highest joy
   I prize her heavenly ways,
   Her sweet communion, solemn vows,
   Her hymns of love and praise.

5 Jesus, Thou Friend Divine,
   Our Saviour and our King,
   Thy hand from every snare and foe
   Shall great deliverance bring.

6 Sure as Thy truth shall last,
   To Zion shall be given
   The brightest glories earth can yield,
   And brighter bliss of heaven.

Rev. Timothy Dwight, 1800

STATE STREET S. M.

Jonathan C. Woodman, 1844

1 I love Thy king - dom, Lord, The house of Thine a - bode, The Church our blest Re-deem -er saved With His own pre - cious blood. A - men.

Note—*This hymn was included by Dr. Dwight in his revision of Watts' "The Psalms of David imitated" as a paraphrase of* Psalm cxxxvii.

The Church and its Fellowship

The fuller text and the "proper tune" as long sung in the chapel of Yale University

(205) YALE COLLEGE S. M. D.   Arranged from J. MICHAEL HAYDN (1737–1806)

1 I love Thy king-dom, Lord, The house of Thine a - bode, The Church our blest Re-
deem - er saved With His own pre-cious blood. I love Thy Church, O God:
Her walls be - fore Thee stand, Dear as the ap - ple of Thine eye,
And grav - en on Thy hand, And grav - en on Thy hand. A - MEN.

2 If e'er to bless Thy sons
 My voice or hands deny,
These hands let useful skill forsake,
 This voice in silence die.
If e'er my heart forget
 Her welfare or her woe,
Let every joy this heart forsake,
 And every grief o'erflow.

3 For her my tears shall fall,
 For her my prayers ascend;
To her my cares and toils be given,
 Till toils and cares shall end.

Beyond my highest joy
 I prize her heavenly ways,
Her sweet communion, solemn vows,
 Her hymns of love and praise.

4 Jesus, Thou Friend Divine,
 Our Saviour and our King,
Thy hand from every snare and foe
 Shall great deliverance bring.
Sure as Thy truth shall last,
 To Zion shall be given
The brightest glories earth can yield,
 And brighter bliss of heaven.

Rev. TIMOTHY DWIGHT, President of Yale College, 1800

206 GOLDEN 8. 6. 8. 6. 6. 6. 6. 6.

JOHN H. GOWER, 1911

1 How pa - tient - ly they trod with Him The hills of Gal - i - lee,—
His sheep who knew their Shepherd's voice And heard His "Fol - low Me"!
O Mas - ter, we are Thine, Thou call - est us to - day;
Thy life and truth still shine Up - on Thy Church's way. A - MEN.

Copyright, 1911, by John H. Gower

Alternative tune, O PARADISE, No. 383

My Church.—ST. MATT. xvi, 18

2 Nor house nor hut the Shepherd had,
  Nor shelter for His flock,
When he exulting said, "My Church
  I build upon this rock."
    Lord Jesus, guard it well
      When faith and courage fail;
    Let not the gates of hell
      Against Thy Church prevail.

3 No gifts were in that empty hand,
  His cross alone in view
From out the shadows, when He said,
  "My peace I leave with you."

O Saviour, at Thy side
  All strife and discord cease;
Where Thou wast crucified
  Thy Church shall find her peace.

4 And now when troubled hearts are turned
  Toward heaven's distant hill,
The Spirit of Remembrance speaks,—
  "Lo! I am with you still:
    Remember Jesus Christ
      Arisen from the dead;
    The Lamb once sacrificed,
      The Church's only Head."

REV. LOUIS F. BENSON, 1922

207 AUSTRIAN HYMN 8. 7. 8. 7. D.

F. Joseph Haydn, for the Emperor
Francis' Birthday, February 12, 1797

1 Glo - rious things of thee are spo - ken, Zi - on, cit - y of our God!
He whose word can - not be bro - ken Formed thee for His own a - bode;
On the Rock of A - ges found - ed, What can shake thy sure re - pose?
With sal - va - tion's walls sur-round-ed, Thou mayst smile at all thy foes. A - MEN.

Glorious things are spoken of thee, O city of God.—Ps. lxxxvii, 3

2 See, the streams of living waters,
    Springing from eternal Love,
Well supply thy sons and daughters,
    And all fear of want remove:
Who can faint, while such a river
    Ever flows their thirst to assuage;
Grace which, like the Lord the Giver,
    Never fails from age to age?

3 Round each habitation hovering,
    See the cloud and fire appear
For a glory and a covering,
    Showing that the Lord is near:

Thus deriving from their banner
    Light by night and shade by day,
Safe they feed upon the manna
    Which He gives them when they pray.

4 Saviour, if of Zion's city
    I, through grace, a member am,
Let the world deride or pity,
    I will glory in Thy Name:
Fading is the worldling's pleasure,
    All his boasted pomp and show;
Solid joys and lasting treasure
    None but Zion's children know.

Rev. John Newton, 1779

208 WAVERTREE L. M.

WILLIAM SHORE, 1840

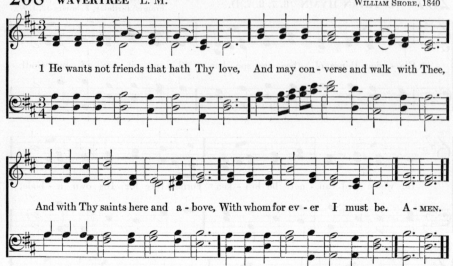

1 He wants not friends that hath Thy love, And may con - verse and walk with Thee,

And with Thy saints here and a - bove, With whom for ev - er I must be. A - MEN.

2 In the communion of Thy saints
  Is wisdom, safety and delight;
  And when my heart declines and faints,
  It's raisèd by their heat and light.

3 As for my friends, they are not lost;
  The several vessels of Thy fleet,
  Though parted now, by tempests tost,
  Shall safely in the haven meet.

4 Still we are centred all in Thee,
  Members, though distant, of one Head;
  In the same family we be,
  By the same faith and spirit led.

5 Before Thy throne we daily meet
  As joint-petitioners to Thee;
  In spirit we each other greet,
  And shall again each other see.

6 The heavenly hosts, world without end,
  Shall be my company above;
  And Thou, my best and surest Friend,
  Who shall divide me from Thy love?

Arranged from Rev. RICHARD BAXTER's "The Resolution," 1681

209 (ST. PETER) C. M.

Where there is neither Greek nor Jew . . . Barbarian, Scythian, bond nor free.—COL. iii, 11

1 In Christ there is no East or West,
  In Him no North or South;
  But one great fellowship of love
  Throughout the whole wide earth.

2 In Him shall true hearts everywhere
  Their high communion find;
  His service is the golden cord
  Close binding all mankind.

3 Join hands, then, brothers of the faith,
  Whate'er your race may be.
  Who serves my Father as a son
  Is surely kin to me.

4 In Christ now meet both East and West,
  In Him meet South and North;
  All Christly souls are one in Him
  Throughout the whole wide earth.

JOHN OXENHAM, 1908

210 BOYLSTON S. M.

LOWELL MASON, 1832

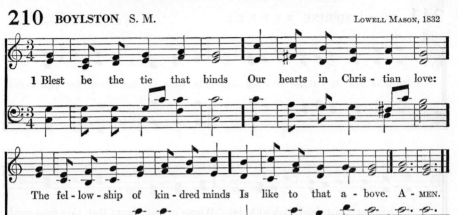

1 Blest be the tie that binds Our hearts in Chris - tian love: The fel - low - ship of kin - dred minds Is like to that a - bove. A - MEN.

2 Before our Father's throne
   We pour our ardent prayers;
   Our fears, our hopes, our aims, are one;
   Our comforts and our cares.

3 We share our mutual woes,
   Our mutual burdens bear,
   And often for each other flows
   The sympathizing tear.

4 When we are called to part
   From those we hold in love,
   We shall be with them still in heart,
   And hope to meet above.

5 This glorious hope revives
   Our courage by the way,
   While each in expectation lives,
   And waits to see the day.

6 From sorrow, toil and pain,
   And sin, we shall be free;
   And perfect love and friendship reign
   Through all eternity.

Rev. JOHN FAWCETT, 1782;
with the fourth verse recast

ST. PETER C. M.

ALEXANDER R. REINAGLE, 1836

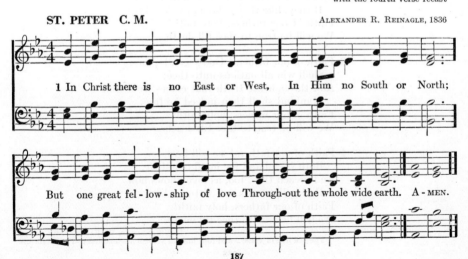

1 In Christ there is no East or West, In Him no South or North; But one great fel - low - ship of love Through-out the whole wide earth. A - MEN.

211 ST. CATHERINE 8. 8. 8. 8. 8. 8.

HENRI F. HEMY, 1864:
arranged by JAMES G. WALTON, 1874

1 Faith of our fa - thers! liv - ing still In spite of dun - geon, fire and sword,

O how our hearts beat high with joy When-e'er we hear that glo - rious word:

Faith of our fa - thers, ho - ly faith! We will be true to thee till death. A - MEN.

2 Our fathers, chained in prisons dark,
    Were still in heart and conscience free;
    And blest would be their children's fate
    If they, like them, should die for thee:
    Faith of our fathers, holy faith!
    We will be true to thee till death.

3 Faith of our fathers! God's great power
    Shall win all nations unto thee;
    And through the truth that comes from God
    Mankind shall then indeed be free:
    Faith of our fathers, holy faith!
    We will be true to thee till death.

4 Faith of our fathers! we will love
    Both friend and foe in all our strife,
    And preach thee, too, as love knows how
    By kindly words and virtuous life:
    Faith of our fathers, holy faith!
    We will be true to thee till death.

Rev. FREDERICK W. FABER, 1849: varied
The 4th line of verse 2 and four lines of verse 3 are adapted to Protestant use

212 SEWARD C. M. D.

LEWIS A. SEWARD, published in 1909

1 O Shep - herd of the Name - less Fold, The bless - ed Church to be,
Our hearts with love and long - ing turn To find their rest in Thee;
"Thy king - dom come," its heaven - ly walls Un - seen a - round us rise,
And deep in lov - ing hu - man hearts Its broad foun - da - tion lies. A - MEN.

By permission of The General Synod of The Church of England in Canada

Alternative tune, LAND OF REST, No. 84

And there shall be one fold, and one Shepherd.—ST. JOHN, x, 16

2 From out our low, unloving state,
　Our centuries of strife,
Thy hand, O Shepherd of the Flock,
　Is lifting into life;
From all our old divided ways
　And fruitless fields, we turn
To Thy dear feet, the simple way
　Of Christian love to learn.

3 O holy kingdom, happy fold,
　O blessèd Church to be,
Our hearts in love and worship turn
　To find themselves in thee:
Thy bounds are known to God alone,
　For they are set above;
The length, the breadth, the height, are one,
　And measured by His love.

MARY A. LATHBURY, "Chautauqua, 1881"

189

213 SARUM 10. 10. 10. 4.

Sir Joseph Barnby, 1869

1 For all the saints who from their la-bors rest, Who Thee by faith be-fore the world con-fessed, Thy Name, O Je-sus, be for ev-er blest. Al - le-lu - ia! Al - le-lu - ia! A-MEN.

2 Thou wast their Rock, their Fortress, and their Might;
Thou, Lord, their Captain in the well-fought fight;
Thou, in the darkness drear, their one true Light. Alleluia!

3 O may Thy soldiers, faithful, true, and bold,
Fight as the saints who nobly fought of old,
And win with them the victor's crown of gold. Alleluia!

4 O blest communion, fellowship divine!
We feebly struggle, they in glory shine;
Yet all are one in Thee, for all are Thine. Alleluia!

5 And when the strife is fierce, the warfare long,
Steals on the ear the distant triumph-song,
And hearts are brave again, and arms are strong. Alleluia!

6 The golden evening brightens in the west;
Soon, soon to faithful warriors cometh rest;
Sweet is the calm of Paradise the blest. Alleluia!

7 But lo! there breaks a yet more glorious day;
The saints triumphant rise in bright array;
The King of Glory passes on His way. Alleluia!

8 From earth's wide bounds, from ocean's farthest coast,
Through gates of pearl streams in the countless host,
Singing to Father, Son, and Holy Ghost.   Alleluia!

Bishop WILLIAM W. How, 1864

For a special setting of this hymn, see No. 406

214   PARADISE   7. 6. 7. 6. D.   FREDERIC WEBER, 1856

1 { From all Thy saints in war - fare, For all Thy saints at rest, }
{ To Thee, O bless - ed Je - sus, All prais - es be ad-dressed; }

Thou, Lord, didst win the bat - tle That they might con - querors be;

Their crowns of liv - ing glo - ry Are lit with rays from Thee. A - MEN.

Alternative tune, AURELIA, No. 25

2 Apostles, prophets, martyrs,
  And all the sacred throng
Who wear the spotless raiment,
  Who raise the ceaseless song;
For these, passed on before us,
  Saviour, we Thee adore,
And, walking in their footsteps,
  Would serve Thee more and more.

3 Then praise we God the Father,
  And praise we God the Son,
And God the Holy Spirit,
  Eternal Three in One;
Till all the ransomed number
  Fall down before the Throne,
And honor, power, and glory
  Ascribe to God alone.

HORATIO, EARL NELSON, 1863

NOTE—*These verses comprise the "general" beginning and conclusion of a hymn of twenty verses for Saints'
Days: the intermediate verses being suitable to the various persons to be commemorated on a special Saint's Day.*

215 HERVEY'S LITANY 7. 7. 7. 6. Rev. Frederick A. J. Hervey, 1875

To be sung in unison

1 Je - sus, with Thy Church a - bide, Be her Sav - iour, Lord, and Guide,

While on earth her faith is tried: We be - seech Thee, hear us. A - men.

Alternative tune, GOWER'S LITANY, No. 240

2 Keep her life and doctrine pure;
Grant her patience to endure,
Trusting in Thy promise sure:
    We beseech Thee, hear us.

3 May she one in doctrine be,
One in truth and charity,
Winning all to faith in Thee:
    We beseech Thee, hear us.

4 May she guide the poor and blind,
Seek the lost until she find,
And the broken-hearted bind:
    We beseech Thee, hear us.

5 Save her love from growing cold,
Make her watchmen strong and bold,
Fence her round, Thy peaceful fold:
    We beseech Thee, hear us.

6 May her lamp of truth be bright,
Bid her bear aloft its light
Through the realms of heathen night;
    We beseech Thee, hear us.

7 Arm her soldiers with the cross,
Brave to suffer toil or loss,
Counting earthly gain but dross:
    We beseech Thee, hear us.

8 May she holy triumphs win,
Overthrow the hosts of sin,
Gather all the nations in:
    We beseech Thee, hear us.

Rev. Thomas B. Pollock, 1871:
as varied in *Hymns ancient and modern*, (the edition of 1875)

Note—*Of the hymns extolling the Church as an institution, with which this section opens, Newton's (No. 207) represents the conception of the Church developed in the 18th century Evangelical Revival, in its fervor and Old Testament flavor; President Dwight's (No. 205) represents the New England Congregationalist conception of the Church at the dawn of the 19th century, in its according to the Church the honors of the Kingdom; Mr. Stone's (No. 201) represents the conception of the Church developed in the Oxford Revival later in that century, in its emphasis on divine authority and corporate unity. Mr. Johnson's (No. 202) represents the modern Liberal view in its tracing the continuity of "the Church of the Spirit" independent of organization. Each hymn makes its contribution to a true doctrine of the Church.*

Baptism

A Collect for the Day of a Child's Baptism

O God, who by Thy Son hast established in Thy Church the sacrament of Baptism as a sign and seal of our engrafting into Christ: Take this child, we beseech Thee, into Thy fatherly tuition, that *he* may abide in Christ for ever. Give us faith to hear Thy covenant, in simple trust that Thou wilt receive and keep the child whom we commit to Thee; and give to those who make answer for *him* grace to fulfil the solemn vows they make in Thy Name. Let Thy Holy Spirit come upon us, and sustain us with the breath of life, and Thy hand guide us beside the still waters of Thy peace; for His sake who is the good Shepherd of Thy sheep, Jesus Christ our Lord. Amen.

216 JESUS, TENDER SHEPHERD 8. 7. 8. 7.

Sir JOHN STAINER, 1898

To be sung in unison

1 Sav-iour, Who Thy flock art feed-ing, With the shep-herd's kind-est care,

All the fee-ble gent-ly lead-ing, While the lambs Thy bo-som share. A-MEN.

Alternative tune, EVENING PRAYER, No. 20

2 Now, *these* little *ones* receiving,
　　Fold *them* in Thy gracious arm;
　　There, we know—Thy word believing—
　　Only there, secure from harm.

3 Never from Thy pasture roving
　　Let *them* be the lion's prey;
　　Let Thy tenderness, so loving,
　　Keep *them* through life's dangerous way.

4 Then, within Thy fold eternal,
　　Let *them* find a resting-place;
　　Feed in pastures ever vernal,
　　Drink the rivers of Thy grace.

Rev. WILLIAM A. MÜHLENBERG, 1826

The Church: Confession of Faith

A Collect for the Confirmation of Baptismal Vows

Almighty God, our Heavenly Father, who hast not withheld Thy loving-kindness from *this* Thy *servant*, but hast given *him* shelter within the covenant of Thy peace, and makest *him* to sit down at Thy Table; we entreat Thee of Thy great mercy to perfect in *him* the good work Thou hast begun: that *he*, being defended by Thy fatherly hand, and strengthened with power through Thy Spirit in the inward man, may be enabled to keep this covenant without spot, unrebukable, until the day of the appearing of our Lord Jesus Christ. Amen.

217 RELIANCE 7. 7. 7. 7. 7. 7. JOHN H. GOWER, in *The Hymnal*, 1895

1 When Thy sol - diers take their swords, When they speak the sol - emn words,

When they kneel be - fore Thee here, Feel - ing Thee, their Fa - ther, near;

These Thy chil - dren, Lord, de - fend; To their help Thy Spir - it send. A-MEN.

2 When the world's sharp strife is nigh,
When they hear the battle-cry,
When they rush into the fight,
Knowing not temptation's might;
   These Thy children, Lord, defend;
   To their zeal Thy wisdom lend.

3 When their hearts are lifted high
With success or victory,
When they feel the conqueror's pride;
Lest they grow self-satisfied,
   These Thy children, Lord, defend;
   Teach their souls to Thee to bend.

4 When the vows that they have made,
When the prayers that they have prayed,
Shall be fading from their hearts;
When their first warm faith departs;
   These Thy children, Lord, defend;
   Keep them faithful to the end.

5 Through life's conflict guard us all,
Or if wounded some should fall
Ere the victory be won,
For the sake of Christ, Thy Son,
   These Thy children, Lord, defend;
   And in death Thy comfort lend.

MRS. FRANCES M. OWEN, c. 1872

Confession of Faith

218 WOODWARD'S LITANY 7. 7. 7. 7.   WILLIAM W. WOODWARD, 1863

1 Thine for ev - er! God of love, Hear us from Thy throne a - bove;
Thine for ev - er may we be Here and in e - ter - ni - ty. A - MEN.

Alternative tune, SEYMOUR, No. 17

Defend, O Lord, this Thy child with Thy heavenly grace; that he may continue Thine for ever.

2 Thine for ever! Lord of life,
Shield us through our earthly strife;
Thou, the Life, the Truth, the Way,
Guide us to the realms of day.

3 Thine for ever! O how blest
They who find in Thee their rest!
Saviour, Guardian, heavenly Friend,
O defend us to the end.

4 Thine for ever! Saviour, keep
These Thy frail and trembling sheep;
Safe alone beneath Thy care,
Let us all Thy goodness share.

5 Thine for ever! Thou our Guide,
All our wants by Thee supplied,
All our sins by Thee forgiven,
Lead us, Lord, from earth to heaven.

MRS. MARY F. MAUDE, 1847

SPANISH HYMN 7. 7. 7. 7. 7. 7.   "The Spanish Hymn, arranged for the Musical Fund Society," by BENJAMIN CARR, Philadelphia, 1826

1 When Thy sol - diers take their swords, When they speak the sol - emn words,

D. C.—These Thy chil - dren, Lord, de - fend; To their help Thy Spir - it send.

When they kneel be - fore Thee here, Feel - ing Thee, their Fa - ther, near; A-MEN.

219 ST. QUINTIN 6. 7. 7. 7.   Rev. HENRY PARR, 1834; adapted for this book

1 I bind my heart this tide To the Gal - i - le - an's side,

To the wounds of Cal - va - ry, To the Christ who died for me. A - MEN.

2 I bind my soul this day
To the brother far away,
And the brother near at hand,
In this town, and in this land.

3 I bind my heart in thrall
To the God, the Lord of All,
To the God, the poor man's Friend,
And the Christ whom He did send.

4 I bind myself to peace,
To make strife and envy cease,
God! Knit Thou sure the cord
Of my thraldom to my Lord.

Rev. LAUCHLAN MACLEAN WATT

DALEHURST C. M.   ARTHUR COTTMAN, 1874

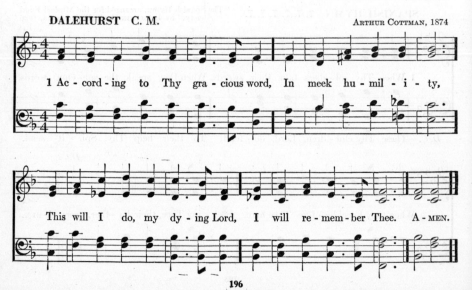

1 Ac - cord - ing to Thy gra - cious word, In meek hu - mil - i - ty,

This will I do, my dy - ing Lord, I will re - mem - ber Thee. A - MEN.

The Communion

A Prayer Before Going to the Lord's Table

Wherewithal shall we come before Thee, O God, or bow ourselves before Thy presence? We will come in the strength of the Lord God, we will make mention of Thy righteousness, even of Thine only. Thou preparest a table before us in the presence of our enemies. We will take the cup of salvation, and call upon the Name of the Lord. We will pay our vows unto the Lord, now in the presence of all Thy people. We will offer ourselves to Thee as the sacrifice of thanksgiving; and to Him who knocketh we will open the door of our heart, that He may come in and feast with us and we with Him: even Jesus Christ our Lord. Amen.

220 MARCOTTE L. M.

Rev. CALVIN W. LAUFER, 1926

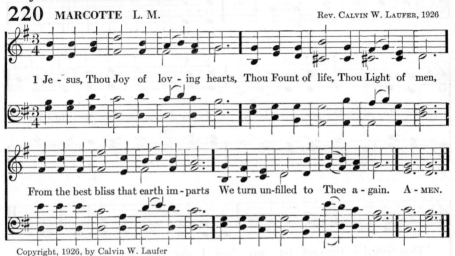

1 Je - sus, Thou Joy of lov - ing hearts, Thou Fount of life, Thou Light of men,

From the best bliss that earth im - parts We turn un-filled to Thee a - gain. A - MEN.

Copyright, 1926, by Calvin W. Laufer

Alternative tune, QUEBEC, No. 79

2 Thy truth unchanged hath ever stood;
   Thou savest those that on Thee call;
To them that seek Thee Thou art good,
   To them that find Thee All in all.

3 We taste Thee, O Thou living Bread,
   And long to feast upon Thee still;
We drink of Thee, the Fountain-head,
   And thirst our souls from Thee to fill.

4 Our restless spirits yearn for Thee,
   Where'er our changeful lot is cast;
Glad when Thy gracious smile we see,
   Blest when our faith can hold Thee fast.

5 O Jesus, ever with us stay,
   Make all our moments calm and bright;
Chase the dark night of sin away,
   Shed o'er the world Thy holy light.

An anonymous 11th century Latin hymn:
translated by Rev. RAY PALMER, 1858

221 (DALEHURST) C. M.

1 According to Thy gracious word,
   In meek humility,
This will I do, my dying Lord,
   I will remember Thee.

2 Thy body, broken for my sake,
   My bread from heaven shall be;
Thy testamental cup I take,
   And thus remember Thee.

3 When to the cross I turn mine eyes,
   And rest on Calvary,

O Lamb of God, my Sacrifice,
   I must remember Thee;

4 Remember Thee, and all Thy pains,
   And all Thy love to me:
Yea, while a breath, a pulse remains
   Will I remember Thee.

5 And when these failing lips grow dumb,
   And mind and memory flee,
When Thou shalt in Thy kingdom come,
   Jesus, remember me.

JAMES MONTGOMERY, 1825

222 HINCHMAN 7. 8. 7. 8. 7. 7.

UZZIAH C. BURNAP, 1869

1 Let Thy blood in mer - cy poured, Let Thy gra - cious bod - y bro - ken,

Be to me, O gra - cious Lord, Of Thy bound-less love the to - ken:

Thou didst give Thy - self for me, Now I give my - self to Thee. A - MEN.

What shall I render unto the Lord for all His benefits toward me?—Ps. cxvi, 12

2 Thou didst die that I might live;
　Blessèd Lord, Thou cams't to save me;
　All that love of God could give
　　Jesus by His sorrows gave me:
　Thou didst give Thyself for me,
　Now I give myself to Thee.

3 By the thorns that crowned Thy brow,
　By the spear wound and the nailing,
　By the pain and death, I now
　　Claim, O Christ, Thy love unfailing:
　Thou didst give Thyself for me,
　Now I give myself to Thee.

4 Wilt Thou own the gift I bring?
　All my penitence I give Thee;
　Thou art my exalted King,
　　Of Thy matchless love forgive me:
　Thou didst give Thyself for me,
　Now I give myself to Thee.

REV. JOHN BROWNLIE, 1907: based on the Greek

NOTE—*Dr. Brownlie, a clergyman of the United Free Church of Scotland (who died during the preparation of this book) gave much of his time and strength, during more than thirty years, to making available the hymns (if they are to be called so) that lie imbedded in the office-books of the Greek Church.* (See also No. 252.)

The Communion

223 MORECAMBE 10. 10. 10. 10.

Frederick C. Atkinson's setting of
"Abide with Me," c. 1870

1 Here, O my Lord, I see Thee face to face; Here would I touch and
han - dle things un - seen, Here grasp with firm - er hand the e - ter - nal grace,
And all my wea - ri - ness up - on Thee lean. A - MEN.

2 Here would I feed upon the Bread of God,
Here drink with Thee the royal Wine of heaven;
Here would I lay aside each earthly load,
Here taste afresh the calm of sin forgiven.

3 This is the hour of banquet and of song;
This is the heavenly table spread for me:
Here let me feast, and, feasting, still prolong
The brief, bright hour of fellowship with Thee.

4 I have no help but Thine, nor do I need
Another arm save Thine to lean upon:
It is enough, my Lord, enough indeed;
My strength is in Thy might, Thy might alone.

5 Mine is the sin, but Thine the righteousness;
Mine is the guilt, but Thine the cleansing blood;
Here is my robe, my refuge, and my peace,
Thy blood, Thy righteousness, O Lord my God.

Rev. Horatius Bonar, 1855

199

224 MELFORD 7. 7. 7.

From a MS. signed "M. B. F."

1 Je - sus, to Thy ta - ble led, Now let ev - ery
heart be fed With the true and liv - ing Bread. A - MEN.

Thou preparest a table before me.—Ps. xxiii, 5

2 While in penitence we kneel,
Thy sweet presence let us feel,
All Thy wondrous love reveal.

3 While on Thy dear cross we gaze,
Mourning o'er our sinful ways,
Turn our sadness into praise.

4 When we taste the mystic Wine,
Of Thine out-poured blood the sign,
Fill our hearts with love divine.

5 Draw us to Thy wounded side,
Whence there flowed the healing tide;
There our sins and sorrows hide.

6 From the bonds of sin release,
Cold and wavering faith increase;
Lamb of God, grant us Thy peace.

7 Lead us by Thy piercèd hand,
Till around Thy throne we stand
In the bright and better land.

Rev. ROBERT H. BAYNES, 1864

NOTE—*This tune was found by James Warrington in a mass of old paper in a Philadelphia shop, and first printed in his "Hymns and Tunes for the Children of the Church," 1886.*

225 (EVENING PRAYER) 8. 7. 8. 7.

1 For the Bread, which Thou hast broken;
For the Wine, which Thou hast poured;
For the Words, which Thou hast spoken;
Now we give Thee thanks, O Lord.

2 By this pledge that Thou dost love us,
By Thy gift of peace restored,
By Thy call to heaven above us,
Hallow all our lives, O Lord.

3 With our sainted ones in glory
Seated at our Father's board,
May the Church that waiteth for Thee
Keep love's tie unbroken, Lord.

4 In Thy service, Lord, defend us,
In our hearts keep watch and ward,
In the world where Thou dost send us
Let Thy kingdom come, O Lord.

Rev. LOUIS F. BENSON, 1924

The following Hymns are also suitable:

(INTROIT) Father, once more within Thy Holy Place, 27
Come, ye disconsolate, where're ye languish, 303
Just as I am, without one plea, 320

(GENERAL) Rock of Ages, cleft for me, 317
I lay my sins on Jesus, 326
Jesus, the very thought of Thee, 342

(POST COMMUNION) O Holy One, 43; "Nunc dimittis," 415

The Kingdom
The Home

226   GERMANY   L. M.   In WILLIAM GARDINER'S *Sacred Melodies*, 1815

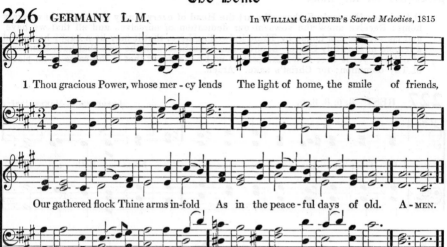

1 Thou gracious Power, whose mer-cy lends   The light of home, the smile of friends,

Our gathered flock Thine arms in-fold   As in the peace-ful days of old.   A - MEN.

2 For all the blessings life has brought,
  For all its sorrowing hours have taught,
  For all we mourn, for all we keep,
  The hands we clasp, the loved that sleep;

3 The noontide sunshine of the past,
  These brief, bright moments fading fast,
  The stars that gild our darkening years,
  The twilight ray from holier spheres;

4 We thank Thee, Father; let Thy grace
  Our narrowing circle still embrace,
  Thy mercy shed its heavenly store,
  Thy peace be with us evermore.

OLIVER WENDELL HOLMES, 1869

NOTE—*The hymn was written for the annual reunion of the Harvard Class of 1829.*

EVENING PRAYER   8. 7. 8. 7.   GEORGE C. STEBBINS, 1878

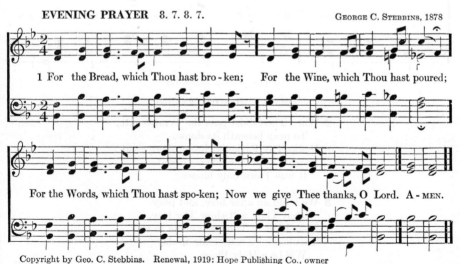

1 For the Bread, which Thou hast bro-ken;   For the Wine, which Thou hast poured;

For the Words, which Thou hast spo-ken; Now we give Thee thanks, O Lord. A - MEN.

The Kingdom: The Home

A Collect for the Home

O God, our Heavenly Father, who art the Head of every family and the Light of every home: Receive anew the vows of our dedication of ourselves and all that we have, and consecrate this house by Thine indwelling here, that it may be a happy home and a temple of the Holy Spirit. Encircle our household with the love that hath been ever of old and yet is ever new: and protect us by the might that is the same in all places of Thy dominion: for Christ's sake. Amen.

227 REST 8. 6. 8. 8. 6. FREDERICK C. MAKER, 1887

1 O Thou whose gra - cious pres - ence blest The home at Beth - a - ny,

This shel - ter from the world's un - rest, This home made read - y

for its Guest, We ded - i - cate to Thee. A - MEN.

For a lower setting, see No. 128

FOR THE CONSECRATION OF A HOME

2 When Thou didst pass the Temple gate,
To pray beneath its dome,
It was Thy Father's House, more great
Because by love made consecrate;
It was Thine only home.

3 We build an altar here, and pray
That Thou wilt show Thy face.
Dear Lord, if Thou wilt come to stay,
This home we consecrate to-day
Will be a Holy Place.

REV. LOUIS F. BENSON, 1925

The Home

228 CROFTON 11. 10. 11. 10.   EDWARD, LORD CROFTON, 1893

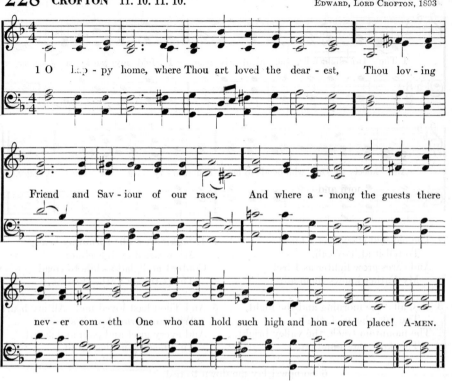

1 O happy home, where Thou art loved the dear-est, Thou lov-ing Friend and Sav-iour of our race, And where a-mong the guests there nev-er com-eth One who can hold such high and hon-ored place! A-MEN.

O SELIG HAUS, WO MAN DICH AUFGENOMMEN

2 O happy home, whose little ones are given
   Early to Thee in humble faith and prayer,
  To Thee, their Friend, who from the heights of heaven
   Guides them, and guards with more than mother's care!

3 O happy home, where each one serves Thee, lowly,
   Whatever his appointed work may be,
  Till every common task seems great and holy,
   When it is done, O Lord as unto Thee!

4 O happy home, where Thou art not forgotten
   When joy is overflowing, full and free,
  O happy home, where every wounded spirit
   Is brought, Physician, Comforter, to Thee,—

5 Until at last, when earth's day's work is ended,
   All meet Thee in the blessèd home above,
  From whence Thou camest, where Thou hast ascended,—
   Thy everlasting home of peace and love.

CARL J. P. SPITTA, 1833
The translation arranged from Mrs. SARAH L. FINDLATER, 1858

The Kingdom: The Home

229 HEBER C. M.

George Kingsley, 1838

1 The twilight falls, the night is near, I fold my work away,
And kneel to One who bends to hear The story of the day: A-MEN.

2 The old, old story; yet I kneel
   To tell it at Thy call,
And cares grow lighter as I feel
   My Father knows them all:

3 Yes, all—the morning and the night,
   The joy, the grief, the loss,
The mountain track, the valley bright,
   The daily thorn and cross.

4 Thou knowest all: I lean my head;
   My wearied eyelids close;
Content and glad awhile to tread
   The path our Father knows.

5 And Thou hast loved me! All my heart
   With answering love is stirred;
And every grief and pain and smart
   Find healing in that word.

6 So now I lay me down to rest,
   As nightly shadows fall,
And lean confiding on His breast
   Who knows and pities all.

The author is unknown and the text is varied

ST. HELEN'S 8. 5. 8. 3.

Sir Robert P. Stewart, 1874

1 Holy Father, in Thy mercy Hear our earnest prayer;
Keep our loved ones, in their absence, 'Neath Thy care. A-MEN.

230 BELLEVILLE 8. 4. 8. 4.

JAMES EDMUND JONES, 1906

1 Lord, for to-mor-row and its needs I do not pray; Keep me, my God, from stain of sin, Just for to-day. A - MEN.

Printed by permission

The morrow shall take thought for the things of itself.—ST. MATT. vi, 34

2 Let me both diligently work
  And duly pray;
Let me be kind in word and deed,
  Just for to-day.

3 Let me be slow to do my will,
  Prompt to obey;
Help me to sacrifice myself,
  Just for to-day.

4 Let me no wrong or idle word
  Unthinking say;
Set Thou a seal upon my lips,
  Just for to-day.

5 Let me in season, Lord, be grave,
  In season gay;
Let me be faithful to Thy grace,
  Just for to-day.

6 Lord, for to-morrow and its needs,
  I do not pray;
But keep me, guide me, love me, Lord,
  Just for to-day.

SYBIL F. PARTRIDGE ("Sister Mary Xavier" in the
Convent of Notre Dame, Liverpool), 1876: the text slightly varied

231 (ST. HELEN'S) 8. 5. 8. 3.

1 Holy Father, in Thy mercy
  Hear our earnest prayer;
Keep our loved ones in their absence,
  'Neath Thy care.

2 Jesus, Saviour, let Thy presence
  Be their light and guide;
Keep, O keep them, in their weakness,
  At Thy side.

3 When in trouble, when in danger,
  When in loneliness,
In Thy love look down and comfort
  Their distress.

4 Holy Spirit, let Thy teaching
  Sanctify their life;
Send Thy grace that they may conquer
  In the strife.

5 Father, Son, and Holy Spirit,
  God the One in Three,
Bless them, guide them, save them, keep them,
  Near to Thee.

ISABELLA S. STEPHENSON, 1889: slightly varied

232 **INTEGER VITÆ** 11. 10. 11. 6.

FREDERICK F. FLEMMING's setting of
HORACE'S "Integer Vitæ," 1810

1 When on my day of life the night is fall-ing, And in the
winds from un-sunned spa-ces blown I hear far voi-ces
out of dark-ness call-ing My feet to paths un-known; A-MEN.

"AT LAST"

2 Thou, who hast made my home of life so pleasant,
    Leave not the tenant when its walls decay;
O Love Divine, O Helper ever present,
    Be Thou my Strength and Stay.

3 Be near me when all else is from me drifting,—
    Earth, sky, home's pictures, days of shade and shine,
And kindly faces to my own uplifting
    The love which answers mine.

4 I have but Thee, my Father; let Thy Spirit
    Be with me then to comfort and uphold!
No gate of pearl, no branch of palm I merit,
    Nor street of shining gold.

5 Suffice it if—my good and ill unreckoned,
    And both forgiven through Thy abounding grace—
I find myself by hands familiar beckoned
    Unto my fitting place,—

The Home

6 Some humble door among Thy many mansions,
  Some sheltering shade where sin and striving cease,
And flows for ever through heaven's green expansions
  The river of Thy peace.

7 There, from the music round about me stealing,
  I fain would learn the new and holy song,
And find at last, beneath Thy trees of healing,
  The life for which I long.

JOHN G. WHITTIER, 1882

NOTE—*This hymn was recited by one of a little group of relatives at the poet's bedside, as the last moment approached.*

233 WOLLASTON C. M. D.

BENJAMIN A. WHAPLES, 1859

1 It sing-eth low in ev-ery heart, We hear it each and all,

A song of those who an-swer not, How-ev-er we may call;

D.S.—kind, the brave, the true, the sweet, Who walk with us no more.

They throng the si-lence of the breast, We see them as of yore,— The A-MEN.

"AULD LANG SYNE"

2 'Tis hard to take the burden up,
  When these have laid it down;
They brightened all the joy of life,
  They softened every frown:
But O 'tis good to think of them,
  When we are troubled sore;
Thanks be to God that such have been,
  Although they are no more.

3 More homelike seems the vast unknown,
  Since they have entered there;
To follow them were not so hard,
  Wherever they may fare:
They cannot be where God is not,
  On any sea or shore;
Whate'er betides, Thy love abides,
  Our God for evermore.

REV. JOHN W. CHADWICK, 1876

207

234 **PERFECT LOVE** 11. 10. 11. 10.

Sir JOSEPH BARNBY, 1889

1 O per - fect Love, all hu - man thought tran - scend - ing,

Low - ly we kneel in prayer be - fore Thy throne,

That theirs may be the love which knows no end - ing,

Whom Thou for ev - er - more dost join in one. A - MEN.

A WEDDING HYMN

2 O perfect Life, be Thou their full assurance
  Of tender charity and steadfast faith,
Of patient hope, and quiet, brave endurance,
  With childlike trust that fears nor pain nor death.

3 Grant them the joy which brightens earthly sorrow;
  Grant them the peace which calms all earthly strife,
And to life's day the glorious unknown morrow
  That dawns upon eternal love and life.

DOROTHY F. BLOMFIELD, 1883

NOTE—*The hymn was written at Pull Wyke, Ambleside, at the suggestion of the author's sister, who wished a hymn for her approaching marriage. It was sung at London weddings and was put into "Hymns ancient and modern" (edition of 1889). Barnby set it to the above music for the wedding of Princess Louise of Fife in 1889, and it has been sung at all the subsequent royal weddings.*

School and College

A Collect for Faithfulness

God help us in this day's duties, and in its pleasures also, to be Thy good and obedient servants: help us to be faithful over a few things, that we may prove worthy to be rulers over many things. When we are tempted to do wrong, remind us of Thy presence: if still we fall into evil, forgive us once more and help us to start afresh. And because Thou lovest all of us, help us to be kind to one another. We ask it for Christ's sake, our Saviour and our Elder Brother. Amen.

235 PENTECOST L. M.

Land of our birth, we pledge to thee
Our love and toil in the years to be,
When we are grown and take our place
As men and women with our race.　　Rev. WILLIAM BOYD, 1868

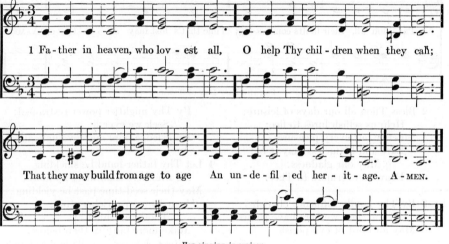

1 Fa-ther in heaven, who lov - est all, O help Thy chil - dren when they call;

That they may build from age to age An un-de-fil-ed her-it-age. A-MEN.

For singing in unison
For a higher setting, see No. 283

2 Teach us to bear the yoke in youth,
With steadfastness and careful truth;
That, in our time, Thy grace may give
The truth whereby the nations live.

3 Teach us to rule ourselves alway,
Controlled and cleanly night and day;
That we may bring, if need arise,
No maimed or worthless sacrifice.

4 Teach us to look in all our ends
On Thee for Judge and not our friends;
That we, with Thee, may walk uncowed
By fear or favor of the crowd.

5 Teach us the strength that cannot seek,
By deed or thought, to hurt the weak;
That, under Thee, we may possess
Man's strength to comfort man's distress.

6 Teach us delight in simple things,
And mirth that has no bitter springs;
Forgiveness free of evil done,
And love to all men 'neath the sun.

Amen.

Land of our birth, our faith, our pride,
For whose dear sake our fathers died;
O Motherland, we pledge to thee
Head, heart, and hand through the years to be.

RUDYARD KIPLING in *Puck of Pook's Hill, 1906*
Printed by his permission and that of Doubleday, Page & Co., the publishers

236 DISMISSAL 8. 7. 8. 7. 8. 7.

WILLIAM L. VINER, 1845

FINE

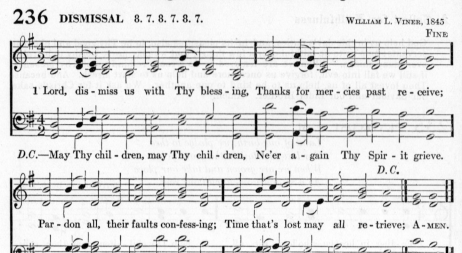

1 Lord, dis-miss us with Thy bless-ing, Thanks for mer-cies past re-ceive;

D.C.—May Thy chil-dren, may Thy chil-dren, Ne'er a-gain Thy Spir-it grieve.

D.C.

Par-don all, their faults con-fess-ing; Time that's lost may all re-trieve; A-MEN.

FOR THE LAST DAY OF TERM

2 Bless Thou all our days of leisure;
   Help us selfish lures to flee;
Sanctify our every pleasure;
   Pure and blameless may it be;
   ||: May our gladness :||
Draw us evermore to Thee.

3 By Thy kindly influence cherish
   All the good we here have gained;
May all taint of evil perish

By Thy mightier power restrained;
   ||: Seek we ever :||
Knowledge pure and love unfeigned.

4 Let Thy father-hand be shielding
   All who here shall meet no more;
May their seed-time past be yielding
   Year by year a richer store;
   ||: Those returning, :||
Make more faithful than before.

Rev. HENRY J. BUCKOLL, for Rugby School, 1843

See also the favorite parting hymn of St. Paul's School, No. 346

237 (ST. ANNE) C. M.

1 Almighty, Merciful and Wise,
   Thy sons before Thee stand,
Attending, ere the hour of strife,
   Thine aid and Thy command.

2 O Mind who knowest all our thought,
   O Heart of loving care,
O Strength of whom our strength is born,
   Hear Thou Thy servants' prayer:

3 That purity may keep our lives,
   That truth in us may shine,
That faithfulness and fearlessness
   In service may combine.

4 Unseen, our ways before us lie;
   Unfelt, our dangers hide;
O Light and Might of all who need,
   None feareth at Thy side!

5 O keep us in Thy service true
   Till every fight be won;
Then may Thy word the victor greet,
   "Thou hast prevailed: well done!"

J. EDMUND BARSS (1871–)

NOTE—*The hymn was written in or about 1905 for the Hotchkiss School.*

School and College

238 **LOG COLLEGE** C. M.
George William Warren in *The Hymnal*, 1895

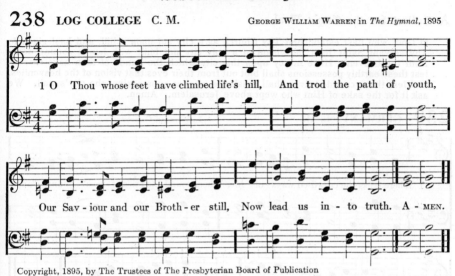

1 O Thou whose feet have climbed life's hill, And trod the path of youth,

Our Sav - iour and our Broth - er still, Now lead us in - to truth. A - MEN.

2 The call is Thine: be Thou the Way,
   And give us men, to guide;
Let wisdom broaden with the day,
   Let human faith abide.

3 Who learn of Thee the truth shall find,
   Who follow, gain the goal;
With reverence crown the earnest mind,
   And speak within the soul.

4 Awake the purpose high which strives,
   And, falling, stands again;
Confirm the will of eager lives
   To quit themselves like men:

5 Thy life the bond of fellowship,
   Thy love the law that rules,
Thy Name, proclaimed by every lip,
   The Master of our schools.

Rev. Louis F. Benson, 1894

ST. ANNE C. M.
The melody is from *Supplement to the New Version*, 1708; and probably by Dr. Croft
To be sung in unison

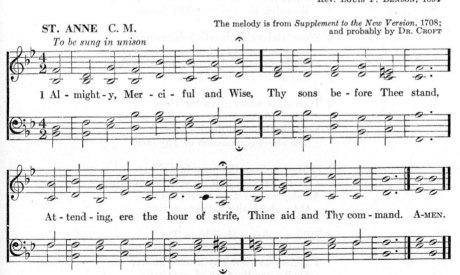

1 Al - might - y, Mer - ci - ful and Wise, Thy sons be - fore Thee stand,

At - tend - ing, ere the hour of strife, Thine aid and Thy com - mand. A-MEN.

For a higher setting, see No. 56

211

The Kingdom: The City

A Collect for the City's Weal

O God, who hast established Thy Church as a city set upon a hill, and hast given to Thy servant Saint John the vision of a holy city not built with hands coming down from the heavens: Have mercy upon this city which the hands of men have reared; lest these earthly possessions shall blot out from their eyes that vision of the heavenlies; and lest these crowded lives shall crush the weaker ones against the city's wall. We ask it for the sake of Him who wept above Jerusalem. Amen.

239 GERMANY L. M.   In WILLIAM GARDINER'S *Sacred Melodies*, 1815

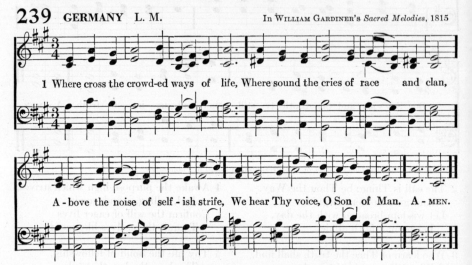

1 Where cross the crowd-ed ways of life, Where sound the cries of race and clan,

A - bove the noise of self - ish strife, We hear Thy voice, O Son of Man. A - MEN.

2 In haunts of wretchedness and need,
   On shadowed thresholds dark with fears,
From paths where hide the lures of greed,
   We catch the vision of Thy tears.

3 From tender childhood's helplessness,
   From woman's grief, man's burdened toil,
From famished souls, from sorrow's stress,
   Thy heart has never known recoil.

4 The cup of water given for Thee
   Still holds the freshness of Thy grace;
Yet long these multitudes to see
   The sweet compassion of Thy face.

5 O Master, from the mountain side,
   Make haste to heal these hearts of pain;
Among these restless throngs abide,
   O tread the city's streets again;

6 Till sons of men shall learn Thy love,
   And follow where Thy feet have trod;
Till glorious from Thy heaven above,
   Shall come the City of our God.

Rev. FRANK MASON NORTH, 1903

The City

240 THE SEVEN WORDS 7. 7. 7. 6.
In *St. Alban's Tune Book*, 1866

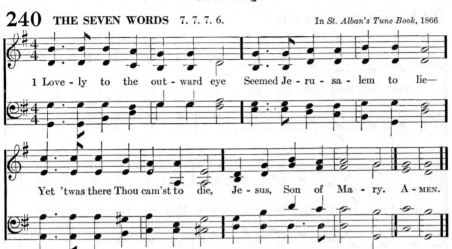

1 Love - ly to the out - ward eye Seemed Je - ru - sa - lem to lie—

Yet 'twas there Thou cam'st to die, Je - sus, Son of Ma - ry. A - MEN.

*And when He was come near, He beheld the city, and wept over it.—*ST. LUKE, xix, 41

2 Far-brought stones and marble rare
Made its towers and circuits fair,
Yet Thy cross was waiting there,
  Wearied Son of Mary.

3 Yea, that whited city's pride,
And its splendors multiplied,
Meant but pain and piercèd side
  To Thee, Son of Mary.

4 And would all the crowded mart,
Wealth and splendid ease and art
Of our own world please Thy heart,
  O Thou Son of Mary?

5 Would'st Thou call our boasting good,
If Thou saw'st our triumphs stood
On the wreck of brotherhood,
  Loving Son of Mary?

6 Or would'st hold our wealth and pride
Cheap because of love denied
And Thy Spirit crucified,
  Patient Son of Mary?

7 Jesus, pardon where we fall;
Jesus, our whole life enthrall;
Let Thy Spirit rule it all,
  Blessèd Son of Mary.

Rev. W. RUSSELL BOWIE, 1909
By permission from *Hymns of the Kingdom*, copyright, 1910, by A. S. Barnes & Co.

GOWER'S LITANY 7. 7. 7. 6.
JOHN H. GOWER, 1891

1 Love - ly to the out - ward eye Seemed Je - ru - sa - lem to lie—

Yet 'twas there Thou cam'st to die, Je - sus, Son of Ma - ry. A - MEN.

241 FARMER 7. 6. 8. 6. D.

JOHN FARMER (1836–1901)

1 The fa - thers built this cit - y How man - y years a - go!
And bus - y in its bus - y streets, They hur - ried to and fro;
The chil - dren played a - round them, And sang the songs of yore,
Till one by one they fell a - sleep, To work and play no more. A - MEN.

Alternative tune, PATMOS, No. 387

2 Yet still the city standeth,
   A hive of toiling men,
And mother's love makes happy home
   For children now as then;
O God of ages, help us
   Such citizens to be
That children's children here may sing
   The songs of liberty.

3 Let all the people praise Thee;
   Give all Thy saving health;
Or vain the laborer's strong right arm
   And vain the merchant's wealth.

Send forth Thy light to banish
   The shadows and the shame,
Till all the civic virtues shine
   Around our city's name.

4 A commonweal of brothers,
   United, great and small;
Upon our banner blazoned be
   The charter, "Each for all!"
Nor let us cease from battle,
   Nor weary sheathe the sword,
Until this city is become
   The city of the Lord.

REV. WILLIAM G. TARRANT (1853–):
the second line varied

The City

242 URBS 6. 10. 6. 10. 6. 10.   Rev. CALVIN W. LAUFER, 1926

1 Not in the sol - i - tude A - lone, may man com-mune with heaven, or see

On - ly in sav - age wood And sun - ny vale, the pres - ent De - i - ty;

Or on - ly hear His voice Where the winds whis-per and the waves re-joice. A - MEN.

Copyright, 1926, by Calvin W. Laufer

"HYMN OF THE CITY"

2   Even here do I behold
Thy steps, Almighty!—here, amidst the crowd
    Through the great city rolled,
With everlasting murmur, deep and loud—
    Choking the ways that wind
Among proud piles, the work of human kind.

3   Thy Spirit is around,
Quickening the restless mass that sweeps along;
    And this eternal sound—
Voices and footfalls of th' unnumbered throng—
    Like the resounding sea,
Or like the rainy tempest, speaks of Thee.

4   And when the hours of rest
Come, like a calm upon the mid-sea brine,
    Hushing its billowy breast—
The quiet of that moment, too, is Thine;
    It breathes of Him who keeps
The vast and helpless city while it sleeps.

WILLIAM CULLEN BRYANT, 1830:
the rhythm of two lines revised

The Kingdom: Brotherhood and Service

A Collect for the Spirit of Service

O Thou from whom cometh every good gift: Help us not only to praise Thee, but to share also Thy grace of giving. O Thou who gavest Thy Son in sacrifice for the world's sin, make us more obedient to His law of sacrifice, and more brotherly to those for whom He died. O Thou who hast called us to serve Thee in His Name, let these songs of service thrill our hearts with the uplift of our heavenly calling, and sweeten the tasks of our earthly labors. Through Jesus Christ our Lord. Amen.

243 ALMSGIVING. 8. 8. 8. 4.

Rev. John B. Dykes, 1865

1 O Lord of heaven and earth and sea, To Thee all praise and glo - ry be; How shall we show our love to Thee Who giv - est all? A - MEN.

Freely ye have received, freely give.—Rom. xiii, 12

2 The golden sunshine, vernal air,
Sweet flowers and fruit, Thy love declare;
When harvests ripen, Thou art there,
Who givest all.

3 For peaceful homes and healthful days,
For all the blessings earth displays,
We owe Thee thankfulness and praise,
Who givest all.

4 For souls redeemed, for sins forgiven,
For means of grace and hopes of heaven,
Father, what can to Thee be given,
Who givest all?

5 We lose what on ourselves we spend;
We have as treasure without end
Whatever, Lord, to Thee we lend,
Who givest all.

Bishop Christopher Wordsworth, 1863

244 (ALMSGIVING) 8. 8. 8. 4.

1 Content to come, content to go,
Content to wrestle or to race,
Content to know or not to know,
Each in his place;

2 Lord, grant us grace to love Thee so
That glad of heart and glad of face
At last we may sit high or low,
Each in his place;

3 Where pleasures flow as rivers flow,
And loss has left no barren trace,
And all that are are perfect so,
Each in his place.

Christina G. Rossetti, before 1893

245 COMRADES 8. 7. 8. 7. D. (Iambic)

Arranged from a German song
by BRADLEY KEELER, 1924

1 The lamps of heaven are burn-ing still Be - yond the wind and wea - ther;

Then lift your heart and brace your will To breast the hill to - geth - er.

It's hill and hol - low, mist or rain, It's fail - ure and en - deav - or,

It's strug - gle al - ways, sometimes pain, And then it's home for ev - er. A - MEN.

Copyright, 1925, by Louis F. Benson

Every one said to his brother, Be of good courage.—ISA. xli, 6

2 So share your hope of heaven to-day,
  If any heart will heed you;
And give, along the narrow way,
  A hand to those who need you:
Till some spent pilgrim in his woe,
  Who feels your arm around him,
Will dream that heaven is bending low
And bless the love that found him.

3 O who would scale life's topmost hill
  Alone amid the heather,
Where he might lead a comrade still
  To enter heaven together?
God lend more kindness to the brave,
  God make faint hearts more daring;
From pride defend, in weakness save,
And prosper our wayfaring.

REV. LOUIS F. BENSON, 1913

246 SCHUMANN S. M.

In MASON AND WEBB'S *Cantica Laudis*, Boston, 1850

1 We give Thee but Thine own, What-e'er the gift may be:
All that we have is Thine a-lone, A trust, O Lord, from Thee. A-MEN.

Remember the words of the Lord Jesus, how He said, It is more blessed to give than to receive.—ACTS xx, 35

2 May we Thy bounties thus
  As stewards true receive,
And gladly, as Thou blessest us,
  To Thee our first-fruits give.

3 O hearts are bruised and dead,
  And homes are bare and cold,
And lambs for whom the Shepherd bled
  Are straying from the fold.

4 To comfort and to bless,
  To find a balm for woe,
To tend the lone and fatherless,
  Is angels' work below.

5 The captive to release,
  To God the lost to bring,
To teach the way of life and peace,—
  It is a Christ-like thing.

6 And we believe Thy word,
  Though dim our faith may be,
Whate'er for Thine we do, O Lord,
  We do it unto Thee.

Bishop W. WALSHAM HOW, 1864

247 (BULLINGER) 8. 5. 8. 3.

1 When thy heart, with joy o'erflowing,
  Sings a thankful prayer;
In thy joy O let thy brother
  With thee share.

2 When the harvest sheaves ingathered
  Fill thy barns with store,
To thy God and to thy brother
  Give the more.

3 If thy soul, with power uplifted,
  Yearn for glorious deed,
Give thy strength to serve thy brother
  In his need.

4 Hast thou borne a secret sorrow
  In thy lonely breast?
Take to thee thy sorrowing brother
  For a guest.

5 Share with him thy bread of blessing,
  Sorrow's burden share;
When thy heart enfolds a brother,
  God is there.

Rev. THEODORE C. WILLIAMS, 1891

248 ORIENTIS PARTIBUS 7. 7. 7. 7.

A mediæval French melody

To be sung in unison

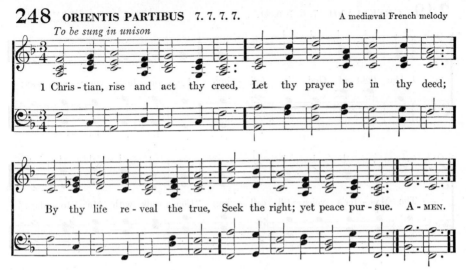

1 Chris-tian, rise and act thy creed, Let thy prayer be in thy deed;

By thy life re-veal the true, Seek the right; yet peace pur-sue. A-MEN.

Alternative tune, INNOCENTS, No. 10

2 Let thine alms be hope and joy,
And thy worship God's employ;
Give Him thanks in humble zeal,
Keen to learn and quick to feel.

3 Hearts around thee sink with care;
Thou canst help their load to bear;
When they falter in the fight,
Thou canst bring them strength and light.

4 Wrong shall die in open day,
Clouds of doubt shall melt away;
Falsehood flee from candor's face,
Health reflect eternal grace.

5 Come then, law divine, and reign,—
Perfect faith assailed in vain,
Perfect love bereft of fear,
Born in heaven and radiant here.

Rev. FRANCIS A. R. RUSSELL, 1893:
recast for this book

BULLINGER 8. 5. 8. 3.

Rev. ETHELBERT W. BULLINGER, 1874

1 When thy heart, with joy o'er-flow-ing, Sings a thank-ful prayer,

In thy joy O let thy broth-er With thee share. A-MEN.

249 **GREENLAND** 7. 6. 7. 6. D.

Arranged from J. Michael Haydn in B. Jacob's *National Psalmody*, 1819

1 The light of God is fall - ing Up - on life's com - mon way;

The Mas - ter's voice still call - ing, "Come, walk with Me to - day:"

No du - ty can seem low - ly To him who lives with Thee,

And all of life grows ho - ly, O Christ of Gal - i - lee. A - MEN.

2 Who shares his life's pure pleasures,
  And walks the honest road,
Who trades with heaping measures,
  And lifts his brother's load,
Who turns the wrong down bluntly,
  And lends the right a hand;
He dwells in God's own country,
  He tills the Holy Land.

3 Where human lives are thronging
  In toil and pain and sin,
While cloistered hearts are longing,
  To bring the kingdom in,

O Christ, the Elder Brother
  Of proud and beaten men,
When they have found each other,
  Thy kingdom will come then.

4 Thy ransomed host in glory,
  All souls that sin and pray,
Turn toward the cross that bore Thee;
  "Behold the man!" they say:
And while Thy Church is pleading
  For all who would do good,
We hear Thy true voice leading
  Our song of brotherhood.

Rev. Louis F. Benson, 1910

Brotherhood and Service

250 **TENNENT** 7. 6. 7. 6. D.   Uzziah C. Burnap in *The Hymnal*, 1895

1 Lead on, O King E - ter - nal, The day of march has come;

Hence - forth in fields of con - quest Thy tents shall be our home:

Through days of prep - a - ra - tion Thy grace has made us strong,

And now, O King E - ter - nal, We lift our bat - tle - song. A - MEN.

2 Lead on, O King Eternal,
   Till sin's fierce war shall cease,
And Holiness shall whisper
   The sweet Amen of peace;
For not with swords loud clashing,
   Nor roll of stirring drums,
But deeds of love and mercy,
   The heavenly kingdom comes.

3 Lead on, O King Eternal:
   We follow, not with fears;
For gladness breaks like morning
   Where'er Thy face appears;
Thy cross is lifted o'er us;
   We journey in its light:
The crown awaits the conquest;
   Lead on, O God of might.

Rev. Ernest W. Shurtleff, 1888

Note—*The hymn was written for the graduation of the Class of 1888 at Andover Theological Seminary.*

251 WORK SONG 7. 6. 7. 5. D.

LOWELL MASON, 1864

1 Work, for the night is com - ing: Work through the morn - ing hours;

Work while the dew is spark - ling; Work 'mid spring - ing flowers;

Work while the day grows bright - er, Un - der the glow - ing sun;

Work, for the night is com - ing, When man's work is done. A - MEN.

The night cometh, when no man can work.—ST. JOHN ix, 4

2 Work, for the night is coming:
  Work through the sunny noon;
  Fill brightest hours with labor,
  Rest comes sure and soon;
  Give every flying minute
  Something to keep in store;
  Work, for the night is coming,
  When man works no more.

3 Work, for the day is coming!
  Darkness will soon be gone,
  Then o'er the night of weeping
  Endless day shall dawn.
  What now we sow in sadness,
  Then we shall reap in joy;
  Hope will be changed to gladness,
  Praise be our employ.

Verses 1 and 2 are by Mrs. ANNA L. COGHILL, 1854, slightly varied: verse 3 is added

NOTE—*Mrs. Coghill's stirring hymn stops short of the more Christian incentive to diligence. In place of her third verse, which only deepens the impending gloom, a substitute is taken from a hymn attributed to Prof. Basil Manly of Louisville.*

252 BANSTEAD S. M. D.

JOHN T. MUSGRAVE, 1916

1 The time is draw - ing near, It can - not tar - ry long,

When they who face the con - flict here Shall join the glo - rious throng,—

REFRAIN

Where glad - ness fills each heart, And hon - or crowns each brow:

For tire - less ser - vice fit me, Lord, By will - ing ser - vice now. A - MEN.

2 Let sunshine fill the soul
   When threatening night descends,
That I may see the light serene
   No sunset ever ends:—REF.

3 Let strength my spirit nerve,
   That, with each labor done,
I may, like those who serve above,
   See some new task begun:—REF.

4 The time is drawing near,—
   Till that bright morning break,
May I, with those who seek Thy face,
   Thy will my pleasure make:—REF.

Rev. JOHN BROWNLIE, based on the Greek, 1911

See the note under No. 222

253 NOX PRÆCESSIT C. M.

J. BAPTISTE CALKIN, 1875

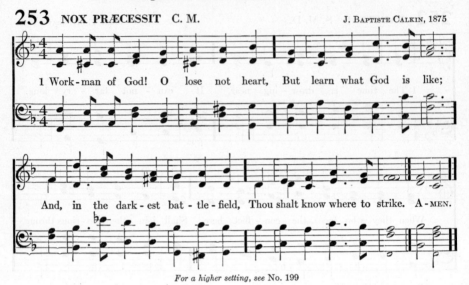

1 Work-man of God! O lose not heart, But learn what God is like;

And, in the dark-est bat-tle-field, Thou shalt know where to strike. A-MEN.

For a higher setting, see No. 199

2 Thrice blest is he to whom is given
The instinct that can tell
That God is on the field when He
Is most invisible.

3 Blest too is he who can divine
Where the real right doth lie,
And dares to take the side that seems
Wrong to man's blindfold eye.

4 Then learn to scorn the praise of men,
And learn to lose with God;
For Jesus won the world through shame,
And beckons thee His road:

5 For right is right, since God is God;
And right the day must win;
To doubt would be disloyalty,
To falter would be sin.

Arranged from Rev. FREDERICK W. FABER's "The Right must win," 1849

NORTHREPPS C. M.

JOSIAH BOOTH, 1887

1 When cour-age fails, and faith burns low, And men are tim-id grown,

Hold fast thy loy-al-ty, and know That truth still mov-eth on. A-MEN.

224

254 MIRFIELD C. M.   ARTHUR COTTMAN, 1874

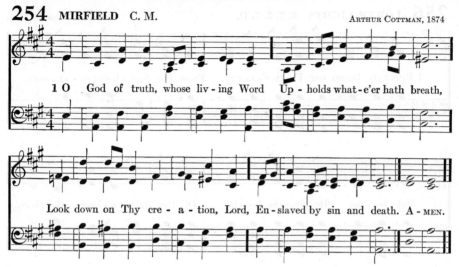

1 O God of truth, whose liv-ing Word Up-holds what-e'er hath breath,

Look down on Thy cre-a-tion, Lord, En-slaved by sin and death. A-MEN.

Strive for truth to the death, and the Lord shall fight for thee.—ECCLUS. iv, 28
Thou desirest truth in the inward parts.—Ps. li, 6

2 Set up Thy standard, Lord, that we
  Who claim a heavenly birth
May march with Thee to smite the lies
  That vex Thy groaning earth.

3 Ah! would we join that blest array,
  And follow in the might
Of Him, the Faithful and the True,
  In raiment clean and white!

4 We fight for truth, we fight for God,
  Poor slaves of lies and sin!
He who would fight for Thee on earth
  Must first be true within.

5 Then, God of truth for whom we long,
  Thou who wilt hear our prayer,
Do Thine own battle in our hearts,
  And slay the falsehood there.

6 Still smite, still burn, till naught is left
  But God's own truth and love;
Then, Lord, as morning dew come down,
  Rest on us from above.

7 Yea, come; then, tried as in the fire,
  From every lie set free,
Thy perfect truth shall dwell in us,
  And we shall live in Thee.

THOMAS HUGHES, author of *Tom Brown's School Days*, 1859

255 (NORTHREPPS) C. M.

1 When courage fails, and faith burns low,
  And men are timid grown,
Hold fast thy loyalty, and know
  That truth still marches on.

2 For unseen messengers she hath
  To work her will and ways,
And even human scorn and wrath
  God turneth to her praise.

3 The race is not unto the swift,
  The battle to the strong,

When dawn her judgment-days that sift
  The claims of right and wrong.

4 And more than thou canst do for truth
  Can she on thee confer,
If thou, O heart, but give thy youth
  And manhood unto her.

5 For she can make thee inly bright,
  Thy self-love purge away,
And lead thee in the path whose light
  Shines to the perfect day.

REV. FREDERICK L. HOSMER, 1881

256 LOWER LIGHTS 8. 7. 8. 7. D.

Philip P. Bliss, 1877

1 Bright-ly beams our Fa-ther's mer-cy From His light-house ev-er-more,

But to us He gives the keep-ing Of the lights a-long the shore.

REFRAIN

Let the low-er lights be burn-ing! Send a gleam a-cross the wave!

Some poor faint-ing, struggling sail-or You may res-cue, you may save. A-MEN.

2 Dark the night of sin has settled,
　Loud the angry billows roar;
　Eager eyes ar watching, longing,
　　For the lights along the shore.—REF.

3 Trim your feeble lamp, my brother;
　Some poor sailor tempest tossed,
　Trying now to make the harbor,
　　In the darkness may be lost.—REF.

Philip P. Bliss, 1877

NOTE—*Mr. Bliss' song was based on a story which Moody, the evangelist, told of a vessel that on a stormy night made the Cleveland harbor by aid of the light-house, but missed the channel because the range-lights had gone out, and was wrecked. "The Master," Mr. Moody said, "will take care of the great light-house: let us keep the lower lights burning."*

257 HOLY CROSS C. M.

Adapted from THOMAS HASTINGS, 1831
in S. SMITH'S *Selection of Psalm and Hymn Tunes*, 1865

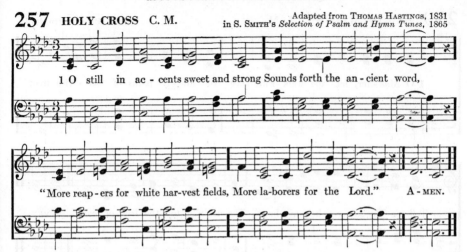

1 O still in ac-cents sweet and strong Sounds forth the an-cient word,

"More reap-ers for white har-vest fields, More la-borers for the Lord." A-MEN.

2 We hear the call; in dreams no more
  In selfish ease we lie,
But, girded for our Father's work,
  Go forth beneath His sky.

3 Where prophets' word, and martyrs' blood,
  And prayers of saints were sown,

We, to their labors entering in,
  Would reap where they have strown.

4 O Thou whose call our hearts has stirred,
  To do Thy will we come;
Thrust in our sickles at Thy word,
  And bear our harvest home.

Rev. SAMUEL LONGFELLOW, 1864

258 HOLY TRINITY C. M.

Sir JOSEPH BARNBY, 1861

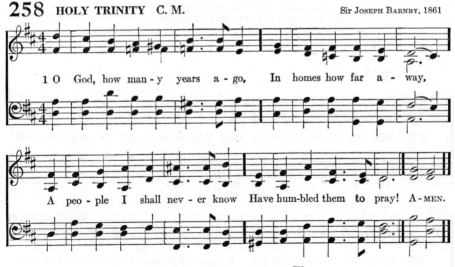

1 O God, how man-y years a-go, In homes how far a-way,

A peo-ple I shall nev-er know Have hum-bled them to pray! A-MEN.

2 Not once or twice we cry to Thee,
  Not once, or now and then,—
Wherever there is misery,
  Wherever there are men.

FREDERIC W. H. MYERS, 1870

259 SUN OF MY SOUL L. M.

Rev. H. Percy Smith, 1874

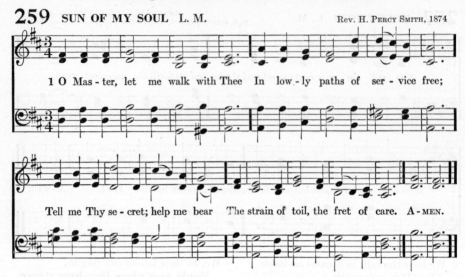

1 O Mas-ter, let me walk with Thee In low-ly paths of ser-vice free;

Tell me Thy se-cret; help me bear The strain of toil, the fret of care. A-men.

2 Help me the slow of heart to move
By some clear winning word of love;
Teach me the wayward feet to stay,
And guide them in the homeward way.

3 Teach me Thy patience; still with Thee
In closer, dearer company,
In work that keeps faith sweet and strong,
In trust that triumphs over wrong;

4 In hope that sends a shining ray
Far down the future's broadening way;
In peace that only Thou canst give,
With Thee, O Master, let me live.

Rev. Washington Gladden, 1879

Note—*Dr. Gladden requested that his hymn should always be sung to this tune.*

RACHEL L. M.

Miss E. M. Wren, 1890

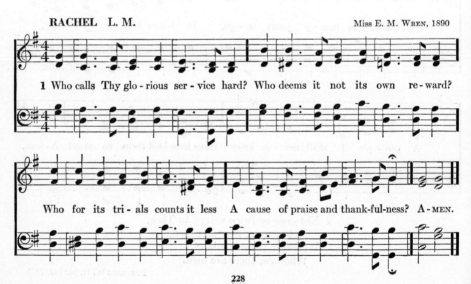

1 Who calls Thy glo-rious ser-vice hard? Who deems it not its own re-ward?

Who for its tri-als counts it less A cause of praise and thank-ful-ness? A-men.

260 CANONBURY L. M.

Arranged from ROBERT A. SCHUMANN'S
Nachtstücke, No. 4, 1839

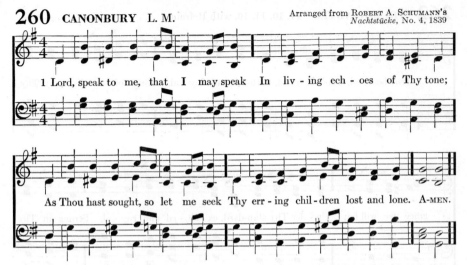

1 Lord, speak to me, that I may speak In liv - ing ech - oes of Thy tone;

As Thou hast sought, so let me seek Thy err - ing chil - dren lost and lone. A-MEN.

2 O lead me, Lord, that I may lead
The wandering and the wavering feet;
O feed me, Lord, that I may feed
Thy hungering ones with manna sweet.

3 O strengthen me, that while I stand
Firm on the Rock, and strong in Thee,
I may stretch out a loving hand
To wrestlers with the troubled sea.

4 O teach me, Lord, that I may teach
The precious things Thou dost impart;
And wing my words, that they may reach
The hidden depths of many a heart.

5 O give Thine own sweet rest to me,
That I may speak with soothing power
A word in season, as from Thee,
To weary ones in needful hour.

6 O use me, Lord, use even me,
Just as Thou wilt, and when, and where;
Until Thy blessèd face I see,
Thy rest, Thy joy, Thy glory share.

FRANCES R. HAVERGAL, 1872

261 (RACHEL) L. M.

1 Who calls Thy glorious service hard?
Who deems it not its own reward?
Who for its trials counts it less
A cause of praise and thankfulness?

2 It may not be our lot to wield
The sickle in the ripened field;
Nor ours to hear, on summer eves,
The reapers' song among the sheaves.

3 Yet where our duty's task is wrought
In unison with God's great thought,
The near and future blend in one,
And whatsoe'er is willed is done.

4 And ours the grateful service whence
Comes day by day the recompense;
The hope, the trust, the purpose stayed,
The fountain and the noonday shade.

5 And were this life the utmost span,
The only end and aim of man,
Better the toil of fields like these
Than waking dream and slothful ease.

6 But life, though falling like our grain,
Like that revives and springs again;
And early called, how blest are they
Who wait in heaven their harvest-day!

Abridged from WHITTIER'S "Seed-time and Harvest," 1850

262 TRUE-HEARTED 11. 10. 11. 10. with Refrain

JOSIAH BOOTH, 1890

1 True-heart-ed, whole-heart-ed, faith-ful and loy-al, King of our lives, by Thy grace we will be; Un-der Thy stan-dard, ex-alt-ed and roy-al, Strong in Thy

REFRAIN

strength, we will bat-tle for Thee. Peal out the watch-word, and si-lence it nev-er, Song of our spir-its re-joic-ing and free; "True-heart-ed, whole-heart-ed, now and for ev-er, King of our lives, by Thy grace we will be." A-MEN.

Brotherhood and Service

2 True-hearted, whole-hearted! fullest allegiance
   Yielding henceforth to our glorious King;
Valiant endeavor and loving obedience
   Freely and joyously now would we bring.—REF.

3 True-hearted! Saviour, Thou knowest our story;
   Weak are the hearts that we lay at Thy feet,
Sinful and treacherous; yet, for Thy glory,
   Heal them, and cleanse them from sin and deceit.—REF.

4 Whole-hearted! Saviour, beloved and glorious,
   Take Thy great power and reign Thou alone,
Over our wills and affections victorious,
   Freely surrendered, and wholly Thine own.—REF.

FRANCES R. HAVERGAL, 1874

263 ST. BEES 7. 7. 7. 7.

REV. JOHN B. DYKES, 1862

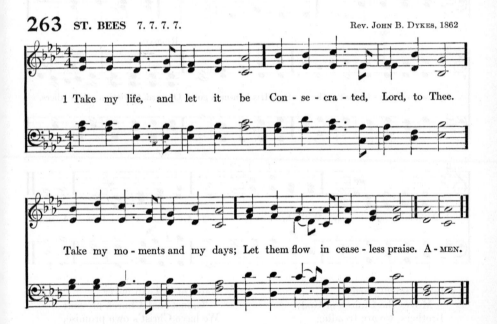

1 Take my life, and let it be Con-se-cra-ted, Lord, to Thee.

Take my mo-ments and my days; Let them flow in cease-less praise. A-MEN.

2 Take my hands, and let them move
   At the impulse of Thy love.
Take my lips, and let them be
   Filled with messages from Thee.

3 Take my silver and my gold;
   Not a mite would I withhold.
Take my intellect, and use
   Every power as Thou shalt choose.

4 Take my will, and make it Thine;
   It shall be no longer mine.
Take my heart, it is Thine own;
   It shall be Thy royal throne.

5 Take my love; my Lord, I pour
   At Thy feet its treasure-store.
Take myself, and I will be
   Ever, only, all for Thee.

FRANCES R. HAVERGAL, 1874

264 ST. GERTRUDE 6.5.6.5. 12 ll.   Sir ARTHUR SULLIVAN, 1871

1 Onward, Christian soldiers, Marching as to war, With the cross of Jesus Going on before: Christ the royal Master Leads against the foe:

Forward into battle See His banners go.

REFRAIN

Onward, Christian soldiers, Marching as to war, With the cross of Jesus Going on before. A-MEN.

2 Like a mighty army
  Moves the Church of God;
Brothers, we are treading
  Where the saints have trod;
We are not divided,
  All one body we,
One in hope and doctrine,
  One in charity.—REF.

3 Crowns and thrones may perish,
  Kingdoms rise and wane,
But the Church of Jesus
  Constant will remain;

Gates of hell can never
  'Gainst that Church prevail;
We have Christ's own promise,
  And that cannot fail.—REF.

4 Onward, then, ye people,
  Join our happy throng,
Blend with ours your voices
  In the triumph-song;
Glory, laud, and honor
  Unto Christ the King;
This through countless ages
  Men and angels sing.—REF.

Rev. SABINE BARING-GOULD, 1865

265 ONWARD 6. 5. 6. 5. 12 ll. J. W. BARRINGTON, 1893

1 For-ward through the a - ges, In un - bro-ken line, Move the faithful spir - its,

At the call di - vine; Gifts in differing meas - ure, Hearts of one ac - cord,

Man - i - fold the serv - ice, One the sure re - ward.

REFRAIN

For-ward through the a - ges, In un - bro-ken line, Move the faith-ful spir-its At the call di - vine. A-MEN.

2 Wider grows the kingdom,
    Reign of love and light;
For it we must labor
    Till our faith is sight;
Prophets have proclaimed it,
    Martyrs testified,
Poets sung its glory,
    Heroes for it died.—REF.

3 Not alone we conquer,
    Not alone we fall;
In each loss or triumph
    Lose or triumph all.
Bound by God's far purpose
    In one living whole,
Move we on together
    To the shining goal!—REF.

Rev. FREDERICK L. HOSMER, 1908

The Kingdom: Brotherhood and Service

266 **PRESBYTER** C. M. D.

WALTER O. WILKINSON, in *The Hymnal*, 1895

To be sung in unison

1 God's trum-pet wakes the slumbering world; Now each man to his post!

The red-cross ban-ner is un-furled; Who joins the glo-rious host?

He who, in feal-ty to the Truth, And count-ing all the cost,

Doth con-se-crate his generous youth,— He joins the no-ble host. A-MEN.

2 He who, no anger on his tongue
  Nor any idle boast,
Bears steadfast witness against wrong,—
  He joins the sacred host.
He who with calm undaunted will
  Ne'er counts the battle lost,
But, though defeated, battles still,—
  He joins the faithful host.

3 He who is ready for the cross,
  The cause despised loves most;
And shuns not pain or shame or loss,—
  He joins the martyr host.
God's trumpet wakes the slumbering world;
  Now each man to his post!
The red-cross banner is unfurled;
  Who joins the glorious host?

REV. SAMUEL LONGFELLOW, 1864

267 ARMAGEDDON 6. 5. 6. 5. 12 ll.

Arranged from a German melody
by Sir JOHN GOSS, 1871

1 Who is on the Lord's side? Who will serve the King? Who will be His help-ers

Oth-er lives to bring? Who will leave the world's side? Who will face the foe?

Who is on the Lord's side? Who for Him will go? By Thy call of mer-cy,

By Thy grace di-vine, We are on the Lord's side, Sav-iour, we are Thine. A-MEN.

2 Not for weight of glory,
   Not for crown and palm,
Enter we the army,
   Raise the warrior psalm;
But for love that claimeth
   Lives for whom He died:
He whom Jesus nameth
   Must be on His side.
     By Thy love constraining,
     By Thy grace divine,
   We are on the Lord's side,
     Saviour, we are Thine.

3 Fierce may be the conflict,
   Strong may be the foe,
But the King's own army
   None can overthrow:
Round His standard ranging,
   Victory is secure;
For His truth unchanging
   Makes the triumph sure.
     Joyfully enlisting
     By Thy grace divine,
   We are on the Lord's side,
     Saviour, we are Thine.

FRANCES R. HAVERGAL, 1877

The Kingdom: The Nation

A Collect for the Fourth of July

Almighty God, who on this day didst direct and inspire the hearts of our fathers to set forth the independence of these United States: We give all glory and praise to Thee, the Author of our liberty, and the sure Defense of our safety. We pray that by Thy grace we may be enabled to build wisely upon these foundations of freedom and of peace; that we may hold our liberties in due subjection to Thy law, and in all things seek that righteousness which exalteth a nation. Kindle in our hearts the pure flame of sacrifice to our country's needs; and grant that the fires of our patriotism may shine as beacon lights upon Thy holy hills, O God, and may point the ways of men toward that universal brotherhood, when the nations of the world shall be one in Jesus Christ our Lord. Amen.

268 **AMERICA** 6. 6. 4. 6. 6. 6. 4.

In *Thesaurus Musicus*, 1740, 1745

1 My coun-try, 'tis of thee, Sweet land of lib-er-ty,
Of thee I sing; Land where my fa-thers died, Land of the pil-grim's pride,
From ev-ery moun-tain side Let free-dom ring. A-MEN.

2 My native country, thee,
    Land of the noble free,
        Thy name I love;
    I love thy rocks and rills,
    Thy woods and templed hills;
    My heart with rapture thrills
        Like that above.

3 Let music swell the breeze,
    And ring from all the trees
        Sweet freedom's song:
    Let mortal tongues awake;
    Let all that breathe partake;
    Let rocks their silence break,
        The sound prolong.

4 Our fathers' God, to Thee,
    Author of liberty,
        To Thee we sing:
    Long may our land be bright
    With freedom's holy light;
    Protect us by Thy might,
        Great God, our King.

Rev. SAMUEL F. SMITH, 1832

236

269 NATIONAL HYMN 10. 10. 10. 10.

GEORGE WILLIAM WARREN, 1892

Trumpets, before each verse. 1 God of our fa-thers, whose al-might-y hand

With organ

Leads forth in beau-ty all the star-ry band

Of shi-ning worlds in splen-dor through the skies,

Our grate-ful songs be-fore Thy throne a-rise. A-MEN.

2 Thy love divine hath led us in the past;
In this free land by Thee our lot is cast;
Be Thou our Ruler, Guardian, Guide, and Stay;
Thy word our law, Thy paths our chosen way.

3 From war's alarms, from deadly pestilence,
Be Thy strong arm our ever sure defence;
Thy true religion in our hearts increase,
Thy bounteous goodness nourish us in peace.

4 Refresh Thy people on their toilsome way,
Lead us from night to never-ending day;
Fill all our lives with love and grace divine,
And glory, laud, and praise be ever Thine.

Rev. DANIEL C. ROBERTS, 1876

NOTE—*Dr. Roberts' hymn was written for a celebration of the Centennial Fourth of July at Brandon, Vermont.*

270 **LEST WE FORGET** 8. 8. 8. 8. 8. 8. GEORGE F. BLANCHARD, 1898

1 God of our fa - thers, known of old, Lord of our far - flung bat - tle line,

Be-neath whose aw - ful hand we hold Do - min - ion o - ver palm and pine:

Lord God of hosts, be with us yet, 1-4. Lest we for - get, Lest we for - get.
5. Thy mer-cy on Thy peo - ple, Lord! A-MEN.

2 The tumult and the shouting dies;
  The captains and the kings depart;
  Still stands Thine ancient sacrifice,
  An humble and a contrite heart:
    Lord God of hosts, be with us yet,
    Lest we forget—lest we forget.

3 Far called our navies melt away;
  On dune and headland sinks the fire;
  Lo, all our pomp of yesterday
  Is one with Nineveh and Tyre!
    Judge of the nations, spare us yet,
    Lest we forget—lest we forget.

4 If, drunk with sight of power, we loose
  Wild tongues that have not Thee in awe,
  Such boastings as the Gentiles use,
  Or lesser breeds without the law:
    Lord God of hosts, be with us yet,
    Lest we forget—lest we forget.

5 For heathen heart that puts her trust
  In reeking tube and iron shard;
  All valiant dust that builds on dust,
  And, guarding, calls not Thee to guard;
    For frantic boast and foolish word,
    Thy mercy on Thy people, Lord.

RUDYARD KIPLING, 1897

Printed by permission of Mr. Kipling and Doubleday, Page & Company

NOTE—*Mr. Kipling's hymn was contributed to "The Times" for July 17, 1897; and included in his "The Five Nations," 1903. Its allusions were made to incidents of the Diamond Jubilee of Queen Victoria, particularly the procession and naval review.*

271 LANCASHIRE 7.6.7.6.D.   HENRY SMART, 1836

1 From o-cean un-to o-cean Our land shall own Thee Lord,
And, filled with true de-vo-tion, O-bey Thy sove-reign word.
Our prai-ries and our moun-tains, For-est and fer-tile field,
Our riv-ers, lakes, and foun-tains, To Thee shall trib-ute yield. A-MEN.

2 O Christ, for Thine own glory,
   And for our country's weal,
We humbly plead before Thee,
   Thyself in us reveal;
And may we know, Lord Jesus,
   The touch of Thy dear hand;
And, healed of our diseases,
   The tempter's power withstand.

3 Where error smites with blindness,
   Enslaves and leads astray,
Do Thou in loving-kindness
   Proclaim Thy gospel day;

Till all the tribes and races
   That dwell in this fair land,
Adorned with Christian graces,
   Within Thy courts shall stand.

4 Our Saviour King, defend us,
   And guide where we should go;
Forth with Thy message send us,
   Thy love and light to show;
Till, fired with true devotion
   Enkindled by Thy word,
From ocean unto ocean
   Our land shall own Thee Lord.

Rev. ROBERT MURRAY, in *The Hymnal of the Presbyterian Church in Canada*, 1880

272 THE STAR-SPANGLED BANNER Irregular JOHN STAFFORD SMITH, c. 1778

1 O say, can you see, by the dawn's ear - ly light, What so proud - ly we
2 On the shore, dim - ly seen through the mists of the deep, Where the foe's haughty
3 O thus be it ev - er when free-men shall stand Be - tween their loved

hailed at the twilight's last gleaming? Whose broad stripes and bright stars, through the
host in dread si - lence re - pos - es, What is that which the breeze, o'er the
home and the war's des - o - la - tion; Blest with vic - tory and peace, may the

per - il - ous fight, O'er the ram - parts we watched were so gal - lant - ly streaming?
tow - er - ing steep, As it fit - ful - ly blows, half con-ceals, half dis-clos - es?
heaven-res-cued land Praise the Power that hath made and pre-served us a na - tion!

And the rock - et's red glare, the bomb bursting in air, Gave proof through the
Now it catch - es the gleam of the morn-ing's first beam, In full glo - ry re -
Then con - quer we must, when our cause it is just; And this be our

240

The Nation

night   that our flag was still there! O   say, does that star-span-gled
flect-ed   now shines in the stream! 'Tis the star-span-gled ban-ner: O
mot-to: "In God is our trust!" And the star-span-gled ban-ner in

ban-ner yet wave O'er the land of the free and the home of the brave?
long may it wave O'er the land of the free and the home of the brave!
tri-umph shall wave O'er the land of the free and the home of the brave!

FRANCIS SCOTT KEY, 1814: three (out of four) verses
from the author's MS. now at Baltimore

273   DEVONSHIRE   7. 6. 7. 6.

An English traditional melody

1 Our coun-try's voice is plead-ing, Ye men of God a - rise!

His prov-i-dence is lead-ing, The land be-fore you lies; A - MEN.

Alternative tune, MURIEL, No. 31

2 Day-gleams are o'er it brightening,
     And promise clothes the soil;
Wide fields, for harvest whitening,
     Invite the reaper's toil.

3 The love of Christ unfolding,
     Speed on from east to west,

Till all, His cross beholding,
     In Him are fully blest.

4 Great Author of salvation,
     Haste, haste the glorious day,
When we, a ransomed nation,
     Thy sceptre shall obey.

Mrs. MARIA F. ANDERSON, 1849

274 **BATTLE HYMN OF THE REPUBLIC** 15. 15. 15. 6. with Refrain

Arranged 1861–2 from an older melody
("Say, Brothers, will you meet us")

1 Mine eyes have seen the glo - ry of the com - ing of the Lord;

He is tramp - ling out the vin - tage where the grapes of wrath are stored;

He hath loosed the fate - ful light - ning of His ter - ri - ble swift sword:

REFRAIN

His truth is march - ing on. Glo - ry! glo - ry! Hal - le - lu - jah!

Glo - ry! glo - ry! Hal - le - lu - jah! Glo - ry! glo - ry! Hal - le -

lu - jah!	1 His truth is march - ing on.	
	2 His day is march - ing on.	
	3 Since God is march - ing on.	
	4 Our God is march - ing on.	
	5 While God is march - ing on.	A - MEN.

2 I have seen Him in the watch-fires of a hundred circling camps;
  They have builded Him an altar in the evening dews and damps;
  I can read His righteous sentence by the dim and flaring lamps;
    His day is marching on.
      Glory! glory! Hallelujah! His day is marching on.

3 I have read a fiery gospel writ in burnished rows of steel:
  "As ye deal with My contemners, so with you My grace shall deal;
  Let the Hero, born of woman, crush the serpent with His heel,
    Since God is marching on."
      Glory! glory! Hallelujah! Since God is marching on.

4 He has sounded forth the trumpet that shall never call retreat;
  He is sifting out the hearts of men before His judgment-seat:
  O be swift, my soul, to answer Him! be jubilant, my feet!
    Our God is marching on.
      Glory! glory! Hallelujah! Our God is marching on.

5 In the beauty of the lilies Christ was born across the sea,
  With a glory in His bosom that transfigures you and me:
  As He died to make men holy, let us die to make men free,
    While God is marching on.
      Glory! glory! Hallelujah! While God is marching on.

                                        Mrs. JULIA WARD HOWE, 1861

275 (AMERICA, No. 268; or HYMN TO THE TRINITY, No. 29)

1 God bless our native land;
  Firm may she ever stand
    Through storm and night:
  When the wild tempests rave,
  Ruler of wind and wave,
  Do Thou our country save
    By Thy great might.

2 For her our prayer shall rise
  To God, above the skies;
    On Him we wait;
  Thou who art ever nigh,
  Guarding with watchful eye,
  To Thee aloud we cry,
    God save the State.

          SIEGFRIED A. MAHLMANN, 1815: the 1st 5 lines translated by
Rev. CHARLES T. BROOKS, c. 1833; the remainder by Rev. JOHN S. DWIGHT, 1844

276 MATERNA C. M. D.

SAMUEL A. WARD, 1882

1 O beau-ti-ful for spa-cious skies, For am-ber waves of grain,

For pur-ple moun-tain maj-es-ties A-bove the fruit-ed plain!

A-mer-i-ca! A-mer-i-ca! God shed His grace on thee,

And crown thy good with broth-er-hood From sea to shin-ing sea! A-MEN.

For a higher setting, see No. 382
"AMERICA THE BEAUTIFUL"

2 O beautiful for pilgrim feet
Whose stern, impassioned stress
A thoroughfare for freedom beat
Across the wilderness!
America! America!
God mend thine every flaw,
Confirm thy soul in self-control,
Thy liberty in law!

3 O beautiful for heroes proved
In liberating strife,
Who more than self their country loved,
And mercy more than life!

America! America!
May God thy gold refine,
Till all success be nobleness,
And every gain divine!

4 O beautiful for patriot dream
That sees beyond the years
Thine alabaster cities gleam
Undimmed by human tears!
America! America!
God shed His grace on thee
And crown thy good with brotherhood
From sea to shining sea!

KATHARINE LEE BATES, 1904

277 JESU DILECTISSIME 7. 6. 7. 6. D.

Robert H. McCartney, 1844–1905

1 "O Beau-ti-ful! My Coun-try"! Be thine a no-bler care
Than all thy wealth of com-merce, Thy har-vests wav-ing fair:
Be it thy pride to lift up The man-hood of the poor;
Be thou to the op-press-ed Fair Free-dom's o-pen door! A-men.

"O Beautiful! My Country!" Lowell's "Commemoration Ode"

2 For thee our fathers suffered,
　For thee they toiled and prayed;
Upon thy holy altar
　Their willing lives they laid;:
Thou hast no common birthright,
　Grand memories on thee shine;
The blood of pilgrim nations
　Commingled flows in thine.

3 O Beautiful! Our Country!
　Round thee in love we draw;
Thine is the grace of freedom,
　The majesty of law:
Be righteousness thy sceptre,
　Justice thy diadem;
And on thy shining forehead
　Be peace the crowning gem!

Rev. Frederick L. Hosmer, 1884

The Kingdom: Social Progress

Cleanse our hearts, O God, from all inordinate desires, and free them from every worldly entanglement and selfish interest that have hushed the voice of our song of brotherly love or hindered our hands from helping to right the wrongs of the downtrodden and to upbuild a commonwealth of civic righteousness and social justice on the earth: through Jesus Christ our Lord. Amen.

278 RHUDDLAN 8. 7. 8. 7. 8. 7.

A Welsh traditional melody

1 Judge E-tern-al, throned in splen-dor, Lord of lords and King of kings,

With Thy liv-ing fire of judg-ment Purge this land of bit-ter things;

Sol-ace all its wide do-min-ion With the heal-ing of Thy wings. A-MEN.

2 Still the weary folk are pining
　For the hour that brings release,
And the city's crowded clangor
　Cries aloud for sin to cease;
And the homesteads and the woodlands
　Plead in silence for their peace.

3 Crown, O God, Thine own endeavor;
　Cleave our darkness with Thy sword;
Feed the faint and hungry heathen
　With the richness of Thy word;
Cleanse the body of this nation
　Through the glory of the Lord.

Rev. HENRY SCOTT HOLLAND, 1902

NOTE—*Dr. Holland, a canon of St. Paul's, London, was a fiery prophet of the Christian social order, and in 1895 founded as his personal organ "The Commonwealth," in which his hymn first appeared.*

279 COMMONWEALTH 7. 6. 7. 6. 8. 8. 8. 5.

Josiah Booth, 1888

1 When wilt Thou save the peo - ple? O God of mer - cy, when?

Not kings and lords, but na - tions! Not thrones and crowns, but men!

Flowers of Thy heart, O God, are they; Let them not pass, like weeds, a - way,

Their her - i - tage a sun - less day. God save the peo - ple! A - men.

2 Shall crime bring crime for ever,
   Strength aiding still the strong?
Is it Thy will, O Father,
   That man shall toil for wrong?
No, say Thy mountains; No, Thy skies;
Man's clouded sun shall brightly rise,
And songs ascend, instead of sighs.
   God save the people!

3 When wilt Thou save the people?
   O God of mercy, when?
The people, Lord, the people,
   Not thrones and crowns, but men!
God save the people; Thine they are,
Thy children, as Thine angels fair.
From vice, oppression, and despair,
   God save the people!

Ebenezer Elliott, "The Corn-law Rhymer," 1850

280 ST. ASAPH 8. 7. 8. 7. D.

WILLIAM S. BAMBRIDGE, 1872

1 Once to ev - ery man and na - tion Comes the mo - ment to de - cide,

In the strife of truth with false-hood, For the good or e - vil side;

Some great cause, God's new Mes - si - ah, Off-ering each the bloom or blight—

And the choice goes by for ev - er 'Twixt that dark - ness and that light. A - MEN.

2 Then to side with truth is noble,
   When we share her wretched crust,
 Ere her cause bring fame and profit,
   And 'tis prosperous to be just;
 Then it is the brave man chooses,
   While the coward stands aside
 Till the multitude make virtue
   Of the faith they had denied.

3 By the light of burning martyrs,
   Christ, Thy bleeding feet we track,
 Toiling up new Calvaries ever
   With the cross that turns not back.

New occasions teach new duties;
   Time makes ancient good uncouth;
 They must upward still and onward
   Who would keep abreast of truth.

4 Though the cause of evil prosper,
   Yet 'tis truth alone is strong;
 Truth for ever on the scaffold,
   Wrong for ever on the throne,
 Yet that scaffold sways the future,
   And, behind the dim unknown,
 Standeth God within the shadow,
   Keeping watch above His own.

Arranged from J. RUSSELL LOWELL's "The Present Crisis," 1844

Social Progress
(Second Tune)

(280) IN BABILONE 8. 7. 8. 7. D. A Dutch traditional melody

1 {Once to ev-ery man and na-tion Comes the mo-ment to de-cide,}
{In the strife of truth with false-hood, For the good or e-vil side;}

Some great cause, God's new Mes-si-ah, Off-ering each the bloom or blight—

And the choice goes by for ev-er 'Twixt that dark-ness and that light. A-MEN.

2 Then to side with truth is noble,
  When we share her wretched crust,
Ere her cause bring fame and profit,
  And 'tis prosperous to be just;
Then it is the brave man chooses,
  While the coward stands aside
Till the multitude make virtue
  Of the faith they had denied.

3 By the light of burning martyrs,
  Christ, Thy bleeding feet we track,
Toiling up new Calvaries ever
  With the cross that turns not back.
New occasions teach new duties;
  Time makes ancient good uncouth;
They must upward still and onward
  Who would keep abreast of truth.

4 Though the cause of evil prosper,
  Yet 'tis truth alone is strong;
Truth for ever on the scaffold,
  Wrong for ever on the throne,
Yet that scaffold sways the future,
  And, behind the dim unknown,
Standeth God within the shadow,
  Keeping watch above His own.

Arranged from J. RUSSELL LOWELL's "The Present Crisis," 1844

281 **DAILY, DAILY** 8. 7. 8. 7. D.

HENRI F. HEMY, 1865

1 We are liv-ing, we are dwell-ing, In a grand and aw-ful time;
In an age on a-ges tell-ing, To be liv-ing is sub-lime.
Hark! the wa-king up of na-tions, Hosts ad-vanc-ing to the fray;
Hark! what sound-eth is cre-a-tion's Mustering for the lat-ter day. A-MEN.

2 Will ye play, then? will ye dally
Far behind the battle-line?
Up! it is Jehovah's rally;
God's own arm hath need of thine.
Worlds are charging, heaven beholding;
Thou hast but an hour to fight;
Now, the blazoned cross unfolding,
On, right onward for the right!

3 Pledged to yield, to waver, **never**,
Consecrated, born again,
Sworn to be Christ's soldiers ever,
O for Christ at least be men!
O let all the soul within you
For the truth's sake go abroad!
Strike! let every nerve and sinew
Tell on ages, tell for God.

Arranged from Bishop A. CLEVELAND COXE, 1840

Social Progress
(Second Tune)

(281) TON-Y-BOTEL 8. 7. 8. 7. D.   A Welsh hymn melody

May be sung in unison

1 { We are liv - ing, we are dwell - ing, In a grand and
   { In an age on a - ges tell - ing, To be liv - ing

aw - ful time; }
is sub-lime. } Hark! the wa - king up of na - tions,

Hosts ad - vanc - ing to the fray: Hark! what sound - eth

is cre - a - tion's Must - er-ing for the lat - ter day. A-MEN.

2 Will ye play, then? will ye dally
  Far behind the battle-line?
Up! it is Jehovah's rally;
  God's own arm hath need of thine.
Worlds are charging, heaven beholding;
  Thou hast but an hour to fight;
Now, the blazoned cross unfolding,
  On, right onward for the right!

3 Pledged to yield, to waver, never,
  Consecrated, born again,
Sworn to be Christ's soldiers ever,
  O for Christ at least be men!
O let all the soul within you
  For the truth's sake go abroad!
Strike! let every nerve and sinew
  Tell on ages, tell for God.

Arranged from Bishop A. CLEVELAND COXE, 1840

251

282 AMERICAN HYMN 10. 10. 10. 10. D. Matthias Keller, 1869

1 An - gel of peace, thou hast wan - dered too long! Spread thy white
2 Joy - ous we meet; on this al - tar of thine Min - gling the
3 An - gels of Beth - le - hem, an - swer the strain! Hark! a new

wings to the sun - shine of love! Come while our voi - ces are
gifts we have gath - ered for thee, Sweet with the o - dors of
birth - song is fill - ing the sky! Loud as the storm - wind that

blend - ed in song, Fly to our ark like the storm - beat - en dove,—
myr - tle and pine, Breeze of the prai - rie and breath of the sea,—
tum - bles the main, Bid the full breath of the or - gan re - ply,—

Fly to our ark on the wings of the dove; Speed o'er the
Mead - ow and moun - tain and for - est and sea; Sweet is the
Let the loud tem - pest of voi - ces re - ply; Roll its long

far - sound - ing bil - lows of song,
frag - rance of myr - tle and pine,
surge like the earth-shak-ing main!

Crowned with thine ol - ive - leaf gar - land of
Sweet - er the in - cense we of - fer to
Swell the vast song till it mounts to the

love; An - gel of peace, thou hast wait - ed too long!
thee, Broth-ers once more round this al - tar of thine!
sky! An - gels of Beth - le - hem, ech - o the strain! A-MEN.

OLIVER WENDELL HOLMES, 1869

NOTE—*The hymn and tune were written to be sung at the Boston "Peace Jubilee," June 15, 1869.*

283 PENTECOST L. M.

REV. WILLIAM BOYD, 1868

1 Let there be light, Lord God of Hosts, Let there be wis-dom on the earth!

Let broad hu-man-i-ty have birth! Let there be deeds, in-stead of boasts! A-MEN.

For a lower setting, see No. 235

2 Within our passioned hearts instill
  The calm that endeth strain and strife;
  Make us Thy ministers of life;
  Purge us from lusts that curse and kill.

3 Give us the peace of vision clear
  To see our brothers' good our own,
  To joy and suffer not alone,
  The love that casteth out all fear.

4 Let woe and waste of warfare cease,
  That useful labor yet may build
  Its homes with love and laughter filled.
  God, give Thy wayward children peace.

WILLIAM M. VORIES, 1908
by permission of *The Advocate of Peace*

284 CAROL C. M. D.

Arranged from Richard S. Willis' "Study No. 23," 1850,
by Uzziah C. Burnap

1 It came up-on the mid-night clear, That glo-rious song of old,
From an-gels bend-ing near the earth, To touch their harps of gold:
"Peace on the earth, good-will to men, From heaven's all-gra-cious King."
The world in sol-emn still-ness lay To hear the an-gels sing. A-MEN.

2 Still through the cloven skies they come,
　With peaceful wings unfurled,
And still their heavenly music floats
　O'er all the weary world:
Above its sad and lowly plains
　They bend on hovering wing,
And ever o'er its Babel sounds
　The blessèd angels sing.

3 And ye, beneath life's crushing load,
　Whose forms are bending low,
Who toil along the climbing way
　With painful steps and slow,—

Look now; for glad and golden hours
　Come swiftly on the wing:
O rest beside the weary road,
　And hear the angels sing.

4 For lo! the days are hastening on,
　By prophet bards foretold,
When with the ever-circling years
　Comes round the age of gold;
When peace shall over all the earth
　Its ancient splendors fling,
And the whole world give back the song
　Which now the angels sing.

Rev. Edmund H. Sears, 1850

254

285 **RUSSIAN HYMN** 11. 10. 11. 9.   ALEKSYEI T. LWOFF, 1833

1 God the Om-nip-o-tent! King, who or-dain-est
Great winds Thy clar-i-ons, light-nings Thy sword;
Show forth Thy pit-y on high where Thou reign-est,
Give to us peace in our time, O Lord. A-MEN.

2 God the All-merciful! earth hath forsaken
   Thy ways of blessedness, slighted Thy word;
Bid not Thy wrath in its terrors awaken;
   Give to us peace in our time, O Lord!

3 God the All-righteous One! man hath defied Thee;
   Yet to eternity standeth Thy word;
Falsehood and wrong shall not tarry beside Thee:
   Give to us peace in our time, O Lord!

4 God the All-pitiful! through fire and wasting
   Earth shall to freedom and truth be restored;
Through the thick darkness Thy kingdom is hasting:
   Thou wilt give peace in Thy time, O Lord!

Arranged from HENRY F. CHORLEY, 1842
and Rev. JOHN ELLERTON, 1870

286 MENDON L. M.

A German melody, arranged by SAMUEL DYER, 1828

1 These things shall be,— a loft - ier race Than e'er the world hath known shall rise

With flame of free-dom in their souls, And light of knowledge in their eyes. A - MEN.

2 They shall be gentle, brave, and strong
To spill no drop of blood, but dare
All that may plant man's lordship firm,
On earth, and fire, and sea, and air.

3 Nation with nation, land with land,
Unarmed shall live as comrades free;
In every heart and brain shall throb
The pulse of one fraternity.

4 Man shall love man with heart as pure
And fervent as the young-eyed throng
Who chant their heavenly psalms before
God's face with undiscordant song.

5 New arts shall bloom of loftier mould,
And mightier music thrill the skies,
And every life shall be a song,
When all the earth is paradise.

6 There shall be no more sin, nor shame,
Though pain and passion may not die;
For man shall be at one with God
In bonds of firm necessity.

Abridged from J. ADDINGTON SYMONDS' "A Vista," 1880

QUEBEC L. M.

HENRY BAKER, 1862 (see No. 79)

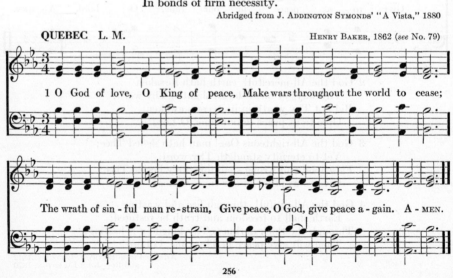

1 O God of love, O King of peace, Make wars throughout the world to cease;

The wrath of sin - ful man re-strain, Give peace, O God, give peace a - gain. A - MEN.

287 ST. MARGUERITE C. M.

Rev. Edward C. Walker, 1876

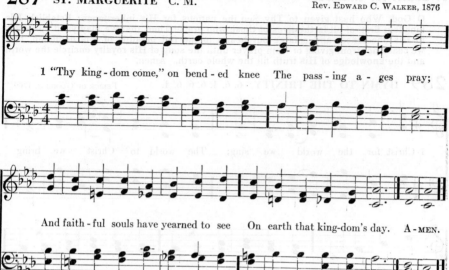

1 "Thy king-dom come," on bend-ed knee The pass-ing a-ges pray;
And faith-ful souls have yearned to see On earth that king-dom's day. A-MEN.

Alternative tune, HEBER, No. 229

2 But the slow watches of the night
   Not less to God belong
And for the everlasting right
   The silent stars are strong.

3 And lo! already on the hills
   The flags of dawn appear;
Gird up your loins, ye prophet souls,
   Proclaim the day is near:

4 The day in whose clear-shining light
   All wrongs shall stand revealed,
When justice shall be throned in might,
   And every hurt be healed;

5 When knowledge, hand in hand with peace,
   Shall walk the earth abroad;—
The day of perfect righteousness,
   The promised day of God.

Rev. Frederick L. Hosmer, 1891

288 (QUEBEC) L. M.

He maketh wars to cease unto the end of the earth.—Ps. xlvi, 9

1 O God of love, O King of peace,
   Make wars throughout the world to cease;
The wrath of sinful man restrain;
   Give peace, O God, give peace again.

2 Remember, Lord, Thy works of old,
   The wonders that our fathers told;
Remember not our sin's dark stain;
   Give peace, O God, give peace again.

3 Whom shall we trust but Thee, O Lord?
   Where rest but on Thy faithful word?
None ever called on Thee in vain;
   Give peace, O God, give peace again.

4 Where saints and angels dwell above
   All hearts are knit in holy love;
O bind us in that heavenly chain;
   Give peace, O God, give peace again.

Rev. Sir Henry W. Baker, Bart., 1861

A Collect for Missions

O God, Who hast given to Thy Son the nations for His inheritance: Establish His kingdom first of all in the lives of those who praise Thee, that we may yield ourselves to His obedience; and enlarge our hearts to the full breadth of His dominion, that we cease not from giving or from prayer until the song of His royalty encircle the world and the knowledge of His truth fill the whole earth. Amen.

289 **HYMN TO THE TRINITY** 6. 6. 4. 6. 6. 6. 4.　　FELICE DE GIARDINI, 1769

1 Christ for the world we sing; The world to Christ we bring
With lov-ing zeal; The poor and them that mourn, The faint and o-ver-borne,
Sin-sick and sor-row-worn, Whom Christ doth heal. A-MEN.

And we have seen and do testify that the Father sent the Son to be the Saviour of the world.—I ST. JOHN iv, 14

2 Christ for the world we sing;
　The world to Christ we bring
　　With fervent prayer;
　The wayward and the lost,
　By restless passions tossed,
　Redeemed at countless cost
　　From dark despair.

3 Christ for the world we sing;
　The world to Christ we bring
　　With one accord;
　With us the work to share,
　With us reproach to dare,
　With us the cross to bear,
　　For Christ our Lord.

4 Christ for the world we sing;
　The world to Christ we bring
　　With joyful song;
　The new-born souls whose days,
　Reclaimed from error's ways,
　Inspired with hope and praise,
　　To Christ belong.

REV. SAMUEL WOLCOTT, 1869

The World

290 **PASTOR REGALIS** 6. 6. 4. 6. 6. 6. 4.   ROBERT BONNER, 1887

1 Thou, whose al-might-y word Cha-os and dark-ness heard, And took their
flight, Hear us, we humb-ly pray; And, where the gos-pel's day
Sheds not its glo-rious ray, Let there be light. A - MEN.

God said, Let there be light: and there was light.—GEN. i, 3

2 Thou, who didst come to bring
In Thy redeeming wing
    Healing and sight,
Health to the sick in mind,
Sight to the inly blind,
O now to all mankind
    Let there be light.

3 Spirit of truth and love,
Life-giving, holy Dove,
    Speed forth Thy flight,;
Move o'er the waters' face,
Bearing the lamp of grace,
And in earth's darkest place
    Let there be light.

4 Holy and blessèd Three,
Glorious Trinity,
    Wisdom, Love, Might!
Boundless as ocean's tide,
Rolling in fullest pride,
Through the world far and wide
    Let there be light.

REV. JOHN MARRIOTT, c. 1813

291 WALTHAM L. M.

J. Baptiste Calkin, 1872

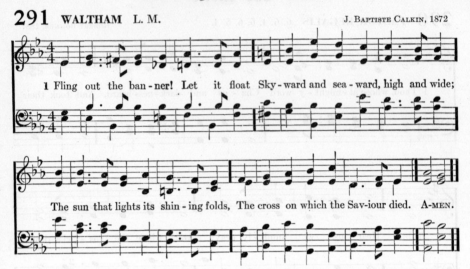

1 Fling out the ban-ner! Let it float Sky-ward and sea-ward, high and wide; The sun that lights its shin-ing folds, The cross on which the Sav-iour died. A-men.

Thou hast given a banner to them that fear Thee, that it may be displayed because of the truth.—Ps. lx, 4

2 Fling out the banner! angels bend
　In anxious silence o'er the sign,
And vainly seek to comprehend
　The wonder of the love divine.

3 Fling out the banner! heathen lands
　Shall see from far the glorious sight,
And nations, crowding to be born,
　Baptize their spirits in its light.

4 Fling out the banner! sin-sick souls,
　That sink and perish in the strife,
Shall touch in faith its radiant hem,
　And spring immortal into life.

5 Fling out the banner! let it float
　Skyward and seaward, high and wide,
Our glory, only in the cross;
　Our only hope, the Crucified!

Bishop George W. Doane, 1848

MISSIONARY CHANT L. M.

Heinrich C. Zeuner, 1832

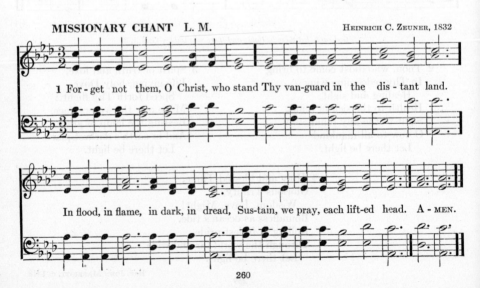

1 For-get not them, O Christ, who stand Thy van-guard in the dis-tant land. In flood, in flame, in dark, in dread, Sus-tain, we pray, each lift-ed head. A-men.

292 PARK STREET L. M.

Arranged from FREDERICK M. A. VENUA, c. 1810

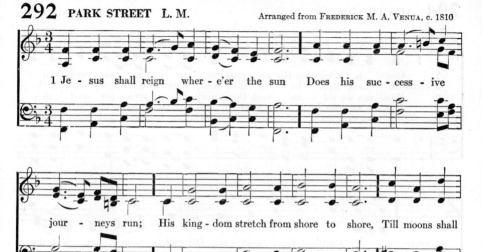

1 Je-sus shall reign wher-e'er the sun Does his suc-cess-ive jour-neys run; His king-dom stretch from shore to shore, Till moons shall wax and wane no more, Till moons shall wax and wane no more. A-MEN.

The kingdoms of this world are become the kingdoms of our Lord, and of His Christ; and He shall reign for ever and ever.—Rev. xi, 15

2 For Him shall endless prayer be made,
And praises throng to crown His head;
His Name, like sweet perfume, shall rise
With every morning sacrifice;

3 People and realms of every tongue
Dwell on His love with sweetest song;
And infant voices shall proclaim
Their early blessings on His Name.

4 Blessings abound where'er He reigns;
The prisoner leaps to lose his chains,
The weary find eternal rest,
And all the sons of want are blest.

5 Let every creature rise and bring
Peculiar honors to our King,
Angels descend with songs again,
And earth repeat the loud Amen.

Rev. Isaac Watts, 1719

293 (MISSIONARY CHANT) L. M.

1 Forget not them, O Christ, who stand
Thy vanguard in the distant land.
In flood, in flame, in dark, in dread,
Sustain, we pray, each lifted head.

2 Thine is the work they strive to do;
Their foes so many, they so few.
Be with Thine own, Thy loved, who stand,
Christ's vanguard, in the storm-swept land.

Mrs. Margaret E. Sangster (1838-1912)

294 AINGER Irregular

MILLICENT D. KINGHAM, 1896

1 God is work-ing His pur-pose out, as year suc-ceeds to year: God is work-ing His pur-pose out, and the time is draw-ing near— Near-er and near-er draws the time, the time that shall sure-ly be, When the earth shall be

2 From ut-most East to ut-most West, wher-e'er man's foot hath trod, By the mouth of man-y mes-sen-gers goes forth the voice of God; Give ear to Me, ye con-ti-nents—ye isles, give ear to Me, That the earth shall be

3 What can we do to work God's work, to pros-per and in-crease The broth-er-hood of all man-kind— the reign of the Prince of Peace? What can we do to hast-en the time, the time that shall sure-ly be, When the earth shall be

4 March we forth in the strength of God, with the ban-ner of Christ un-furled, That the light of the glo-ri-ous gos-pel of truth may shine through-out the world: Fight we the fight with sor-row and sin to set their cap-tives free, That the earth shall be

5 All we can do is noth-ing worth, un-less God bless-es the deed; Vain-ly we hope for the har-vest tide, till God gives life to the seed; Yet near-er and near-er draws the time, the time that shall sure-ly be, When the earth shall be

The World

filled with the glo - ry of God, as the wa - ters cov-er the sea. A - MEN.

ARTHUR C. AINGER, 1894

295 WESLEY 11. 10. 11. 10.

LOWELL MASON, 1833

1 Hail to the bright-ness of Zi - on's glad morn - ing, Joy to the
lands that in dark-ness have lain! Hushed be the ac - cents of sor - row and
mourn-ing; Zi - on in tri - umph be - gins her mild reign. A - MEN.

2 Hail to the brightness of Zion's glad morning,
 Long by the prophets of Isreael foretold!
 Hail to the millions from bondage returning!
 Gentiles and Jews the blest vision behold.

3 Lo! in the desert rich flowers are springing,
 Streams ever copious are gliding along;
 Loud from the mountain-tops echoes are ringing,
 Wastes rise in verdure, and mingle in song.

4 See, from all lands, from the isles of the ocean,
 Praise to Jehovah ascending on high;
 Fallen are the engines of war and commotion,
 Shouts of salvation are rending the sky.

THOMAS HASTINGS, 1832

296 WEBB 7. 6. 7. 6. D.   GEORGE J. WEBB, 1837

1 The morn-ing light is break-ing, The dark-ness dis-ap-pears;
The sons of earth are wak-ing To pen-i-ten-tial tears;
Each breeze that sweeps the o-cean Brings ti-dings from a-far
Of na-tions in com-mo-tion, Pre-pared for Zi-on's war. A-MEN.

For a lower setting, see No. 351

2 See heathen nations bending
  Before the God we love,
And thousand hearts ascending
  In gratitude above;
While sinners, now confessing,
  The gospel call obey,
And seek the Saviour's blessing,
  A nation in a day.

3 Blest river of salvation,
  Pursue thy onward way;
Flow thou to every nation,
  Nor in thy richness stay:
Stay not till all the lowly
  Triumphant reach their home;
Stay not till all the holy
  Proclaim, "The Lord is come."

REV. SAMUEL F. SMITH, 1832

297 MISSIONARY HYMN 7. 6. 7. 6. D.

Lowell Mason, 1823

1 From Green-land's i-cy moun-tains, From In-dia's cor-al strand,
Where Af-ric's sun-ny fount-ains Roll down their gold-en sand,
From man-y an an-cient riv-er, From man-y a palm-y plain,
They call us to de-liv-er Their land from er-ror's chain. A-MEN.

*Come over . . . and help us.—*Acts xvi, 9

2 What though the spicy breezes
Blow soft o'er Ceylon's isle;
Though every prospect pleases,
And only man is vile:
In vain with lavish kindness
The gifts of God are strown;
The heathen in his blindness
Bows down to wood and stone.

3 Can we, whose souls are lighted
With wisdom from on high,
Can we to men benighted
The lamp of life deny?

Salvation! O salvation!
The joyful sound proclaim,
Till each remotest nation
Has learned Messiah's Name.

4 Waft, waft, ye winds, His story,
And you, ye waters, roll,
Till like a sea of glory
It spreads from pole to pole;
Till o'er our ransomed nature
The Lamb for sinners slain,
Redeemer, King, Creator,
In bliss returns to reign.

Bishop Reginald Heber, 1819

298 ANGELIC SONGS 11. 10. 11. 10. 9. 11.

James Walch's setting of "Hark! hark, my soul," 1875

1 O Zi-on, haste, thy mis-sion high ful-fill-ing, To tell to all the world that God is Light; That He who made all na-tions is not will-ing One soul should per-ish, lost in shades of night. Pub-lish glad ti-dings, ti-dings of peace; Ti-dings of Je-sus, re-demp-tion and re-lease. A-MEN.

2 Behold how many thousands still are lying
　Bound in the darksome prison-house of sin,
With none to tell them of the Saviour's dying,
　Or of the life He died for them to win.—REF.

3 Proclaim to every people, tongue, and nation
　That God, in whom they live and move, is Love:
Tell how He stooped to save His lost creation,
　And died on earth that man might live above.—REF.

4 Give of thy sons to bear the message glorious;
　Give of thy wealth to speed them on their way;
Pour out thy soul for them in prayer victorious;
　And all thou spendest Jesus will repay.—REF.

The World

5 He comes again: O Zion, ere thou meet Him,
   Make known to every heart His saving grace;
   Let none whom He hath ransomed fail to greet Him,
   Through thy neglect, unfit to see His face.—REF.

Mrs. MARY ANN THOMSON, 1870

299 LUCKNOW 7. 7. 8. 7. 8. 7.

Rev. EDWARD HUSBAND, c. 1882

1 Com-ing, com-ing— yes, they are, Com-ing, com-ing, from a-far— From the wild and scorch-ing des-ert, Af-ric's sons of col-or deep; Je-sus' love has drawn and won them, At His cross they bow and weep. A-MEN.

And they shall come from the east, and from the west, and from the north, and from the south,
and shall sit down in the kingdom of God.—ST. LUKE xiii, 29

2 Coming, coming—yes, they are,
  Coming, coming, from afar—
From the fields and crowded cities
  China gathers to His feet;
In His love Shem's gentle children
  Now have found a safe retreat.

3 Coming, coming—yes, they are,
  Coming, coming, from afar—
From the Indus and the Ganges
  Steady flows the living stream,
To love's ocean, to His bosom,
  Calvary their wondering theme.

4 Coming, coming—yes, they are,
  Coming, coming, from afar—
From the frozen realms of midnight,
  Over many a weary mile,
To exchange their souls' long winter
  For the summer of His smile.

5 Coming, coming—yes, they are,
  Coming, coming, from afar—
All to meet in plains of glory,
  All to sing His praises sweet,
What a chorus, what a meeting,
  With a family complete.

JACOB W. MACGILL, 1897

267

300   **MESSAGE**   10. 8. 8. 7. 7. with Refrain   H. Ernest Nichol, 1896: abridged

With spirit

1 We've a sto - ry to tell to the na - tions That shall turn their hearts to the right, A sto - ry of truth and mer - cy, A sto - ry of peace and light, A sto - ry of peace and light.

REFRAIN

For the dark-ness shall turn to dawn-ing, And the dawn-ing to noon-day bright, And Christ's great kingdom shall come on earth, The king-dom of love and light. A-men.

The World

2 We've a message to give to the nations,
   That the Lord who reigneth above
   Hath sent us His Son to save us,
   And show us that God is love.—REF.

3 We've a Saviour to show to the nations
   Who the path of sorrow has trod,
   That all of the world's great peoples
   Might come to the truth of God.—REF.

COLIN STERNE, 1896

301 MOEL LLYS 7. 5. 7. 5. 7. 7.   SARAH G. STOCK, published in 1899

1 Let the song go round the earth, Je - sus Christ is Lord!
Sound His prais - es, tell His worth, Be His Name a - dored;
Ev - ery clime and ev - ery tongue Join the grand, the glo - rious song! A - MEN.

Sing unto the Lord, all the earth.—Ps. xcvi, 1

2 Let the song go round the earth!
   From the eastern sea,
   Where the daylight has its birth,
   Glad, and bright, and free!
   China's millions join the strains,
   Waft them on to India's plains.

3 Let the song go round the earth!
   Lands where Islam's sway
   Darkly broods o'er home and hearth,
   Cast their bonds away!
   Let His praise from Afric's shore
   Rise and swell her wide lands o'er!

4 Let the song go round the earth!
   Where the summer smiles;
   Let the notes of holy mirth
   Break from distant isles!
   Inland forests, dark and dim,
   Ice-bound coasts give back the hymn.

5 Let the song go round the earth—
   Jesus Christ is King!
   With the story of His worth
   Let the whole world ring!
   Him creation all adore
   Evermore and evermore.

SARAH G. STOCK, 1898

302 SALVE DOMINE 7. 6. 7. 6. D.

LAWRENCE W. WATSON, 1909

1 Hail to the Lord's A - noint - ed, Great Da - vid's great - er Son!

Hail, in the time ap - pont - ed, His reign on earth be - gun!

He comes to break op - pres - sion, To set the cap - tive free,

To take a - way trans - gres - sion, And rule in e - qui - ty. A-MEN.

A PARAPHRASE OF PSALM LXXII

2 He shall come down like showers
Upon the fruitful earth;
Love, joy, and hope, like flowers,
Beside Him spring to birth;
Before Him on the mountains
Shall peace, the herald, go,
And righteousness, in fountains,
From hill to valley flow.

3 Kings shall fall down before Him,
And gold and incense bring;
Nations shall all adore Him,
His praise all people sing;

For Him shall prayer unceasing
And daily vows ascend;
His kingdom still increasing,
A kingdom without end.

4 O'er every foe victorious,
Upon His throne at rest,
Hail Him the King most glorious,
All blessing and all-blest:
The tide of time shall never
His covenant remove,
His Name shall stand for ever,—
That Name to us is Love.

JAMES MONTGOMERY, 1821:
with the rhythm of several lines revised

The Spiritual Life
The Call

303   CONSOLATION   11. 10. 11. 10

Adapted from Samuel Webbe's setting of "Alma Redemptoris Mater," 1792

1 Come, ye dis-con-so-late, wher-e'er ye lan-guish,

Come to the mer-cy-seat, fer-vent-ly kneel;

Here bring your wound-ed hearts, here tell your an-guish;

Earth has no sor-rows that heaven can-not heal.   A-MEN.

I will not leave you comfortless.—St. John xiv, 18

2 Joy of the comfortless, light of the straying,
   Hope of the penitent, fadeless and pure!
   Here speaks the Comforter, in mercy saying,
   "Earth has no sorrows that heaven cannot cure."

3 Here see the Bread of Life; see waters flowing
   Forth from the throne of God, pure from above:
   Come to the feast prepared; come, ever knowing
   Earth has no sorrows but heaven can remove.

Verses 1 and 2 by Thomas Moore, 1816; varied, and verse 3 added, by Thomas Hastings, 1831

304 ILSLEY 8. 7. 8. 7. D.

FRANK G. ILSLEY, 1887

1 Was there ev - er kind-est shep-herd Half so gen - tle, half so sweet As the Sav - iour who would have us Come and gath - er round His feet? It is God; His love looks might - y, But is might - ier than it seems: 'Tis our Fa - ther; and His fond-ness Goes far out be - yond our dreams. A-MEN.

2 There's a wideness in God's mercy,
   Like the wideness of the sea;
There's a kindness in His justice,
   Which is more than liberty.

There is welcome for the sinner,
   And more graces for the good;
There is mercy with the Saviour,
   There is healing in His blood:

3 For the love of God is broader
   Than the measures of man's mind,
And the heart of the Eternal
   Is most wonderfully kind:

But we make His love too narrow
   By false limits of our own,
And we magnify His strictness
   With a zeal He will not own.

4 There is plentiful redemption
   In the blood that has been shed;
There is joy for all the members
   In the sorrows of the Head.

If our love were but more simple,
   We should take Him at His word;
And our lives would be all sunshine
   In the sweetness of our Lord.

Rev. FREDERICK W. FABER, 1854

May be sung to either tune opposite by dividing the verses.

272

The Call

305 **GALILEE** 8. 7. 8. 7.   WILLIAM H. JUDE, 1887

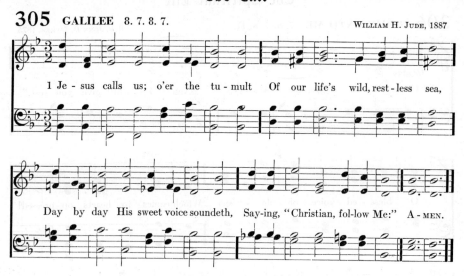

1 Je - sus calls us; o'er the tu - mult Of our life's wild, rest-less sea,

Day by day His sweet voice soundeth, Say-ing, "Christian, fol-low Me:" A - MEN.

One of the two which . . . followed Him was Andrew.— St. JOHN i, 40

2 As, of old, Saint Andrew heard it
  By the Galilean lake,
  Turned from home and toil and kindred,
  Leaving all for His dear sake.

3 Jesus calls us from the worship
  Of the vain world's golden store,
  From each idol that would keep us,
  Saying, "Christian, love Me more."

4 In our joys and in our sorrows,
  Days of toil and hours of ease,
  Still He calls, in cares and pleasures,
  "Christian, love Me more than these."

5 Jesus calls us: by Thy mercies
  Saviour, may we hear Thy call,
  Give our hearts to Thy obedience,
  Serve and love Thee best of all.

   MRS. CECIL F. ALEXANDER, 1852

LOWTON 8. 7. 8. 7.   ALBERT LOWE, 1875

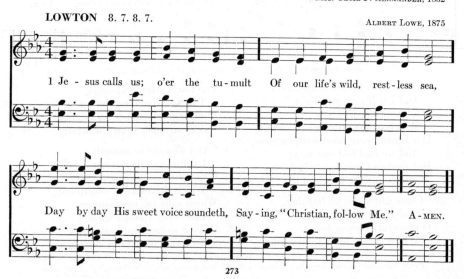

1 Je - sus calls us; o'er the tu - mult Of our life's wild, rest-less sea,

Day by day His sweet voice soundeth, Say - ing, "Christian, fol-low Me." A - MEN.

306 COME UNTO ME 7. 6. 7. 6. D.

Rev. John B. Dykes, 1875

Organ

1 "Come un - to Me, ye wea - ry, And I will give you rest."

O bless - ed voice of Je - sus Which comes to hearts op - pressed!

It tells of ben - e - dic - tion, Of par - don, grace, and peace,

Of joy that hath no end - ing, Of love which can - not cease. A - MEN.

Him that cometh to Me I will in no wise cast out.—St. John vi, 37

2 "Come unto Me, dear children,
 And I will give you light."
O loving voice of Jesus
 Which comes to cheer the night!
Our hearts were filled with sadness,
 And we had lost our way;
But morning brings us gladness,
 And songs the break of day.

3 "Come unto Me, ye fainting,
 And I will give you life."
O peaceful voice of Jesus
 Which comes to end our strife!

The foe is stern and eager,
 The fight is fierce and long;
But Thou hast made us mighty,
 And stronger than the strong.

4 "And whosoever cometh
 I will not cast him out."
O patient love of Jesus
 Which drives away our doubt;
Which calls us, very sinners,
 Unworthy though we be
Of love so free and boundless,
 To come, dear Lord, to Thee!

William C. Dix, 1867

The first two lines of each verse may be sung by Tenors and Basses only or in Octaves by all the voices

274

The Call

(Second Tune)

(306) **LLANGLOFFAN** 7. 6. 7. 6. D.

In D. Evans' *Hymnau a Thonau*, 1865

1 "Come un - to Me, ye wea - ry, And I will give you rest."

O bless - ed voice of Je - sus, Which comes to hearts op - pressed!

It tells of ben - e - dic - tion, Of par - don, grace, and peace,

Of joy that hath no end - ing, Of love which can - not cease. A-MEN.

2 "Come unto Me, dear children,
　　And I will give you light."
　O loving voice of Jesus
　　Which comes to cheer the night!
　Our hearts were filled with sadness,
　　And we had lost our way;
　But morning brings us gladness,
　　And songs the break of day.

3 "Come unto Me, ye fainting,
　　And I will give you life."
　O peaceful voice of Jesus
　　Which comes to end our strife!

The foe is stern and eager,
　　The fight is fierce and long;
　But Thou hast made us mighty,
　　And stronger than the strong.

4 "And whosoever cometh
　　I will not cast him out."
　O patient love of Jesus
　　Which drives away our doubt;
　Which calls us, very sinners,
　　Unworthy though we be
　Of love so free and boundless,
　　To come, dear Lord, to Thee!

WILLIAM C. DIX, 1867

307 VOX DILECTI C. M. D.

Rev. John B. Dykes, 1868

1 I heard the voice of Je - sus say, "Come un - to Me and rest;

Lay down, thou wea - ry one, lay down Thy head up - on My breast."

I came to Je - sus as I was, — Wea - ry and worn and sad;
2 Of that life - giv - ing stream;
3 In Him my Star, my Sun;

I found in Him a rest - ing-place, And He has made me glad. A - MEN.

2 I heard the voice of Jesus say,
  "Behold, I freely give
The living water; thirsty one,
  Stoop down and drink, and live."
I came to Jesus, and I drank
  Of that life-giving stream;
My thirst was quenched, my soul revived
  And now I live in Him.

3 I heard the voice of Jesus say,
  "I am this dark world's Light;
Look unto Me, thy morn shall rise,
  And all thy day be bright."
I looked to Jesus, and I found
  In Him my Star, my Sun;
And in that light of life I'll walk,
  Till travelling days are done.

Rev. Horatius Bonar, 1846

The Call

(*Second Tune*)

(307) **KINGSFORD** C. M. D.

An English traditional melody
arranged by R. Vaughan Williams, 1906

1 I heard the voice of Je-sus say, "Come un-to Me and rest;

Lay down, thou wea-ry one, lay down Thy head up-on My breast."

I came to Je-sus as I was, — Wea-ry and worn and sad;
2 Of that life-giv-ing stream;
3 In Him my Star, my Sun;

I found in Him a rest-ing-place, And He has made me glad. A-MEN.

Org.

2 I heard the voice of Jesus say,
  "Behold, I freely give
The living water; thirsty one,
  Stoop down and drink, and live."
I came to Jesus, and I drank
  Of that life-giving stream;
My thirst was quenched, my soul revived,
  And now I live in Him.

3 I heard the voice of Jesus say,
  "I am this dark world's Light;
Look unto Me, thy morn shall rise,
  And all thy day be bright."
I looked to Jesus, and I found
  In Him my Star, my Sun;
And in that light of life I'll walk,
  Till travelling days are done.

Rev. HORATIUS BONAR, 1846

277

308 ST. EDITH 7. 6. 7. 6. D.

Justin H. Knecht, 1799
and Rev. Edward Husband, 1871

1 O Je - sus, Thou art stand - ing Out - side the fast-closed door,

In low - ly pa - tience wait - ing To pass the thresh - old o'er:

We bear the name of Chris - tians, His Name and sign we bear,

O shame, thrice shame up - on us, To keep Him stand-ing there! A - MEN.

Behold, I stand at the door, and knock.—Rev. iii, 20

2 O Jesus, Thou art knocking;
  And lo! that hand is scarred,
And thorns Thy brow encircle,
  And tears Thy face have marred;
O love that passeth knowledge,
  So patiently to wait!
O sin that hath no equal,
  So fast to bar the gate!

3 O Jesus, Thou art pleading
  In accents meek and low,
"I died for you, My children,
  And will ye treat Me so?"
O Lord, with shame and sorrow
  We open now the door;
Dear Saviour, enter, enter,
  And leave us never more.

Bishop William W. How, 1867

The Call

309 BEULAH 7. 6. 7. 6. D.

HENRI F. HEMY, 1865

1 The King of Glo - ry stand - eth Be - side that heart of sin,

His might - y voice com - mand - eth The ra - ging waves with - in;

The floods of deep - est an - guish Roll back - ward at His will,

As o'er the storm a - ris - eth His man-date, "Peace, be still." A - MEN.

2 At times, with sudden glory,
    He speaks, and all is done!
Without one stroke of battle
    The victory is won:
While we, with joy beholding,
    Can scarce believe it true,
That e'en our kingly Jesus
    Can form such hearts anew.

3 But sometimes in the stillness,
    He gently draweth near,
And whispers words of welcome
    Into the sinner's ear;

With anxious heart He waiteth
    The answer of His cry,
That oft repeated question,
    "O wherefore wilt thou die?"

4 O Christ, His love is mighty!
    Long-suffering is His grace!
And glorious is the splendor
    That beameth from His face!
Our hearts up-leap in gladness,
    When we behold that love,
As we go singing onward
    To dwell with Him above.

MRS. CHARITIE LEES BANCROFT, 1867

310 I LOVE TO TELL THE STORY 7. 6. 7. 6. D. with Refrain

WILLIAM G. FISCHER, 1869

1 I love to tell the sto - ry Of un - seen things a - bove,

Of Je - sus and His glo - ry, Of Je - sus and His love.

I love to tell the sto - ry, Be - cause I know it's true;

It sat - is - fies my long - ings As noth - ing else could do.

REFRAIN

I love to tell the sto - ry, 'Twill be my theme in glo - ry

The Call

To' tell the old, old sto-ry Of Je-sus and His love. A-MEN.

2 I love to tell the story;
More wonderful it seems
Than all the golden fancies
Of all our golden dreams.
I love to tell the story,
It did so much for me;
And that is just the reason
I tell it now to thee.—REF.

3 I love to tell the story;
'Tis pleasant to repeat
What seems, each time I tell it,
More wonderfully sweet.

I love to tell the story,
For some have never heard
The message of salvation
From God's own holy word.—REF.

4 I love to tell the story;
For those who know it best
Seem hungering and thirsting
To hear it, like the rest.
And when, in scenes of glory,
I sing the new, new song,
'Twill be the old, old story
That I have loved so long.—REF.

KATHERINE HANKEY, 1866

NOTE—*Miss Hankey's hymn was written in four-line verses, which the composer coupled; adding also the refrain.*

311 RETURN C. M. with Refrain   JOHN E. GOULD, 1869

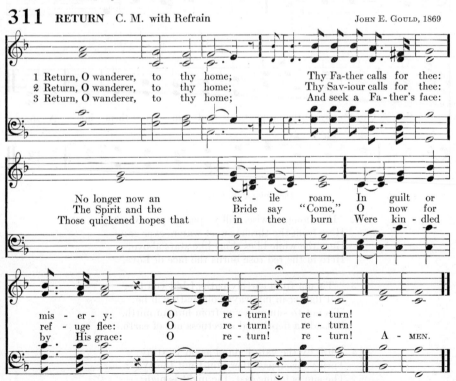

1 Return, O wanderer, to thy home;   Thy Fa-ther calls for thee:
2 Return, O wanderer, to thy home;   Thy Sav-iour calls for thee:
3 Return, O wanderer, to thy home;   And seek a Fa-ther's face:

No longer now an   ex - ile   roam,   In   guilt   or
The Spirit and the   Bride say "Come," O   now   for
Those quickened hopes that in thee burn Were kin - dled

mis - er - y: O   re - turn!   re - turn!
ref - uge flee: O   re - turn!   re - turn!
by   His grace: O   re - turn!   re - turn!   A - MEN.

Arranged from THOMAS HASTINGS, 1831, and Rev. WILLIAM B. COLLYER, 1812

NOTE—*By a conjunction quite undesigned the composers of the two tunes happen to have been partners in the Philadelphia business firm of "Gould and Fischer," dealers in pianos, and their tunes were written in the same year.*

281

The Spiritual Life

DALKEITH 10. 10. 10. 10.

THOMAS HEWLETT, 1866

1 Christ in His heaven-ly gar-den walks all day, And calls to souls upon the world's high-way; Wea-ried with tri-fles, maimed and sick with
sin, Christ by the gate stands, and in-vites them in. A-MEN.

*The garden of the Lord.—*ISA. li, 3

2 "How long, unwise, will ye pursue your woe?
Here from the throne sweet waters ever go:
Here the while lilies shine like stars above:
Here in the red rose burns the face of Love.

3 "'Tis not from earthly paths I bid you flee,
But lighter in my ways your path will be:
'Tis not to summon you from human mirth,
But add a depth and sweetness not of earth.

4 "Still by the gate I stand as on ye stray:
Turn your steps hither: am I not the Way?
The sun is falling fast; the night is nigh:
Why will ye wander? wherefore will ye die?"

FRANCIS T. PALGRAVE, 1867

The Call

313 ST. AIDAN 8.8.8.

Rev. the Hon. F. R. GREY, 1866

1 I say to thee, do thou re-peat To the first man thou may-est meet In lane, high-way, or o-pen street— A-MEN.

2 That he and we and all men move
Beneath a canopy of love,
As broad as the blue sky above;

3 That doubt and trouble, fear and pain
And anguish, all are shadows vain,
That death itself shall not remain;

4 That if we will one Guide obey,
The dreariest path, the darkest way
Shall issue out in heavenly day;

5 And we, on divers shores now cast,
Shall meet, the voyage's peril past,
All in our Father's house at last.

6 And ere thou leave him, say thou this,
Yet one word more—they only miss
The winning of that final bliss,

7 Who will not count it true that love,
For ever blessing, rules above,
And that in it we live and move.

Archbishop RICHARD C. TRENCH, 1835
with the rhythm of three lines revised.

MONKWEARMOUTH 8.8.8.

CHARLES STEGGALL, 1890

1 I say to thee, do thou re-peat To the first man thou may-est meet In lane, high-way, or o-pen street—A-MEN.

NOTE.—*As the hymn is virtually a single sentence, the pause between the verses should not be too marked.*

314 BEACHLEY 7. 6. 7. 6. 7. 7. 7. 6.

ARTHUR COTTMAN, 1876

1 "Fol - low Me," the Mas - ter said; We will fol - low Je - sus:

By His word and Spir - it led, We will fol - low Je - sus.

Still for us He lives to plead, At the throne doth in - ter - cede,

Of - fers help in time of need: We will fol - low Je - sus. A-MEN.

May be sung to SUNSHINE, *No. 365 (noting the slurs in line 6)*

2 Should the world and sin oppose,
　We will follow Jesus:
He is greater than our foes;—
　We will follow Jesus.
On His promise we depend;
He will succor and defend,
Help and keep us to the end:
　We will follow Jesus.

3 Though the way may dark appear,
　We will follow Jesus:
He will make our pathway clear;
　We will follow Jesus.

In our daily round of care,
As we plead with God in prayer,
With the cross which we must bear,
　We will follow Jesus.

4 Ever with the goal in view,
　We will follow Jesus:
All His promises are true;
　We will follow Jesus.
When this earthly course is run,
And the Master says, "Well done!"
Life eternal we have won:
　We will follow Jesus.

WILLIAM STEVENSON, 1880

The Call

315 **FLEE AS A BIRD** 8. 7. 8. 7. 8. 8. 8. 8.   Arranged by Mrs. Mary S. B. Dana, 1840

1 Flee as a bird to your moun-tain, Thou who art wea-ry of sin;
2 He will pro-tect thee for ev - er, Wipe ev - ery fall - ing tear;

Go to the clear-flow-ing foun-tain, Where you may wash and be clean;
He will for-sake thee O nev-er, Shel - tered so ten - der - ly there!

Fly, for temp-ta-tion is near thee, Call, and the Sav - iour will
Haste then, the hours are fly - ing, Spend not the mo - ments in

hear thee; He on His bos - om will bear thee, O thou who art
sigh - ing, Cease from your sor - row and cry - ing, The Sav - iour will

wea - ry of sin, O thou who art wea - ry of sin.
wipe ev - ery tear, The Sav - iour will wipe ev - ery tear. A - MEN.

Mrs. Mary S. B. Dana, 1840

285

316 **STEPHANOS** 8. 5. 8. 3. Rev. Sir HENRY W. BAKER, Bart., 1868

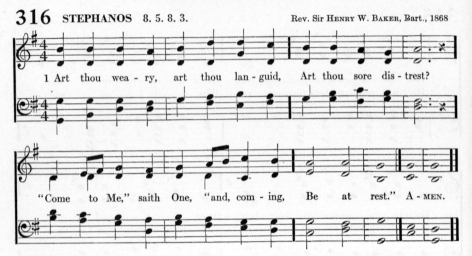

1 Art thou wea - ry, art thou lan - guid, Art thou sore dis - trest?

"Come to Me," saith One, "and, com - ing, Be at rest." A - MEN.

2 Hath He marks to lead me to Him,
    If He be my Guide?
  "In His feet and hands are wound-prints,
    And His side."

3 Is there diadem, as Monarch,
    That His brow adorns?
  "Yea, a crown, in very surety,
    But of thorns."

4 If I find Him, if I follow,
    What His guerdon here?
  "Many a sorrow, many a labor,
    Many a tear."

5 If I still hold closely to Him,
    What hath He at last?
  "Sorrow vanquished, labor ended,
    Jordan passed."

6 If I ask Him to receive me,
    Will He say me nay?
  "Not till earth and not till heaven
    Pass away."

7 Finding, following, keeping, struggling,
    Is He sure to bless?
  "Saints, apostles, prophets, martyrs,
    Answer, 'Yes.'"

Rev. JOHN M. NEALE, 1862: verse 7, line 3, varied.

BULLINGER 8. 5. 8. 3. Rev. ETHELBERT W. BULLINGER, 1874

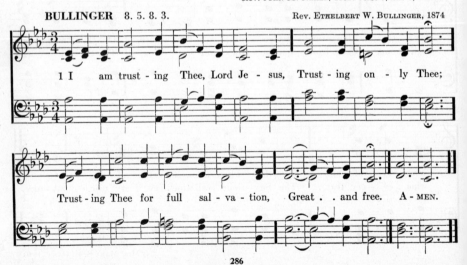

1 I am trust - ing Thee, Lord Je - sus, Trust - ing on - ly Thee;

Trust - ing Thee for full sal - va - tion, Great . . and free. A - MEN.

Repentance and Faith

A Collect for Confidence

Incline Thine ear unto us, O God, as unto one that singeth songs out of the night; for we have no refuge save only the abundance of Thy mercy. I said, I will confess my sins unto the Lord, and Thou scatterest the darkness with the light of Thy forgiveness and awakenest a new song in the hearts of them that trust Thee, through Jesus Christ our Saviour. Amen.

317 **TOPLADY** 7. 7. 7. 7. 7. 7.

THOMAS HASTINGS, 1830

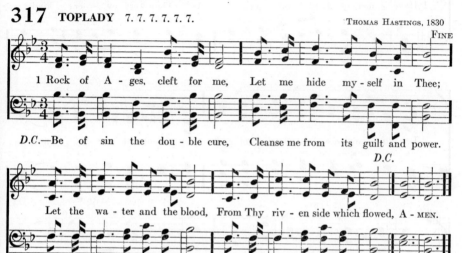

1 Rock of A - ges, cleft for me, Let me hide my - self in Thee;

D.C.—Be of sin the dou - ble cure, Cleanse me from its guilt and power.

Let the wa - ter and the blood, From Thy riv - en side which flowed, A - MEN.

2 Not the labors of my hands
   Can fulfil Thy law's demands;
   Could my zeal no respite know,
   Could my tears for ever flow,
   All for sin could not atone;
   Thou must save, and Thou alone.

3 Nothing in my hand I bring,
   Simply to Thy cross I cling;
   Naked, come to Thee for dress,

Helpless, look to Thee for grace;
Foul, I to the fountain fly,
Wash me, Saviour, or I die.

4 While I draw this fleeting breath,
   When my eyelids close in death,
   When I soar to worlds unknown,
   See Thee on Thy judgment throne,
   Rock of Ages, cleft for me,
   Let me hide myself in Thee.

Rev. AUGUSTUS M. TOPLADY, 1776
verse 4, line 2, varied by Rev. THOMAS COTTERILL, 1815

NOTE.—*The tune* RELIANCE, *No. 217, was composed for this hymn.*

318 **(BULLINGER)** 8. 5. 8. 3.

1 I am trusting Thee, Lord Jesus,
   Trusting only Thee;
   Trusting Thee for full salvation,
   Great and free.

2 I am trusting Thee for pardon;
   At Thy feet I bow;
   For Thy grace and tender mercy,
   Trusting now.

3 I am trusting Thee to guide me;
   Thou alone shalt lead,

Every day and hour supplying
   All my need.

4 I am trusting Thee for power,
   Thine can never fail;
   Words which Thou Thyself shalt give me
   Must prevail.

5 I am trusting Thee, Lord Jesus;
   Never let me fall;
   I am trusting Thee for ever,
   And for all.

FRANCES R. HAVERGAL, 1874

319 PASTOR BONUS S. M. D.

ALFRED J. CALDICOTT, 1890

1 Have mer-cy, Lord, on me, As Thou wert ev-er kind;
Let me, op-pressed with loads of guilt, Thy wont-ed mer-cy find.
A - gainst Thee, Lord, a - lone, And on - ly in Thy sight,
Have I trans-gressed; and though con-demned Must own Thy judg-ment right. A - MEN.

Alternative tune, EVENING SHADOWS, No. 394

A PARAPHRASE OF PSALM LI

2 Blot out my crying sin,
　Nor me in anger view;
Create in me a heart that's clean,
　An upright mind renew.
Withdraw not Thou Thy help,
　Nor cast me from Thy sight;
Nor let Thy Holy Spirit take
　His everlasting flight.

3 The joy Thy favor gives
　Let me again obtain;
And Thy free Spirit's firm support
　My fainting soul sustain.
Do thou unlock my lips,
　With sorrow closed and shame;
So shall my mouth Thy wondrous praise
　To all the world proclaim.

Abridged from the 1698 edition of TATE & BRADY'S
New Version of the Psalms of David: with "His" for "its" at the end of verse 2.

320 JUST AS I AM 8. 8. 8. 6.

Sir Joseph Barnby, 1893

1 Just as I am, with-out one plea But that Thy blood was shed for me,

Slower

And that Thou bidd'st me come to Thee, O Lamb of God, I come. A-MEN.

2 Just as I am, and waiting not
To rid my soul of one dark blot,
To Thee, whose blood can cleanse each spot,
   O Lamb of God, I come.

3 Just as I am, though tossed about
With many a conflict, many a doubt,
Fightings and fears within, without,
   O Lamb of God, I come.

4 Just as I am, poor, wretched, blind;
Sight, riches, healing of the mind,

Yea, all I need, in Thee to find,
   O Lamb of God, I come.

5 Just as I am! Thou wilt receive,
Wilt welcome, pardon, cleanse, relieve;
Because Thy promise I believe,
   O Lamb of God, I come.

6 Just as I am! Thy love unknown
Has broken every barrier down;
Now, to be Thine, yea, Thine alone,
   O Lamb of God, I come.

Charlotte Elliott, 1836

WOODWORTH 8. 8. 8. 6.

William B. Bradbury, 1849

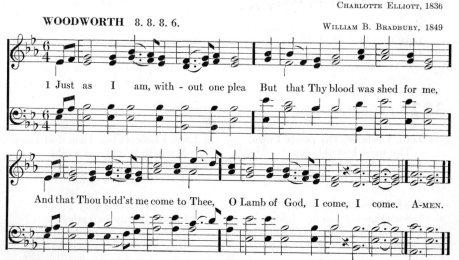

1 Just as I am, with - out one plea But that Thy blood was shed for me,

And that Thou bidd'st me come to Thee, O Lamb of God, I come, I come. A-MEN.

321 **GOWER'S LITANY** 7. 7. 7. 6.

JOHN H. GOWER, 1891

1 Fa-ther, hear Thy chil-dren's call; Hum-bly at Thy feet we fall,
Prod-i-gals, con-fess-ing all: We be-seech Thee, hear us. A-MEN.

2 Christ, beneath Thy cross we blame
All our life of sin and shame,
Penitent, we breathe Thy Name:
    We beseech Thee, hear us.

3 Holy Spirit, grieved and tried,
Oft forgotten and defied,
Now we mourn our stubborn pride:
    We beseech Thee, hear us.

4 Love that caused us first to be,
Love that bled upon the tree,
Love that draws us lovingly:
    We beseech Thee, hear us.

5 We Thy call have disobeyed,
Into paths of sin have strayed,
And repentance have delayed:
    We beseech Thee, hear us.

6 Sick, we come to Thee for cure,
Guilty, seek Thy mercy sure,
Evil, long to be made pure:
    We beseech Thee, hear us.

7 By the love that bids Thee spare,
By the heaven Thou dost prepare,
By Thy promises to prayer,
    We beseech Thee, hear us.

Rev. THOMAS B. POLLOCK, 1875

322 (LAMBETH) C. M.

1 Lord, I believe; Thy power I own,
    Thy word I would obey;
I wander comfortless and lone
    When from Thy truth I stray.

2 Lord, I believe; but gloomy frears
    Sometimes bedim my sight;
I look to Thee with prayers and tears,
    And cry for strength and light.

3 Lord, I believe; but Thou dost know
    My faith is cold and weak;
Pity my frailty, and bestow
    The confidence I seek.

4 Yes, I believe; and only Thou
    Canst give my soul relief:
Lord, to Thy truth my spirit bow;
    Help Thou mine unbelief.

Rev. JOHN R. WREFORD, 1837

Repentance and Faith

323 **HOMEWARD** 8. 8. 8. 6.

Uzziah C. Burnap, 1898

1 Our wil - ful hearts have gone a - stray; Our feet have wan-dered far a - way;

O God, re - mem - ber not the day When we for - sook Thy love. A - MEN.

Copyright, 1925, by Louis F. Benson.

And he arose, and came to his father.—St. Luke xv, 20

2 O patient Eyes that saw us go!
O careless hearts to grieve Thee so!
O feet how swift to leave, how slow
    When we came back to Love!

3 We followed far the wayward will;
Our eyes turned home from every hill;
They saw Thee waiting, watching still
    When we looked back to Love.

4 We found no home to east or west;
We bore no peace within the breast,
Until once more we were at rest
    When we came back to Love.

5 "Our Father!" Hallowed be the Name
That all within Thy house proclaim;
Their prayer and ours at last the same,—
    Thy will be done, O Love.

Rev. Louis F. Benson, 1897

LAMBETH C. M.

William Schulthes, 1871

1 Lord, I be - lieve; Thy power I own, Thy word I would o - bey;

I wan - der com - fort - less and lone When from Thy truth I stray. A - MEN.

291

The Spiritual Life

324 INTERCESSION NEW 7. 5. 7. 5. D. with Refrain
WILLIAM H. CALLCOTT, 1867:
the refrain from "Look down on us" in MENDELSSOHN's *Elijah*, 1846

1 When the wea-ry, seek-ing rest, To Thy good-ness flee; When the heav-y-la-den cast All their load on Thee; When the troubled, seek-ing peace, On Thy Name shall call; When the sin-ner, seek-ing life, At Thy feet shall fall: Hear then in love, O Lord, the cry In heaven, Thy dwell-ing place on high. A-MEN.

What prayer or what supplication soever shall be made of any man . . . when every one shall know . . . his own sore and his own grief—Then hear Thou from heaven Thy dwelling place.—2 CHRON. vi, 29, 30

2 When the worldling, sick at heart,
   Lifts his soul above:
When the prodigal looks back
   To his Father's love;
When the proud man, in his pride,
   Stoops to seek Thy face;
When the burdened brings his guilt
   To Thy throne of grace:—REF.

3 When the man of toil and care
   In the city crowd,
When the shepherd on the moor
   Names the Name of God;
When the learnèd and the high,
   Tired of earthly fame,
Upon higher joys intent,
   Name the blessèd Name:—REF.

Rev. HORATIUS BONAR, 1866

325 OLIVET 6. 6. 4. 6. 6. 6. 4.   LOWELL MASON, 1832

1 My faith looks up to Thee, Thou Lamb of Cal-va-ry,

Sav-iour Di-vine: Now hear me while I pray, Take all my

guilt a-way, O let me from this day Be whol-ly Thine. A-MEN.

2 May Thy rich grace impart
Strength to my fainting heart,
  My zeal inspire;
As Thou hast died for me,
O may my love to Thee
Pure, warm, and changeless be,
  A living fire.

3 While life's dark maze I tread,
And griefs around me spread,
  Be Thou my Guide;
Bid darkness turn to day,
Wipe sorrow's tears away,
Nor let me ever stray
  From Thee aside.

4 When ends life's transient dream,
When death's cold, sullen stream
  Shall o'er me roll,
Blest Saviour, then, in love,
Fear and distrust remove;
O bear me safe above
  A ransomed soul.

Rev. RAY PALMER, 1830

NOTE—*Dr. Palmer follows the older tradition of hymnody in deepening the shadows of life and death. It may be allowable to suggest that the first two verses make a beautiful and complete hymn of faith.*

326 ELIM 7. 6. 7. 6. D.

J. Baptiste Calkin, 1867

1 I lay my sins on Je - sus, The spot - less Lamb of God;

He bears them all, and frees me From the ac - curs - ed load.

I bring my guilt to Je - sus, To wash my crim - son stains

White in His blood most pre - cious, Till not a spot re - mains. A - MEN.

2 I lay my wants on Jesus;
    All fullness dwells in Him;
In every hurt He heals me,
    He doth my soul redeem:
I lay my griefs on Jesus,
    My burdens and my cares;
He all my labors lightens,
    He every sorrow shares.

3 I rest my soul on Jesus,
    This weary soul of mine;
His right hand me embraces,
    I on His breast recline:

I love the Name of Jesus,
    Emmanuel, Christ, the Lord;
Upon the winds, like fragrance,
    His Name abroad is poured.

4 I long to be like Jesus,
    Meek, loving, lowly, mild;
I long to be like Jesus,
    The Father's holy child:
I long to be with Jesus
    Amid the heavenly throng,
To sing with saints His praises,
    To learn the angels' song.

Rev. Horatius Bonar, 1843: here revised

NOTE—*The changes in the text are merely in avoidance of certain rhymes in the original.*

327 ANGEL'S STORY 7. 6. 7. 6. D.   ARTHUR H. MANN, 1883

1 O Je-sus, I have prom-ised To serve Thee to the end;

Be Thou for ev-er near me, My Mas-ter and my Friend:

I shall not fear the bat-tle If Thou art by my side,

Nor wan-der from the path-way If Thou wilt be my Guide. A-MEN.

If any man serve Me, let him follow Me.—ST. JOHN xii, 26

2 O let me feel Thee near me,
 The world is ever near;
I see the sights that dazzle,
 The tempting sounds I hear:
My foes are ever near me,
 Around me and within;
But, Jesus, draw Thou nearer,
 And shield my soul from sin.

3 O let me hear Thee speaking
 In accents clear and still,
Above the storms of passion,
 The murmurs of self-will:

O speak to re-assure me,
 To hasten or control;
O speak, and make me listen,
 Thou Guardian of my soul.

4 O Jesus, Thou hast promised
 To all who follow Thee
That where Thou art in glory
 There shall Thy servant be;
And, Jesus, I have promised
 To serve Thee to the end;
O give me grace to follow
 My Master and my Friend.

REV. JOHN E. BODE, 1868

The Spiritual Life: Love and Loyalty

A Collect for Holy Love

O Thou who knowest that we love Thee: Hallow the lips that sing because Thou lovest us, and help the hands that feed Thy sheep because Thou lovest them: even Jesus Christ our Lord. Amen.

328 ST. MARGARET 8. 8. 8. 8. 6. ALBERT L. PEACE, 1885

1 O Love that wilt not let me go, I rest my wea-ry soul in Thee; I give Thee back the life I owe, That in Thine o-cean depths its flow May rich-er, full-er be. A-MEN.

2 O Light that followest all my way,
   I yield my flickering torch to Thee;
My heart restores its borrowed ray,
That in Thy sunshine's blaze its day
    May brighter, fairer be.

3 O Joy that seekest me through pain
   I cannot close my heart to Thee;
I trace the rainbow through the rain,
And feel the promise is not vain
    That morn shall tearless be.

4 O Cross that liftest up my head,
   I dare not ask to fly from Thee;
I lay in dust life's glory dead,
And from the ground there blossoms red
    Life that shall endless be.

REV. GEORGE MATHESON, 1882

Love and Loyalty

329 BROOKFIELD L. M.

THOMAS B. SOUTHGATE, 1855

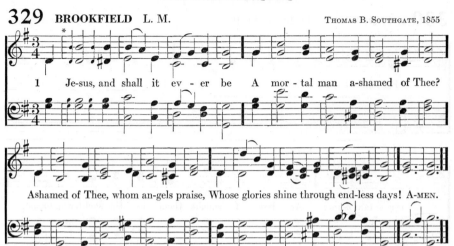

1 Jesus, and shall it ever be A mortal man ashamed of Thee?

Ashamed of Thee, whom angels praise, Whose glories shine through endless days! A-MEN.

Small notes for the first verse.

2 Ashamed of Jesus! sooner far
Let evening blush to own a star:
He sheds the beams of light divine
O'er this benighted soul of mine.

3 Ashamed of Jesus! just as soon
Let midnight be ashamed of noon:
'Tis midnight with my soul till He,
Bright Morning Star, bid darkness flee.

4 Ashamed of Jesus, that dear Friend
On whom my hopes of heaven depend!

No; when I blush, be this my shame,
That I no more revere His Name.

5 Ashamed of Jesus! yes, I may
When I've no guilt to wash away,
No tear to wipe, no good to crave,
No fears to quell, no soul to save.

6 Till then—nor is my boasting vain—
Till then I boast a Saviour slain;
And O may this my glory be,
That Christ is not ashamed of me.

Rev. JOSEPH GRIGG, 1765: varied by Rev. BENJAMIN FRANCIS, 1787

ST. STEPHEN'S CHURCH L. M.

DAVID D. WOOD, in *The Hymnal*, 1895

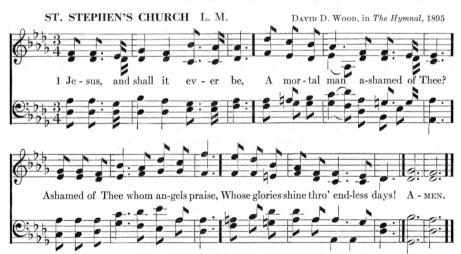

1 Jesus, and shall it ever be, A mortal man ashamed of Thee?

Ashamed of Thee whom angels praise, Whose glories shine thro' endless days! A - MEN.

NOTE—*Dr. Wood was the blind organist of St. Stephen's Church, Philadelphia, where for many years his tune was a favorite.*

The Spiritual Life

330 SUNDOWN 10. 10. 10. 10. 10. 10. JOHN H. GOWER, 1890

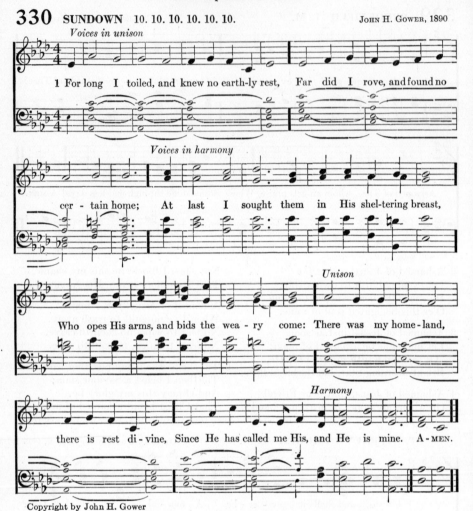

Voices in unison

1 For long I toiled, and knew no earth-ly rest, Far did I rove, and found no

Voices in harmony

cer - tain home; At last I sought them in His shel-tering breast,

Unison

Who opes His arms, and bids the wea - ry come: There was my home-land,

Harmony

there is rest di-vine, Since He has called me His, and He is mine. A-MEN.

2 The good I have is from His stores supplied,
　　What seemeth ill is what He deemeth best;
　With Him for Friend, I'm rich with naught beside,
　　Poorer without Him, though of all possessed:
　Changes may happen; I could all resign,
　Content, while I am His, while He is mine.

3 Whate'er may change, in Him no change is seen,
　　All glorious Sun that wanes not nor declines;
　Above the clouds He walks in light serene
　　And on His people's darkness brightly shines;
　Were all to leave me, I should not repine,
　While I my Saviour's am, while He is mine.

Love and Loyalty

4 While here, alas! I know but half His love,
   I half discern Him, and but half adore;
   But when I meet Him in the realms above
   Then I shall love Him better, praise Him more;
   Telling for ever, 'mid the choir divine,
   How fully I am His, and He is mine.

Rev. HENRY F. LYTE's imitation, 1833, of JOHN QUARLES (1624–65): recast for this book

331 ST. JUDE 8. 7. 8. 8. 7. CHARLES J. VINCENT, 1877

1 O the bit - ter shame and sor - row That a time could ev - er be, When I let the Sav - iour's pit - y Plead in vain, and proud - ly an-swered, "All of self, and none of Thee." A - MEN.

He died for all, that they which live should not henceforth live unto themselves.—2 COR. v, 15

2 Yet He found me; I beheld Him
   Bleeding on the accursèd tree,
   Heard Him pray, "Forgive them, Father!"
   And my wistful heart said faintly,
   "Some of self, and some of Thee."

3 Day by day His tender mercy,
   Healing, helping, full and free,
   Sweet and strong, and, ah! so patient,
   Brought me lower, while I whispered,
   "Less of self, and more of Thee."

4 Higher than the highest heavens,
   Deeper than the deepest sea,
   Lord, Thy love at last hath conquered;
   Grant me now my soul's desire,
   "None of self, and all of Thee."

Rev. THEODORE MONOD, 1874

NOTE—*This hymn was written in English by the French evangelist during a series of consecration meetings held at Broadlands, England, in July, 1874.*

332 HOLLINGSIDE 7. 7. 7. 7. D.

Rev. JOHN B. DYKES, 1861

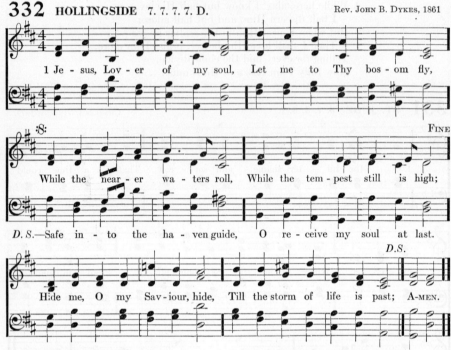

1 Je - sus, Lov - er of my soul, Let me to Thy bos - om fly,

While the near - er wa - ters roll, While the tem - pest still is high;

FINE

D. S.—Safe in - to the ha - ven guide, O re - ceive my soul at last.

Hide me, O my Sav - iour, hide, Till the storm of life is past; A-MEN.

D.S.

2 Other refuge have I none;
　Hangs my helpless soul on Thee;
Leave, ah! leave me not alone,
　Still support and comfort me.
All my trust on Thee is stayed,
　All my help from Thee I bring;
Cover my defenceless head
　With the shadow of Thy wing.

3 Wilt Thou not regard my call?
　Wilt Thou not accept my prayer?
Lo! I sink, I faint, I fall!
　Lo! on Thee I cast my care;
Reach me out Thy gracious hand!
　While I of Thy strength receive,
Hoping against hope I stand,
　Dying, and behold I live!

4 Thou, O Christ, art all I want;
　More than all in Thee I find:
Raise the fallen, cheer the faint,
　Heal the sick, and lead the blind.
Just and holy is Thy Name;
　I am all unrighteousness;
False and full of sin I am,
　Thou art full of truth and grace.

5 Plenteous grace with Thee is found,
　Grace to cover all my sin;
Let the healing streams abound;
　Make and keep me pure within.
Thou of life the Fountain art,
　Freely let me take of Thee;
Spring Thou up within my heart,
　Rise to all eternity.

Rev. CHARLES WESLEY, 1740

For a Welsh setting of this hymn, see No. 407

For a Welsh setting of this hymn, see No. 407

REFUGE 7. 7. 7. 7. D.

JOSEPH P. HOLBROOK, 1862

1 Je - sus, Lov - er of my soul, Let me to Thy bos - om fly,

Love and Loyalty

While the near - er wa - ters roll, While the tem - pest still is high:

Hide me, O my Sav - iour, hide, Till the storm of life is past;

Safe in - to the ha - ven guide, O re - ceive my soul at last. A - MEN.

MARTYN 7. 7. 7. 7. D.

SIMEON B. MARSH, 1834

FINE

1 { Je - sus, Lov - er of my soul, Let me to Thy bos - om fly,
While the near - er wa - ters roll, While the tem - pest still is high:

D. C.—Safe in - to the ha - ven guide, O re - ceive my soul at last.

D. C.

Hide me, O my Sav - iour, hide, Till the storm of life is past; A - MEN.

301

333 THE SWEETEST NAME 8. 7. 8. 7. D. (Iambic)   WILLIAM B. BRADBURY, 1861

1 There is no name so sweet on earth, No name so sweet in heav-en,

The Name be-fore His won-drous birth To Christ the Sav-iour giv-en.

REFRAIN

We love to sing a-round our King, And hail Him bless-ed Je-sus;

For there's no word ear ev-er heard So dear, so sweet as "Je-sus." A-MEN.

2 And, when He hung upon the tree,
   They wrote this Name above Him;
That all might see the reason we
For evermore must love Him.
   We love to sing, *etc.*

3 So now, upon His Father's throne,
   Almighty to release us
From sin and pains, He gladly reigns,
The Prince and Saviour Jesus.
   We love to sing, *etc.*

4 To Jesus every knee shall bow,
   And every tongue confess Him,
And we unite with saints in light,
   Our only Lord, to bless Him.
   We love to sing, *etc.*

5 O Jesus, by that matchless Name,
   Thy grace shall fail us never;
To-day as yesterday the same,
   Thou art the same for ever.
   We love to sing, *etc.*

Anonymous: c. 1858

NOTE—*This hymn is attributed (doubtfully) to the Rev. George W. Bethune, an eminent (Dutch Reformed) American clergyman.*

Love and Loyalty

334 **CONSTANCE** 8. 7. 8. 7. D. (Iambic) Sir Arthur Sullivan, 1875

1 I've found a Friend; O such a Friend! He loved me ere I knew Him;

He drew me with the cords of love, And thus He bound me to Him;

And round my heart still close - ly twine Those ties which naught can sev - er,

For I am His, and He is mine, For ev - er and for ev - er. A - men.

A Friend that sticketh closer than a brother.—Prov. xviii, 24

2 I've found a Friend; O such a Friend!
　He bled, He died to save me;
And not alone the gift of life,
　But His own self He gave me.
Naught that I have mine own I'll call,
　I'll hold it for the Giver;
My heart, my strength, my life, my all,
　Are His, and His for ever.

3 I've found a Friend; O such a Friend,
　So kind and true and tender!
So wise a Counsellor and Guide,
　So mighty a Defender!
From Him who loves me now so well
　What power my soul shall sever?
Shall life or death, shall earth or hell?
　No: I am His for ever.

Rev. James G. Small, 1863

335 ST. CHRYSOSTOM 8. 8. 8. 8. 8. 8.

Sir JOSEPH BARNBY, 1872

1 Je-sus, my Lord, my God, my All, Hear me, blest Sav-iour, when I call;

Hear me, and from Thy dwell-ing-place Pour down the rich-es of Thy grace:

Je-sus, my Lord, I Thee a-dore; O make me love Thee more and more. A-MEN.

2 Jesus, too late I Thee have sought;
How can I love Thee as I ought?
And how extol Thy matchless fame,
The glorious beauty of Thy Name?
    Jesus, my Lord, I Thee adore;
    O make me love Thee more and more.

3 Jesus, what didst Thou find in me
That Thou hast dealt so lovingly?
How great the joy that Thou hast brought,
So far exceeding hope or thought!
    Jesus, my Lord, I Thee adore;
    O make me love Thee more and more.

4 Jesus, of Thee shall be my song;
To Thee my heart and soul belong:
All that I have or am is Thine;
And Thou, blest Saviour Thou art mine:
    Jesus, my Lord, I Thee adore;
    O make me love Thee more and more.

Rev. HENRY COLLINS, 1854

336 WHAT A FRIEND 8. 7. 8. 7. D.

C. CROZAT CONVERSE, 1868

1 What a Friend we have in Je - sus, All our sins and griefs to bear!
What a priv - i - lege to car - ry Ev - ery-thing to God in prayer!
O what peace we of - ten for - feit, O what need - less pain we bear,
All be-cause we do not car - ry Ev - ery-thing to God in prayer. A-MEN.

Alternative tune, EMMELAR, No. 46

2 Have we trials and temptations?
　Is there trouble anywhere?
We should never be discouraged:
　Take it to the Lord in prayer!
Can we find a friend so faithful,
　Who will all our sorrows share?
Jesus knows our every weakness—
　Take it to the Lord in prayer!

3 Are we weak and heavy laden,
　Cumbered with a load of care?
Precious Saviour, still our Refuge,—
　Take it to the Lord in prayer!
Do thy friends despise, forsake thee?
　Take it to the Lord in prayer!
In His arms He'll take and shield thee,
　Thou wilt find a solace there.

JOSEPH SCRIVEN, 1857

337 DOMINUS REGIT ME 8. 7. 8. 7. Iambic

Rev. JOHN B. DYKES, 1868

1 The King of love my Shep-herd is, Whose good-ness fail-eth nev-er;

I noth-ing lack if I am His And He is mine for ev-er. A-MEN.

A PARAPHRASE OF PSALM XXIII

2 Where streams of living water flow
  My ransomed soul He leadeth,
And, where the verdant pastures grow,
  With food celestial feedeth.

3 Perverse and foolish oft I strayed,
  But yet in love He sought me,
And on his shoulder gently laid,
  And home, rejoicing, brought me.

4 In death's dark vale I fear no ill
  With Thee, dear Lord, beside me;

Thy rod and staff my comfort still,
  Thy cross before to guide me.

5 Thou spread'st a table in my sight;
  Thy unction grace bestoweth;
And O what transport of delight
  From Thy pure chalice floweth.

6 And so through all the length of days
  Thy goodness faileth never:
Good Shepherd, may I sing Thy praise
  Within Thy house for ever.

Rev. Sir HENRY W. BAKER, Bart., 1868

GREENWOOD S. M.

JOSEPH E. SWEETSER, 1849

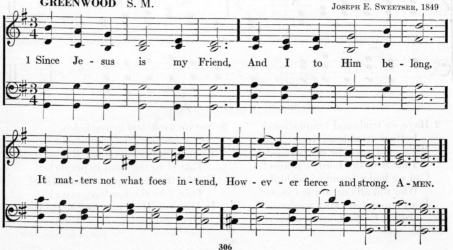

1 Since Je-sus is my Friend, And I to Him be-long,

It mat-ters not what foes in-tend, How-ev-er fierce and strong. A-MEN.

338 PAX TECUM 10. 10.

G. T. CALDBECK, 1877

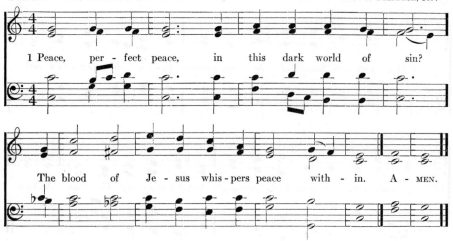

1 Peace, per - fect peace, in this dark world of sin?
The blood of Je - sus whis - pers peace with - in. A - MEN.

Thou wilt keep him in perfect peace, whose mind is stayed on Thee.—ISA. xxvi, 8

2 Peace, perfect peace, by thronging duties pressed?
To do the will of Jesus, this is rest.

3 Peace, perfect peace, with sorrows surging round?
On Jesus' bosom naught but calm is found.

4 Peace, perfect peace, with loved ones far away?
In Jesus' keeping we are safe, and they.

5 Peace, perfect peace, our future all unknown?
Jesus we know, and He is on the throne.

6 Peace, perfect peace, death shadowing us and ours?
Jesus has vanquished death and all its powers.

7 It is enough: earth's struggles soon shall cease,
And Jesus call us to heaven's perfect peace.

Bishop EDWARD H. BICKERSTETH, 1875

339 (GREENWOOD) S. M.

IST GOTT FÜR MICH, SO TRETE

1 Since Jesus is my Friend,
And I to Him belong,
It matters not what foes intend,
However fierce and strong.

2 He whispers in my breast
Sweet words of holy cheer,
How they who seek in God their rest
Shall ever find Him near;

3 How God hath built above
A city fair and new,
Where eye and heart shall see and prove
What faith has counted true.

4 My heart for gladness springs;
It cannot more be sad:
For very joy it laughs and sings,—
Sees naught but sunshine glad.

5 The sun that lights mine eyes
Is Christ, the Lord I love;
I sing for joy of that which lies
Stored up for us above.

Rev. PAUL GERHARDT, 1656
Translated by CATHERINE WINKWORTH, 1855: arranged, and verses 1 and 2 varied

340 ST. PETER C. M.

ALEXANDER R. REINAGLE, 1836

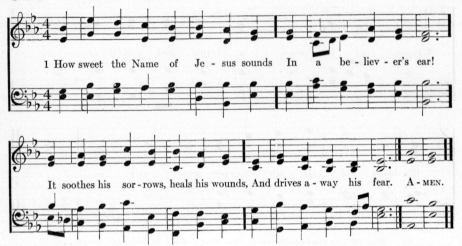

1 How sweet the Name of Je - sus sounds In a be - liev - er's ear!

It soothes his sor - rows, heals his wounds, And drives a - way his fear. A - MEN.

2 It makes the wounded spirit whole,
   And calms the troubled breast;
'Tis Manna to the hungry soul,
   And to the weary Rest.

3 Dear Name! the Rock on which I build,
   My Shield and Hiding-place,
My never-failing Treasury, filled
   With boundless stores of grace;

4 Jesus, my Shepherd, Brother, Friend,
   My Prophet, Priest, and King,
My Lord, my Life, my Way, my End,
   Accept the praise I bring.

5 Weak is the effort of my heart,
   And cold my warmest thought;
But when I see Thee as Thou art,
   I'll praise Thee as I ought.

6 Till then I would Thy love proclaim
   With every fleeting breath;
And may the music of Thy Name
   Refresh my soul in death.

Rev. JOHN NEWTON, 1779: verse 4, line 1, varied

341 (SAWLEY) C. M.

Whom having not seen, ye love.—1 PET. i, 8

1 Jesus, these eyes have never seen
   That radiant form of Thine;
The veil of sense hangs dark between
   Thy blessèd face and mine.

2 I see Thee not, I hear Thee not,
   Yet art Thou oft with me;
And earth hath ne'er so dear a spot
   As where I meet with Thee.

3 Like some bright dream that comes un-
   When slumbers o'er me roll,   [sought,
Thine image ever fills my thought,
   And charms my ravished soul.

4 Yet though I have not seen, and still
   Must rest in faith alone;
I love Thee, dearest Lord, and will,
   Unseen, but not unknown.

5 When death these mortal eyes shall seal,
   And still this throbbing heart,
The rending veil shall Thee reveal,
   All glorious as Thou art.

Rev. RAY PALMER, 1858

Love and Loyalty

342 ST. AGNES C. M.

Rev. John B. Dykes, 1866

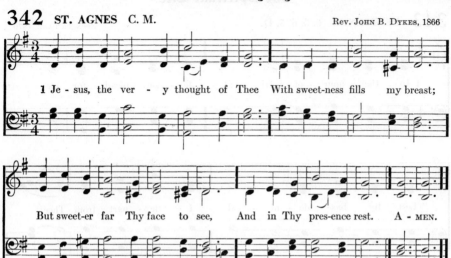

1 Je - sus, the ver - y thought of Thee With sweet-ness fills my breast;

But sweet-er far Thy face to see, And in Thy pres-ence rest. A - men.

JESU DULCIS MEMORIA

2 No voice can sing, nor heart can frame,
  Nor can the memory find,
A sweeter sound than Thy blest Name,
  O Saviour of mankind.

3 O Hope of every contrite heart,
  O Joy of all the meek,
To those who fall, how kind Thou art!
  How good to those who seek!

4 But what to those who find? Ah! this
  Nor tongue nor pen can show:
The love of Jesus, what it is
  None but His loved ones know.

5 Jesus, our only Joy be Thou,
  As Thou our Prize wilt be;
Jesus, be Thou our Glory now,
  And through eternity.

An anonymous Latin hymn of the 11th century
translated by Rev. Edward Caswall, 1849

SAWLEY C. M.

James Walch, 1860

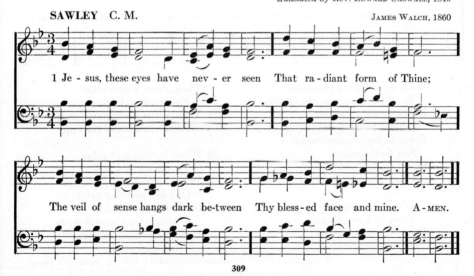

1 Je - sus, these eyes have nev - er seen That ra - diant form of Thine;

The veil of sense hangs dark be-tween Thy bless - ed face and mine. A - men.

343 PENITENCE 6. 5. 6. 5. D.

Spencer Lane, 1879

1 In the hour of tri - al, Je - sus, plead for me;

Lest by base de - ni - al I de - part from Thee:

When Thou seest me wa - ver, With a look re - call,

Nor for fear or fa - vor Suf - fer me to fall. A - MEN.

2 With its witching pleasures
  Would this vain world charm,
Or its sordid treasures
  Spread to work me harm,
Bring to my remembrance
  Sad Gethsemane,
Or, in darker semblance,
  Cross-crowned Calvary.

3 If with sore affliction
  Thou in love chastise,
Pour Thy benediction
  On the sacrifice;

Then, upon Thine altar
  Freely offered up,
Though the flesh may falter,
  Faith shall drink the cup.

4 When in dust and ashes
  To the grave I sink,
While heaven's glory flashes
  O'er the shelving brink,
On Thy truth relying
  Through that mortal strife,
Lord, receive me, dying,
  To eternal life.

James Montgomery, 1834: the second line varied

Love and Loyalty

344   JEWETT   6. 6. 6. 6. D.   Arranged from the overture to CARL M. VON WEBER'S *Der Freischütz*, 1821, by JOSEPH P. HOLBROOK, 1862

1 My Sav-iour, as Thou wilt! O may Thy will be mine;

In-to Thy hand of love I would my all re-sign.

Through sor-row, or through joy, Con-duct me as Thine own;

And help me still to say, My Lord, Thy will be done. A-MEN.

MEIN JESU, WIE DU WILLT

2 My Saviour, as Thou wilt!
　If needy here and poor,
Give me Thy people's bread,
　Their portion rich and sure.
The manna of Thy word
　Let my soul feed upon;
And if all else should fail,
　My Lord, Thy will be done.

3 My Saviour, as Thou wilt!
　Though seen through many a tear,
Let not my star of hope
　Grow dim or disappear.

Since Thou on earth hast wept
　And sorrowed oft alone,
If I must weep with Thee,
　My Lord, Thy will be done.

4 My Saviour, as Thou wilt!
　All shall be well for me;
Each changing future scene
　I gladly trust with Thee.
Straight to my home above
　I travel calmly on,
And sing, in life or death,
　My Lord, Thy will be done.

Rev. BENJAMIN SCHMOLCK, c. 1704.   Translated by JANE BORTHWICK, 1854

NOTE—*In the original and in the translation each verse begins with "My Jesus:" a familiarity of address that has caused many to turn from what is a true lyric, and which it is thought best to avoid here.*

345 HARVARD 8. 6. 8. 6. 8. 8.   ARTHUR BERRIDGE, 1905

1 In Christ I feel the heart of God Throbbing from heaven through earth;

Life stirs a - gain with - in the clod; Re - newed in beau - teous birth,

The soul springs up, a flower of prayer, Breathing His breath out on the air.   A - MEN.

2 In Christ I touch the hand of God,
    From His pure height reached down,
By blessèd ways before untrod,
    To lift us to our crown;
Victory that only perfect is
Through loving sacrifice, like His.

3 Holding His hand, my steadied feet
    May walk the air, the seas;
On life and death His smile falls sweet,
    Lights up all mysteries:
Stranger nor exile can I be
In new worlds where He leadeth me.

4 Not my Christ only; He is ours;
    Humanity's close bond;
Key to its vast, unopened powers,
    Dream of our dreams beyond.
What yet we shall be none can tell:
Now are we His, and all is well.

LUCY LARCOM, 1881

312

346 **NETTLETON** 8. 7. 8. 7. D.

Rev. Asahel Nettleton, 1826
arranged by James C. Knox, 1911

1 Sav-iour, Source of ev-ery bless-ing, Tune my heart to grate-ful lays:

Streams of mer - cy, nev-er ceas-ing, Call for cease-less songs of praise.

2 Teach me some mel-o-dious meas-ure, Sung by rap-tured saints a-bove;

Fill my soul with sa-cred pleas-ure, While I sing re-deem-ing love. A-MEN.

3 Thou didst seek me when a stranger,
   Wandering from the fold of God;
Thou, to save my soul from danger,
   Didst redeem me with Thy blood.

4 By Thy hand restored, defended,
   Safe through life thus far I've come;
Safe, O Lord, when life is ended,
   Bring me to my heavenly home.

Rev. Robert Robinson's "Come, Thou Fount of every blessing," 1758
as recast for *Hymns of the Protestant Episcopal Church*, 1826

Note—*The text and music as here given constitute "the one favorite hymn" of St. Paul's School, Concord, where it is sung at the close of each term with deep feeling, especially on the last night of the school year in June. The use of the hymn goes back to the earliest days of the school.*

347 LOVE DIVINE 8. 7. 8. 7. D.

GEORGE F. LE JEUNE, 1887

1 Love Di - vine, all loves ex - cel - ling, Joy of heaven, to earth come down:

Fix in us Thy hum - ble dwell - ing, All Thy faith - ful mer - cies crown:

Je - sus, Thou art all com - pas - sion, Pure, un - bound - ed love Thou art;

Vis - it us with Thy sal - va - tion, En - ter ev - ery trem-bling heart. A-MEN.

Copyright renewed, 1914, by L. Kendrick Le Jeune

2 Breathe, O breathe Thy loving Spirit
Into every troubled breast;
Let us all in Thee inherit,
Let us find the promised rest:
Take away the love of sinning;
Alpha and Omega be;
End of faith, as its Beginning,
Set our hearts at liberty.

3 Come, Almighty to deliver,
Let us all Thy life receive;
Suddenly return, and never,
Never more Thy temples leave.

Thee we would be always blessing,
Serve Thee as Thy hosts above,
Pray, and praise Thee, without ceasing,
Glory in Thy perfect love.

4 Finish, then, Thy new creation;
Pure and spotless let us be:
Let us see Thy great salvation
Perfectly restored in Thee;
Changed from glory into glory,
Till in heaven we take our place,
Till we cast our crowns before Thee,
Lost in wonder, love, and praise.

REV. CHARLES WESLEY, 1747: verse 2, lines 4 and 5 varied

For a Welsh setting of this hymn, see No. 408

Courage

A Collect for Steadfastness

We thank Thee, O God, for the long succession of Thy singers who have lifted Thy people's hearts and brightened their way with music; and we pray that we also may learn to greet the hard places of life with a song, and climbing steadfastly may enter into the fellowship of Thy white-robed choristers in heaven: through Jesus Christ our Lord. Amen.

348 BEECHER 8. 7. 8. 7. D. JOHN ZUNDEL, 1870

1 Cour - age, broth - er! do not stum - ble, Though thy path be dark as night;

There's a star to guide the hum - ble; "Trust in God, and do the right."

D.S.—Foot it brave - ly, strong or wea - ry; Trust in God, and do the right.

Let the road be rough and drear-y, And its end far out of sight, A - MEN.

2 Perish policy and cunning!
   Perish all that fears the light!
Whether losing, whether winning,
   Trust in God, and do the right.
Trust no party, sect, or faction;
   Trust no leaders in the fight;
But in every word and action
   Trust in God, and do the right.

3 Trust no lovely forms of passion,—
   Fiends may look like angels bright;
Trust no custom, school, or fashion:
   Trust in God, and do the right.

Simple rule, and safest guiding,
   Inward peace, and inward might,
Star upon our path abiding,—
   "Trust in God, and do the right."

4 Some will hate thee, some will love thee,
   Some will flatter, some will slight;
Cease from man, and look above thee:
   Trust in God, and do the right.
Courage, brother! do not stumble,
   Though thy path be dark as night;
There's a star to guide the humble:—
   "Trust in God, and do the right."

REV. NORMAN MACLEOD, 1857

349 VALOR 6. 5. 6. 5. 6. 6. 6. 5.   JOSIAH BOOTH, 1916

Voices in unison

1 Who would true val - or see, Let him come hith - er;

One here will con - stant be, Come wind, come weath - er.

Harmony

There's no dis - cour - age - ment Shall make him once re - lent

Unison

His first a - vowed in - tent To be a pil - grim. A - MEN.

Harmony

They that say such things declare plainly that they seek a country.—HEB. xi, 14

2 Who so beset him round
  With dismal stories,
Do but themselves confound;
  His strength the more is.
No lion can him fright,
He'll with a giant fight,
But he will have a right
  To be a pilgrim.

3 No goblin nor foul fiend
  Can daunt his spirit:
He knows he at the end
  Shall life inherit.
Then fancies fly away,
He'll fear not what men say,
He'll labor night and day
  To be a pilgrim.

JOHN BUNYAN, in *The Pilgrim's Progress: Second Part*, 1654

"*Greatheart*—'Then this was your Victory, even your Faith.'
"*Valiant*—'It was so, I believed and therefore came out, got into the Way, fought all that set themselves against me, and by believing am come to this Place'."—*The Pilgrim's Progress.*

Courage

350 ALFORD 7. 6. 8. 6. D.   Rev. John B. Dykes, 1875

1 Stand fast for Christ thy Saviour! Stand fast, what-e'er be-tide!

Keep thou the Faith, un-stained, un-shamed, By keep-ing at His side;

Be faith-ful, ev-er faith-ful, Wher-e'er thy lot be cast;

Stand fast for Christ, stand fast for Christ! Stand faith-ful to the last! A-MEN.

For a higher setting see No. 180

2 Stout-hearted like a soldier,
   Who never leaves the fight,
But meets the foeman face to face
   And meets him with his might,
So bear thee in thy battles
   Until the war be past;
Stand fast for Christ, stand fast for Christ,
Stand faithful to the last.

3 Stand fast for Christ thy Saviour,
   He once stood fast for thee,
And standeth still, and still shall stand
   For all eternity;
Be faithful O be faithful,
   To love so true, so vast;
Stand fast in Christ, stand fast in Christ,
Stand faithful to the last.

Rev. Walter J. Mathams, 1913

317

351 STAND UP FOR JESUS

7. 6. 7. 6. D. with Refrain

Adam Geibel, 1901

Voices in unison

1 Stand up, stand up for Je - sus, Ye sol - diers of the cross;

Lift high His roy - al ban - ner, It must not suf - fer loss:

From vic - tory un - to vic - tory His ar - my He shall lead,

Till ev - ery foe is van - quished, And Christ is Lord in - deed.

REFRAIN. *Harmony*

Stand up for Je - sus, Ye sol - diers of the cross; Lift
Stand up, stand up for Je - sus,

Courage

high His roy-al ban-ner; It must not, it must not suf-fer loss. A-MEN.

Copyright, 1901, by Geibel & Lehman. Assigned, 1906, to Adam Geibel Music Co.

2 Stand up, stand up for Jesus,
　The trumpet call obey;
Forth to the mighty conflict
　In this His glorious day:
Ye that are men now serve Him
　Against unnumbered foes;
Let courage rise with danger,
　And strength to strength oppose.

3 Stand up, stand up for Jesus,
　Stand in His strength alone;
The arm of flesh will fail you,
　Ye dare not trust your own:

Put on the gospel armor,
　Each piece put on with prayer;
Where duty calls, or danger,
　Be never wanting there.

4 Stand up, stand up for Jesus,
　The strife will not be long;
This day the noise of battle,
　The next the victor's song:
To him that overcometh
　A crown of life shall be;
He with the King of Glory
　Shall reign eternally.

Rev. GEORGE DUFFIELD, 1858

(Second Tune)

WEBB   7. 6. 7. 6. D.

GEORGE J. WEBB, 1837

May be sung in unison

1 Stand up, stand up for Je-sus, Ye sol-diers of the cross;

Lift high His roy-al ban-ner, It must not suf-fer loss:

FINE

D.S.—Till ev-ery foe is van-quished, And Christ is Lord in-deed.

D.S.

From vic-tory un-to vic-tory His ar-my He shall lead, A-MEN.

For a higher setting see No. 296

352 ALL SAINTS NEW C. M. D.

HENRY S. CUTLER, 1872

1 The Son of God goes forth to war, A king-ly crown to gain;

His blood-red ban-ner streams a-far: Who fol-lows in His train?

Who best can drink his cup of woe, Tri-um-phant o-ver pain,

Who pa-tient bears his cross be-low, He fol-lows in His train. A-MEN.

2 The martyr first, whose eagle eye
  Could pierce beyond the grave,
Who saw his Master in the sky,
  And called on Him to save:
Like Him, with pardon on his tongue
  In midst of mortal pain,
He prayed for them that did the wrong:
  Who follows in his train?

3 A glorious band, the chosen few
  On whom the Spirit came,
Twelve valiant saints, their hope they knew,
  And mocked the cross and flame:

They met the tyrant's brandished steel,
  The lion's gory mane;
They bowed their necks the death to feel:
  Who follows in their train?

4 A noble army, men and boys,
  The matron and the maid,
Around the Saviour's throne rejoice,
  In robes of light arrayed:
They climbed the steep ascent of heaven
  Through peril, toil, and pain:
O God, to us may grace be given
  To follow in their train.

Bishop REGINALD HEBER: published in 1827

320

Courage

(Second Tune)

CRUSADER C. M. D.

SAMUEL B. WHITNEY, 1889

1 The Son of God goes forth to war, A king-ly crown to gain;

His blood-red ban-ner streams a-far: Who fol-lows in His train?

REFRAIN

The Son of God* goes forth to war;*

Who best can drink his cup of woe, Tri-um-phant o-ver pain,

Who pa-tient bears his cross be-low, He fol-lows in His train. A-MEN.

* These words are to be repeated in every verse.

353 WATCHWORD 6. 5. 6. 5. D. with Refrain Sir John Stainer, 1875: slightly varied

1 For-ward! said the proph-et, Point-ing to the sea, March, ye roy-al
peo-ple, Through it fear-less-ly! What though foes are gath-ering,
Darken-ing all the plain, God's right arm ex-tend-ed, Shall their force re-strain.

Refrain

Roll back, rush-ing wa-ters! Stay thy waves, O sea!
That I may gain the bless-ed land My God has prom-ised me. A-men.

Courage

And the Lord said unto Moses, . . . speak unto the children of Israel, that they go forward.—Ex. xiv, 15

2 What though broad before you
    Spreads a tossing tide?
  God is strong and mighty
    Waters to divide.
  With my rod uplifted,
    Forward see me go;
  Back! ye hungry billows,
    Let the people through.—REF.

3 Dread not threatening billows
    Which like walls uprear;
  Dread not hosts pursuing,
    Armed with sword and spear.

  Wherefore now faint-hearted?
    Trust ye in your God!
  Look on me, your leader,
    With uplifted rod.—REF.

4 Soon shall all be gathered
    Safe on yonder shore;
  Foes who long have daunted,
    Ye shall see no more;
  Looking back, shall wonder
    What ye had to fear;
  Marvel how ye doubted
    When your help was near.—REF.

Rev. SABINE BARING-GOULD, 1874

354 PURFLEET   5. 5. 5. 5. 6. 5. 6. 5.

WILLIAM C. FILBY, 1875

1 Breast the wave, Chris-tian, When it is strong-est; Watch for day, Chris-tian,
2 Fight the fight, Chris-tian, Je - sus is o'er thee; Run the race, Chris-tian,
3 Lift the eye, Chris-tian, Just as it clos - eth; Raise the heart, Chris-tian,

When the night's long - est; On - ward and on - ward still Be thine en - deav - or;
Heaven is be - fore thee; He who hath prom-is - ed Fal - ter - eth nev - er;
Ere it re - pos - eth; Thee from the love of Christ Noth - ing shall sev - er;

The rest that re - main - eth, Will be for ev - er.
The love of e - ter - ni - ty Flows on for ev - er.
— And, when thy work is done, Praise Him for ev - er. A - MEN.

JOSEPH STAMMERS, 1830: verse 3, line 7, varied

323

355 MOZART L. M.

Arranged from the Kyrie in the *Twelfth Mass*
attributed to Mozart

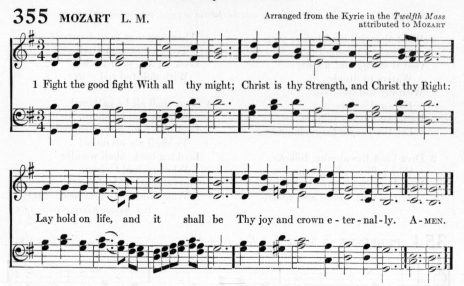

1 Fight the good fight With all thy might; Christ is thy Strength, and Christ thy Right:

Lay hold on life, and it shall be Thy joy and crown e - ter - nal - ly. A - MEN.

2 Run the straight race
Through God's good grace,
Lift up thine eyes, and seek His face;
Life with its way before us lies,
Christ is the Path, and Christ the Prize,

3 Cast care aside;
Upon thy Guide
Lean, and His mercy will provide;

Lean, and the trusting soul shall prove,
Christ is its Life, and Christ its Love.

4 Faint not, nor fear,
His arms are near;
He changeth not, and thou art dear;
Only believe, and thou shalt see
That Christ is All in all to thee.

Rev. JOHN S. B. MONSELL, 1863

SOLDIERS OF CHRIST S. M.

Rev. WILLIAM P. MERRILL, in *The Hymnal*, 1895

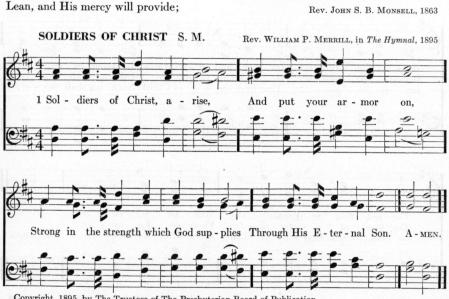

1 Sol - diers of Christ, a - rise, And put your ar - mor on,

Strong in the strength which God sup - plies Through His E - ter - nal Son. A - MEN.

Courage

356 STEWART 2. 10. 10. 10. C. HAROLD LOWDEN, 1915

1 Be strong! We are not here to play, to dream, to drift;
We have hard work to do and loads to lift; Shun not the strug-gle:
face it, 'tis God's gift. Be strong,...... be strong. A - MEN.
Be strong,

Copyright, 1915, by The Heidelberg Press

2   Be strong!
Say not the days are evil—who's to blame?
And fold the hands and acquiesce—O shame!
Stand up, speak out, and bravely, in God's Name.

3   Be strong!
It matters not how deep intrenched the wrong,
How hard the battle goes, the day, how long;
Faint not, fight on! To-morrow comes the song.

Rev. MALTBIE D. BABCOCK, 1901

357 (SOLDIERS OF CHRIST) S. M.

Put on the whole armor of God.—EPH. vi, 11

1 Soldiers of Christ, arise,
  And put your armor on;
Strong in the strength which God supplies
  Through His Eternal Son.

2 Strong in the Lord of Hosts,
  And in His mighty power,
Who in the strength of Jesus trusts
  Is more than conqueror.

3 Stand then in his great might,
  With all His strength endued;

And take, to arm you for the fight,
  The panoply of God.

4 From strength to strength go on,
  Wrestle, and fight, and pray;
Tread all the powers of darkness down,
  And win the well-fought day.

5 That having all things done,
  And all your conflicts past,
Ye may o'ercome, through Christ alone,
  And stand entire at last.

Rev. CHARLES WESLEY, 1749

325

A Collect for Hopefulness

Lighten our hearts, O God, with the music of Thy gospel, and grant us Thine aid in reaching forth unto the things which are before; that as we press toward the mark of our high calling we may win the friendship of the open Way and grow into the likeness of Him who hath called us; even Jesus Christ our Lord. Amen.

358 LANGRAN 10. 10. 10. 10.

JAMES LANGRAN, 1862

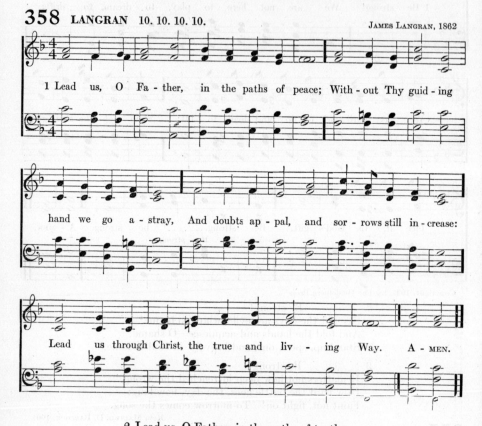

1 Lead us, O Fa-ther, in the paths of peace; With-out Thy guid-ing hand we go a-stray, And doubts ap-pal, and sor-rows still in-crease: Lead us through Christ, the true and liv-ing Way. A-MEN.

2 Lead us, O Father, in the paths of truth;
Unhelped by Thee, in error's maze we grope,
While passion stains and folly dims our youth,
And age comes on uncheered by faith and hope.

3 Lead us, O Father, in the paths of right;
Blindly we stumble when we walk alone,
Involved in shadows of a moral night;
Only with Thee we journey safely on.

4 Lead us, O Father, to Thy heavenly rest,
However rough and steep the path may be;
Through joy or sorrow, as Thou deemest best,
Until our lives are perfected in Thee.

WILLIAM H. BURLEIGH, 1868

359 GOSHEN 6. 5. 6. 5. D. Miss MARCHEL DAVIS, 1847

1 On our way re-joi-cing, As we home-ward move,

Heark-en to our prais-es, O Thou God of love.

Is there grief or sad-ness? Thou our Joy shalt be;

Is our sky be-cloud-ed? There is light in Thee. A-MEN.

Rejoice in the Lord alway.—PHIL. iv, 4

2 If with honest-hearted
   Love for God and man,
Day by day Thou find us
   Doing all we can,
Thou who giv'st the seed-time
   Wilt give large increase,
Crown the head with blessings,
   Fill the heart with peace.

3 On our way rejoicing
   Gladly let us go;
Victor is our Leader,
   Vanquished is the foe:

Christ without, our safety;
   Christ within, our joy;
Who, if we be faithful,
   Can our hope destroy?

4 Unto God the Father
   Joyful songs we sing;
Unto God the Saviour
   Thankful hearts we bring;
Unto God the Spirit
   Bow we and adore;
On our way rejoicing
   Ever, evermore.

Rev. JOHN S. B. MONSELL, 1863, 1873: lines 6 and 8 varied

327

360 BETHANY 6. 4. 6. 4. 6. 6. 6. 4.

LOWELL MASON, 1856;
apparently based on "Oft in the stilly night"

1 Near-er, my God, to Thee, Near-er to Thee! E'en though it be a cross

That rais-eth me; Still all my song shall be, Near-er, my God, to Thee,

Near-er, my God, to Thee, Near-er to Thee! A-MEN.

2 Though like the wanderer,
   The sun gone down,
Darkness be over me,
   My rest a stone,
Yet in my dreams I'd be
Nearer, my God, to Thee,
   Nearer to Thee!

3 There let the way appear,
   Steps unto heaven,
All that Thou sendest me
   In mercy given,
Angels to beckon me
Nearer, my God, to Thee,
   Nearer to Thee!

4 Then, with my waking thoughts
   Bright with Thy praise,
Out of my stony griefs
   Bethel I'll raise;
So by my woes to be
Nearer, my God, to Thee.
   Nearer to Thee!

5 Or if on joyful wing
   Cleaving the sky,
Sun, moon, and stars forgot,
   Upward I fly,
Still all my song shall be,
Nearer, my God, to Thee,
   Nearer to Thee!

Mrs. SARAH F. ADAMS, 1841: the fifth line varied

328

Hope

361 ST. EDMUND 6. 4. 6. 4. 6. 6. 6. 4.

Sir ARTHUR SULLIVAN'S setting of "I'm but a stranger here," 1872

1 Draw Thou my soul, O Christ, Clos-er to Thine; Breathe in-to ev-ery wish Thy will di-vine: Raised my low self a-bove, Won by Thy death-less love, Ev-er, O Christ, through mine Let Thy life shine. A-MEN.

2 Lead forth my soul, O Christ,
  One with Thine own,
Joyful to follow Thee
  Through paths unknown.
In Thee my strength renew;
Give me Thy work to do;
Through me Thy truth be shown,
  Thy love made known.

3 Not for myself alone
  May my prayer be;
Lift Thou Thy world, O Christ,
  Closer to Thee!
Cleanse it from guilt and wrong,
Teach it salvation's song,
Till earth, as heaven, fulfil
  God's holy will.

4 Nearer to Thee, O Christ,
  Nearer to Thee!
Till we in Thy dear face
  God's glory see:
Heavenward our hopes ascend,
Saviour and Lord and Friend;
O draw us all to Thee,
  Nearer to Thee!

LUCY LARCOM, 1892: verse 3, lines 7 and 8, varied

BETHANY *and* ST. EDMUND *are interchangeable*

362 MOUNT VERNON C. M. D.

CHARLES S. BROWN, 1906

1 I feel the winds of God to-day; To-day my sail I lift,

Though heav-y oft with drench-ing spray, And torn with man-y a rift:

If hope but light the wa-ter's crest, And Christ my barque will use,

I'll seek the seas at His be-hest And brave an-oth-er cruise. A-MEN.

Copyright, 1906, by Charles S. Brown. Used by permission

2 It is the wind of God that dries
  My vain regretful tears,
Until with braver thoughts shall rise
  The purer, brighter years:
If cast on shores of selfish ease
  Or pleasure I should be,
Lord, let me feel Thy freshening breeze
  And I'll put back to sea.

3 If ever I forget Thy love
  And how that love was shown,
Lift high the blood-red flag above;
  It bears Thy Name alone.
Great Pilot of my onward way,
  Thou wilt not let me drift:
I feel the winds of God to-day,
  To-day my sail I lift.

Of unknown date and authorship

363 GABRIEL C. M. D.

GOTTFRIED W. FINK, 1842

1 Send forth, O God, Thy light and truth, And let them lead me still,

Un - daunt - ed, in the paths of right, Up to Thy ho - ly hill:

Then to Thy al - tar will I spring, And in my God re - joice;

And praise shall tune the trem-bling string, And grat - i - tude my voice. A - MEN.

A PARAPHRASE OF PSALM XLIII

2 O why, my soul, art thou cast down?
    Within me why distressed?
Thy hopes the God of grace shall crown;
    He yet shall make thee blessed:
To Him, my never-failing Friend,
    I bow, and kiss the rod;
To Him shall thanks and praise ascend,
    My Saviour and my God.

JOHN QUINCY ADAMS, sixth President of the United States, 1841

NOTE—*Mr. Adams, in 1841, placed in his pastor's hand the MS. of a complete metrical version of the Psalms with some hymns.*

364 DISCIPLE 8. 7. 8. 7. D.

In Rev. Joshua Leavitt's *Christian Lyre*, 1831

1 Jesus, I my cross have taken, All to leave, and follow Thee;
Destitute, despised, forsaken, Thou from hence my All shalt be:
Perish every fond ambition, All I've sought, or hoped, or known;
Yet how rich is my condition, God and heaven are still my own. A-MEN.

2 Man may trouble and distress me,
 'Twill but drive me to Thy breast;
Life with trials hard may press me,
 Heaven will bring me sweeter rest:
O 'tis not in grief to harm me
 While Thy love is left to me;
O 'twere not in joy to charm me,
 Were that joy unmixed with Thee.

3 Take, my soul, thy full salvation,
 Rise o'er sin and fear and care;
Joy to find in every station
 Something still to do or bear;

Think what Spirit dwells within thee,
 What a Father's smile is thine,
What a Saviour died to win thee:
 Child of heaven, shouldst thou repine?

4 Haste then on from grace to glory,
 Armed by faith, and winged by prayer;
Heaven's eternal day's before thee,
 God's own hand shall guide thee there.
Soon shall close thy earthly mission;
 Swift shall pass thy pilgrim days;
Hope soon change to glad fruition,
 Faith to sight, and prayer to praise.

Rev. Henry F. Lyte, 1824 (his text of 1833)

365 SUNSHINE 7. 6. 7. 6. D. (Trochaic)

Arranged from a German melody

1 Look - ing up - ward ev - ery day, Sun - shine on our fa - ces;

Press - ing on - ward, ev - ery day, Toward the heaven - ly pla - ces.

Grow - ing ev - ery day in awe, For Thy Name is ho - ly;

Learn - ing ev - ery day to love With a love more low - ly. A - MEN.

Alternative tune, ST. KEVIN, No. 154

2 Walking every day more close
  To our Elder Brother;
Growing every day more true
  Unto one another.
Every day more gratefully
  Kindnesses receiving;
Every day more readily
  Injuries forgiving.

3 Leaving every day behind
  Something which might hinder;
Running swifter every day,
  Growing purer, kinder.
Lord, so pray we every day;
  Hear us in Thy pity,
That we enter in at last
  To the holy city.

MARY BUTLER, 1881

366 ST. THERESA 6. 5. 6. 5. 12 ll.

Sir ARTHUR SULLIVAN, 1874

1 Bright-ly gleams our ban-ner, Point-ing to the sky, Wa-ving on Christ's
sol-diers To their home on high. Marching through the des-ert, Glad-ly thus we pray,
Still with hearts u-ni-ted, Sing-ing on our way.

REFRAIN

Bright-ly gleams our ban-ner, Point-ing to the sky, Wa-ving on Christ's soldiers To their home on high. A-MEN.

2 Jesus, Lord and Master,
   At Thy sacred feet,
Here, with hearts rejoicing,
   See Thy children meet.
Often have we left Thee,
   Often gone astray;
Keep us, mighty Saviour,
   In the narrow way.
      Brightly gleams, *etc.*

3 Pattern of our childhood,
   Once Thyself a child,
Make our childhood holy,
   Pure, and meek, and mild.
In the hour of danger
   Whither can we flee.
Save to Thee, dear Saviour,
   Only unto Thee?
      Brightly gleams, *etc.*

334

4 All our days direct us,
  In the way we go;
Crown us still victorious
  Over every foe:
Bid Thine angels shield us
  When the storm-clouds lower;
Pardon Thou and save us
  In the last dread hour.
    Brightly gleams, *etc.*

5 Then with saints and angels
  May we join above,
Offering prayers and praises
  At Thy throne of love.
When the march is over,
  Then come rest and peace,
Jesus in His beauty,
  Songs that never cease.
    Brightly gleams, *etc.*

Rev. THOMAS J. POTTER, 1860: recast in MORRELL and How's
Psalms and Hymns, 1867, and S. P. C. K. *Psalms and Hymns*, 1869

367 STAR OF MORN AND EVEN 6. 6. 5. 5. 5. 5.   JAMES TILLEARD, 1868

Moderately fast

1 Star of morn and e - ven, Sun of heav - en's heav - en,
Sav - iour high and dear, Toward us turn Thine ear;
Through what - e'er may come, Thou canst lead us home. A - MEN.

Until the day dawn, and the day star arise in your hearts.—1 PETER i, 19

2 Though the gloom be grievous,
  Those we leant on leave us,
    Though the coward heart
    Quit its proper part,
    Though the tempter come,
    Thou wilt lead us home.

3 Saviour pure and holy,
  Lover of the lowly,
    Sign us with Thy sign,

Take our hands in Thine,
Take our hands and come,
Lead Thy children home.

4 Star of morn and even,
  Shine on us from heaven;
    From Thy glory-throne
    Hear Thy very own:
    Lord and Saviour, come,
    Lead us to our home.

FRANCIS T. PALGRAVE, 1862

368 SAWLEY C. M.

James Walch, 1860

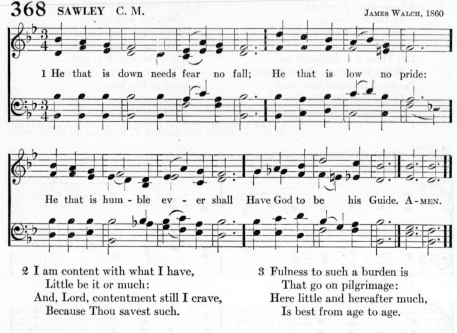

1 He that is down needs fear no fall; He that is low no pride:
He that is hum-ble ev-er shall Have God to be his Guide. A-MEN.

2 I am content with what I have,
   Little be it or much:
And, Lord, contentment still I crave,
   Because Thou savest such.

3 Fulness to such a burden is
   That go on pilgrimage:
Here little and hereafter much,
   Is best from age to age.

369 LAMBETH C. M.

William Schulthes, 1871

1 Let the Most Bless-ed be my Guide, If't be His bless-ed will,
Un-to His gate, in-to His fold, Up to His ho-ly hill. A-MEN.

2 And let Him never suffer me
   To swerve or turn aside
From His free grace and holy ways,
   Whate'er shall me betide.

3 And let Him gather them of mine
   That I have left behind.
Lord, make them pray they may be Thine,
   With all their heart and mind.

Both of these hymns appeared in
John Bunyan's *The Pilgrim's Progress: Second Part*, 1684

370 LYNDHURST 6. 5. 6. 5. D.

In *Church Praise*, 1883 ("composer unknown")

1 Pur - er yet and pur - er I would be in mind,
Dear - er yet and dear - er Ev - ery du - ty find;
Ho - ping still, and trust - ing God with - out a fear,
Pa - tient - ly be - liev - ing He will make all clear; A - MEN.

2 Calmer yet and calmer
  In the hours of pain;
Surer yet and surer
  Peace at last to gain;
Bearing still and doing,
  To my lot resigned,
And to right subduing
  Heart and will and mind;

3 Higher yet and higher,
  Out of clouds and night,
Nearer yet and nearer
  Rising to the light,—

Light serene and holy,
  Where my soul may rest,
Purified and lowly,
  Sanctified and blest;

4 Swifter yet and swifter
  Ever onward run,
Firmer yet and firmer
  Step as I go on;—
Oft these earnest longings
  Swell within my breast;
Yet their inner meaning
  Ne'er can be expressed.

In *Iphigenia in Tauris, with original Poems*, 1851: slightly varied

The Spiritual Life

371 **PILOT** 7. 7. 7. 7. 7. 7. JOHN E. GOULD, 1871

FINE

1 Je - sus, Sav - iour, pi - lot me O - ver life's tem-pest-uous sea;

D.C.—Chart and com - pass came from Thee: Je - sus, Sav - iour, pi - lot me.

Un-known waves be - fore me roll, Hi - ding rock and treacherous shoal; A - MEN.

2 As a mother stills her child,
  Thou canst hush the ocean wild;
  Boisterous waves obey Thy will
  When Thou say'st to them, "Be still."
  Wondrous Sovereign of the sea,
  Jesus, Saviour, pilot me.

3 When at last I near the shore,
  And the fearful breakers roar
  'Twixt me and the peaceful rest,
  Then, while leaning on Thy breast,
  May I hear Thee say to me,
  "Fear not, I will pilot thee."

REV. EDWARD HOPPER, 1871

HANFORD 8. 8. 8. 4. Sir ARTHUR SULLIVAN, 1871

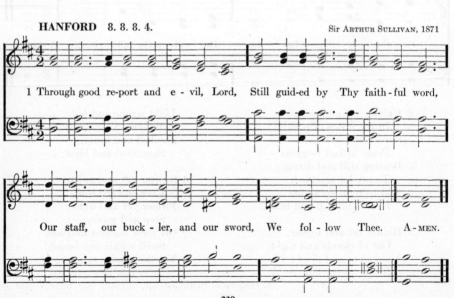

1 Through good re-port and e - vil, Lord, Still guid-ed by Thy faith-ful word,

Our staff, our buck - ler, and our sword, We fol - low Thee. A - MEN.

Hope

372 CHRISTMAS C. M. From "Non vi piacque" in Händel's *Siroe*, 1728

1 A - wake, my soul, stretch ev - ery nerve,
And press with vig - or on! A heaven - ly race de - mands thy zeal,
And an im - mor - tal crown, And an im - mor - tal crown. A - MEN.

I press toward the mark for the prize of the high calling of God in Christ Jesus.—PHILL. iii, 14

2 A cloud of witnesses around
   Hold thee in full survey:
Forget the steps already trod,
   And onward urge thy way.

3 'Tis God's all-animating voice
   That calls thee from on high;
'Tis His own hand presents the prize
   To thine aspiring eye:

4 That prize with peerless glories bright,
   Which shall new lustre boast,
When victors' wreaths and monarchs' gems
   Shall blend in common dust.

5 Blest Saviour, introduced by Thee,
   Have I my race begun;
And, crowned with victory, at Thy feet
   I'll lay my honors down.

Rev. PHILIP DODDRIDGE, published in 1755

373 (HANFORD) 8. 8. 8. 4.

1 Through good report and evil, Lord,
   Still guided by Thy faithful word,
Our staff, our buckler and our sword,
   We follow Thee.

2 In silence of the lonely night,
   In the full glow of day's clear light,
Through life's strange windings, dark or
   We follow Thee.   [bright,

3 Strengthened by Thee we forward go,
   'Mid smile or scoff of friend or foe,

Through pain or ease, through joy or woe,
   We follow Thee.

4 O Master, point Thou out the way,
   Nor suffer Thou our steps to stray;
Then in the path that leads to day
   We follow Thee.

5 Thou hast passed on before our face
   Thy footsteps on the way we trace:
O keep us, aid us by Thy grace;
   We follow Thee.

Rev. HORATIUS BONAR, 1866

374 BEATITUDO C. M.

Rev. John B. Dykes, 1875

1 Search-er of hearts, from mine e-rase All thoughts that should not be,

And in its deep re-cess-es trace My grat-i-tude to Thee. A-MEN.

2 Hearer of prayer, O guide aright
Each word and deed of mine;
Life's battle teach me how to fight,
And be the victory Thine.

3 Giver of all—for every good
In the Redeemer came—

For raiment, shelter, and for food,
I thank Thee in His Name.

4 Father, and Son, and Holy Ghost,
Thou glorious Three in One,
Thou knowest best what I need most,
And let Thy will be done.

George P. Morris, 1838

375 (BEATITUDO) C. M.

And Enoch walked with God.—Gen. v, 24

1 O for a closer walk with God,
A calm and heavenly frame,
A light to shine upon the road
That leads me to the Lamb!

2 What peaceful hours I once enjoyed!
How sweet their memory still!
But they have left an aching void
The world can never fill.

3 Return, O Holy Dove; return,
Sweet Messenger of rest:

I hate the sins that made Thee mourn,
And drove Thee from my breast.

4 The dearest idol I have known,
Whate'er that idol be,
Help me to tear it from Thy throne,
And worship only Thee.

5 So shall my walk be close with God,
Calm and serene my frame;
So purer light shall mark the road
That leads me to the Lamb.

William Cowper, 1769

376 (VITTEL WOODS) C. M.

"A Melody of Love and Life"

1 O Love that lights the eastern sky
And shrouds the evening rest,
From out whose hand the swallows fly,
Within whose heart they nest!

2 O life, content beneath the blue!
Or, if God will the gray,
Then tranquil yet, till light breaks through
To melt the mist away!

3 O death that sails so close to shore
At twilight! From my gate
I scan the darkening sea once more,
And for its message wait.

4 What lies beyond the afterglow?
To life's new dawn how far?
As if an answer, spoken low,
Love lights the evening star.

Rev. Louis F. Benson, 1923

Hope

377 ST. STEPHEN C. M.

Rev. WILLIAM JONES, 1789

1 God moves in a mys-te-rious way His won-ders to per-form;
He plants His foot-steps in the sea, And rides up-on the storm. A-MEN.

2 Deep hidden in unfathomed mines
   Of never-failing skill
He treasures up His bright designs,
   And works His sovereign will.

3 Ye fearful saints, fresh courage take;
   The clouds ye so much dread
Are big with mercy, and shall break
   In blessings on your head.

4 Judge not the Lord by feeble sense,
   But trust Him for His grace;

Behind a frowning providence
   He hides a smiling face.

5 His purposes will ripen fast,
   Unfolding every hour;
The bud may have a bitter taste,
   But sweet will be the flower.

6 Blind unbelief is sure to err,
   And scan His work in vain;
God is His own Interpreter,
   And He will make it plain.

WILLIAM COWPER, 1772 or 1773: with the fifth line varied

NOTE—*For actual use in singing it may be permissible to alter here Cowper's line, "Deep in unfathomable mines." Wrong in rhythm and almost unpronounceable, it has hitherto deterred musicians from attempting an adequate setting of the hymn.*

VITTEL WOODS C. M.

BRADLEY KEELER, 1924

1 O Love that lights the east-ern sky And shrouds the eve-ning rest,
From out whose hand the swal-lows fly, With-in whose heart they nest! A-MEN.

Immortal Life

We lift up our eyes, O God, unto the hills where abideth for ever the life we have hidden in Christ, and in our songs we celebrate the place He hath gone to prepare: Beseeching Thee to illumine our daily tasks with the pure light of heaven, that by serving Thee more gladly now we may be fitted for the service that hath no end. Through Jesus Christ our Lord. Amen.

378 ABENDS L. M.

HERBERT S. OAKELEY, 1874

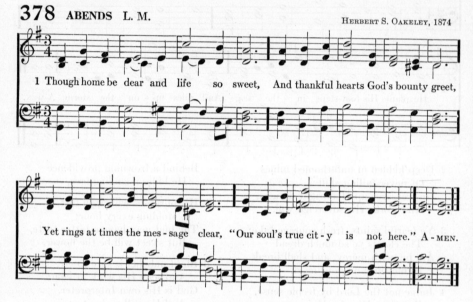

1 Though home be dear and life so sweet, And thankful hearts God's bounty greet,

Yet rings at times the mes - sage clear, "Our soul's true cit - y is not here." A - MEN.

But the things which are not seen are eternal.—2 COR. iv, 18

2 'Mid changing scenes of joy and pain,
There comes again and yet again
A vision of the changeless rest
Where God's own face shall make us blest.

3 And through the web of earthly life,
Its grief and gladness, work and strife,
There runs a thread divine to tie
The life of time to that on high.

4 O help us, Lord, with thankful heart
To grasp each day's eternal part,
And build a home on that calm height
Where saints do walk with Thee in white.

Mrs. ELLA S. ARMITAGE: printed in 1894: verse 3, line 4, varied

379 (DOLOMITE CHANT) 6. 4. 6. 4. 6. 6.

When thou art bidden, go and sit down in the lowest room.—ST. LUKE xiv, 10

1 Give me the lowest place; Not that I dare
   Ask for that lowest place, But Thou
      hast died
That I might live and share
   Thy glory by Thy side.

2 Give me the lowest place; Or if for me
   That lowest place too high, Make one
      more low
Where I may sit and see
   My God and love Thee so.

CHRISTINA G. ROSSETTI, July 25, 1863

Immortal Life

380 ACHNASHEEN 9. 8. 10. 5.

CHARLES H. LLOYD, 1903

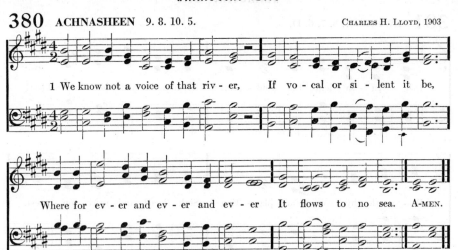

1 We know not a voice of that riv - er, If vo - cal or si - lent it be,

Where for ev - er and ev - er and ev - er It flows to no sea. A-MEN.

And he showed me a pure river of water of life, clear as crystal, proceeding out of the throne of God and of the Lamb.—REV. xxii, 1

2 More deep than the seas is that river,
 More full than their manifold tides,
Where for ever and ever and ever
 It flows and abides.

3 Pure gold is the bed of that river,
 (The gold of that land is the best),
Where for ever and ever and ever
 It flows on at rest.

4 O goodly the banks of that river,
 O goodly the fruits that they bear,
Where for ever and ever and ever
 It flows and is fair.

5 For lo! on each bank of that river,
 The tree that is life-giving grows,
Where for ever and ever and ever
 The pure river flows.

CHRISTINA G. ROSSETTI, before 1893: with the rhythm of one line revised

DOLOMITE CHANT 6. 4. 6. 4. 6. 6.

An Austrian melody: harmonized by J. T. COOPER

1 { Give me the low - est place; Not that I dare } That I might
 { Ask for that low - est place, But Thou hast died }

live and share Thy glo - ry by Thy side.......... A - MEN.

For a higher setting see No. 97

343

Immortal Life

381 EWING 7.6.7.6.D.

ALEXANDER EWING, 1853

1 Je - ru - sa - lem the gold - en, With milk and hon - ey blest!
Be - neath thy con - tem - pla - tion Sink heart and voice op - prest.
I know not, O I know not, What joys a - wait us there;
What ra - dian - cy of glo - ry, What bliss be - yond com - pare. A-MEN.

URBS SYON AUREA, PATRIA LACTEA, CIVE DECORA

2 They stand, those halls of Zion,
　All jubilant with song,
And bright with many an angel
　And all the martyr throng.
The Prince is ever in them,
　The daylight is serene;
The pastures of the blessèd
　Are decked in glorious sheen.

3 There is the throne of David;
　And there, from care released,
The song of them that triumph,
　The shout of them that feast;

And they who with their Leader
　Have conquered in the fight,
For ever and for ever
　Are clad in robes of white.

4 O sweet and blessèd country
　The home of God's elect!
O sweet and blessèd country
　That eager hearts expect!
Jesus, in mercy bring us
　To that dear land of rest;
Who art, with God the Father,
　And Spirit, ever blest.

Arranged from Rev. JOHN M. NEALE's translation, 1851,
of BERNARD of Cluny's *De Contemptu Mundi*, c. 1145

344

Immortal Life

(Second Tune)

URBS BEATA   7. 6. 7. 6. D. with Refrain

GEORGE F. LE JEUNE, 1887

1 Je - ru - sa - lem the gold - en, With milk and hon - ey blest!

Be - neath thy con - tem - pla - tion Sink heart and voice op - prest.

I know not, O I know not, What joys a - wait us there;

What ra - dian - cy of glo - ry, What bliss be - yond com - pare.

REFRAIN

Je - ru - sa - lem the gold - en!

Je - ru - sa - lem the gold - en, With milk and hon - ey blest!

Be - neath thy con - tem - pla - tion Sink heart and voice op - prest. A - MEN.

Org.

382 MATERNA C. M. D.

SAMUEL A. WARD, 1882

1 O Moth-er dear, Je-ru-sa-lem, When shall I come to thee?
When shall my la-bors have an end? Thy joys when shall I see?
O hap-py har-bor of the saints! O sweet and pleas-ant soil!
In thee no sor-row may be found, No grief, no care, no toil. A-MEN.

For a lower setting see No. 276

2 No dampish mist is seen in thee,
    No cold, nor darksome night;
  There every soul shines as the sun;
    There God Himself gives light;
  There lust and lucre cannot dwell;
    There envy bears no sway;
  There is no hunger, heat, nor cold,
    But pleasure every way.

3 Thy gardens and thy gallant walks
    Continually are green,
  There grow such sweet and pleasant
    As nowhere else are seen.   [flowers

Quite through the streets, with silver
    The flood of life doth flow;   [sound,
  Upon whose banks on every side
    The wood of life doth grow.

4 There trees for evermore bear fruit,
    And evermore do spring;
  There evermore the angels sit,
    And evermore do sing.
  Jerusalem! Jerusalem!
    God grant I once may see
  Thy endless joys, and of the same
    Partaken aye may be!

"F. B. P.," in a MS. of late 16th cent.: slightly varied

346

Immortal Life

383 O PARADISE 8. 6. 8. 6. 6. 6. 6. 6.   Sir Joseph Barnby, 1866

1 O Par - a - dise! O Par - a - dise! Who would not win thy rest?

Who would not seek the hap - py land Where they that loved are blest?

Refrain
Where loy - al hearts and true

Where loy - - - - al hearts and true Stand ev - er in the light,
Where loy - - al

All rap - ture through and through, In God's most ho - ly sight. A - men.

Alternative tune, GOLDEN No. 206

The paradise of God.—Rev. ii, 7

2 O Paradise! O Paradise!
 I want to sin no more;
I want to be as pure on earth
 As on thy spotless shore;—REF.

3 O Paradise! O Paradise!
 When faith is growing cold
The doubting heart that thinks of thee
 Finds shelter in that fold;—REF

4 Lord Jesus, King of Paradise,
 O keep us in Thy love
And fit us for that holy land
 Of perfect peace above;—REF.

Rev. Frederick W. Faber, 1862: recast for this book

Immortal Life

HENRY SMART, 1868

1 Hark! hark, my soul! An-gel-ic songs are swell-ing O'er earth's green fields and o-cean's wave-beat shore: How sweet the truth those bless-ed strains are tell-ing Of that new life when sin shall be no more! An-gels of Je-sus, an-gels of light, Sing-ing to wel-come the pil-grims of the night! A-MEN.

2 Onward we go, for still we hear them singing,
   "Come, weary souls, for Jesus bids you come,"
   And through the dark, its echoes sweetly ringing,
   The music of the gospel leads us home.—REF.

3 Far, far away, like bells at evening pealing,
   The voice of Jesus sounds o'er land and sea;
   And laden souls, by thousands meekly stealing,
   Kind Shepherd, turn their weary steps to Thee.—REF.

4 Angels, sing on, your faithful watches keeping,
   Sing us sweet fragments of the songs above;
   Till morning's joy shall end the night of weeping,
   And life's long shadows break in cloudless love.—REF.

Rev. FREDERICK W. FABER, 1854: verse 4, lines 3 and 4, varied

Immortal Life

385 **RUTHERFORD** 7. 6. 7. 6. 7. 6. 7. 5.

Adapted from CHRÉTIEN URHAN, 1834,
by EDWARD F. RIMBAULT, 1867

1 The sands of time are sink-ing, The dawn of heav-en breaks,

The sum-mer morn I've sighed for, The fair sweet morn a-wakes;

Dark, dark hath been the mid-night, But day-spring is at hand,

And glo-ry, glo-ry dwell-eth In Em-man-uel's land. A-MEN.

2 The King there in His beauty
   Without a veil is seen;
It were a well-spent journey
   Though seven deaths lay between:
The Lamb with His fair army
   Doth on Mount Zion stand,
And glory, glory dwelleth
   In Emmanuel's land.

3 O Christ, He is the Fountain
   The deep sweet Well of love!
The streams on earth I've tasted
   More deep I'll drink above:

There to an ocean fulness
   His mercy doth expand,
And glory, glory dwelleth
   In Emmanuel's land.

4 With mercy and with judgment
   My web of time He wove,
And aye the dews of sorrow
   Were lustred by His love:
I'll bless the hand that guided,
   I'll bless the heart that planned,
When throned where glory dwelleth
   In Emmanuel's land.

From Mrs. ANNE R. COUSIN's
"The Last Words of Rev. Samuel Rutherford," 1857

Immortal Life

386 REDEMPTION 8. 6. 8. 6. 8. 8. 8. P. R. RICHARDS, 1881

1 Je - ru - sa - lem is built of gold, Of crys - tal, pearl, and gem:

O fair thy lus - tres man - i - fold, Thou fair Je - ru - sa - lem!

Thy cit - i - zens who walk in white Have naught to do with day or night,

And drink the riv - er of de - light. A - MEN.

The holy city, new Jerusalem.—REV. xxi, 2

2 Jerusalem makes melody
   For simple joy of heart;
An organ of full compass she,
   One-tuned through every part:
While not to day or night belong
Her matins and her evensong,
The one thanksgiving of her throng.

3 Jerusalem a garden is,
   A garden of delight;
Leaf, flower, and fruit, make fair her trees,
   Which see not day or night:

Beside her river clear and calm
The tree of life grows with the palm,
For triumph and for food and balm.

4 Jerusalem, where song nor gem
   Nor fruit nor waters cease,
God bring us to Jerusalem,
   God bring us home in peace:
The strong who stand, the weak who fall,
The first and last, the great and small,
Home one by one, home one and all.

CHRISTINA G. ROSSETTI, before 1882

350

Immortal Life

387 PATMOS 7. 6. 8. 6. D.

HENRY J. STORER, 1891

1 I heard a sound of voi - ces A - round the great white throne,

With harp - ers harp - ing on their harps To Him who sat there - on;

"Sal - va - tion, glo - ry, hon - or," I heard the song a - rise,

As through the courts of heaven it rolled In won - drous har - mo - nies. A - MEN.

Alternative tune, ALFORD No. 180

2 From every clime and kindred,
　And nations from afar,
As serried ranks returning home
　In triumph from a war,
I heard the saints upraising,
　The myriad hosts among,
In praise of Him who died, and lives,
　Their one glad triumph-song.

3 I saw the holy city,
　The New Jerusalem,
Come down from heaven a Bride adorned
　With jewelled diadem:

And there His servants serve Him,
　And, life's long battle o'er,
Enthroned with Him, their Saviour, King,
　They reign for evermore.

4 O Lamb of God who reignest,
　Thou Bright and Morning Star,
Whose glory lightens that new earth
　Which now we see from far;
O worthy Judge Eternal,
　When Thou dost bid us come,
Then open wide the gates of pearl,
　And call Thy servants home.

Rev. GODFREY THRING, 1886: with the third verse arranged

351

Immortal Life

388 SHINING SHORE 8. 7. 8. 7. D.

GEORGE F. ROOT, 1859

1 My days are gli - ding swift-ly by, And I, a pil - grim stran - ger,
Would not de - tain them as they fly, Those hours of toil and dan - ger:

REFRAIN

For O we stand on Jor - dan's strand, Our friends are pass - ing o - ver;
And, just be - fore, the shi - ning shore We may al - most dis - cov - er. A - MEN.

2 We'll gird our loins, my brethren dear,
  Our distant home discerning;
  Our absent Lord has left us word,
  "Let every lamp be burning."—REF.

3 Should coming days be cold and dark,
  We need not cease our singing;
  That perfect rest naught can molest,
  Where golden harps are ringing.—REF.

4 Let sorrow's rudest tempest blow,
  Each cord on earth to sever;
  Our King says, "Come," and there's our home,
  For ever, O for ever.—REF.

Rev. DAVID NELSON, 1835

NOTE—*The composer, in his "Story of a Musical Life," narrates the spontaneous way in which the melody sang itself as he read the verses in a newspaper, and seeks in vain to probe the secret of "the mysterious life" in his song. It was no doubt this naïveté and unconsciousness of art that gave his composition something of the perennial charm of folk-song.*

352

Immortal Life

389 MEDITATION C. M.

JOHN H. GOWER, 1890

1 There is a land of pure de-light, Where saints im-mor-tal reign;

In-fin-ite day ex-cludes the night, And pleas-ures ban-ish pain. A-MEN.

Copyright by John H. Gower

And Moses went up . . . to the top of Pisgah. And the Lord showed him all the land.—DEUT. xxxix, 1

2 There everlasting spring abides,
　And never-withering flowers;
　Death, like a narrow sea, divides
　This heavenly land from ours.

3 Sweet fields beyond the swelling flood
　Stand dressed in living green;
　So to the Jews old Canaan stood,
　While Jordan rolled between

4 But timorous mortals start and shrink
　To cross this narrow sea;
　And linger, shivering, on the brink,
　And fear to launch away.

5 O could we make our doubts remove,
　Those gloomy doubts that rise,
　And see the Canaan that we love
　With unbeclouded eyes;

6 Could we but climb where Moses stood,
　And view the landscape o'er,
　Not Jordan's stream, nor death's cold flood,
　Should fright us from the shore.

Rev. ISAAC WATTS, 1707

WILTSHIRE C. M.

Sir GEORGE T. SMART, c. 1795

1 There is a land of pure de-light, Where saints im-mor-tal reign;

In-fin-ite day ex-cludes the night, And pleas-ures ban-ish pain. A-MEN.

" There are some of us who can never look upon a green field with the spring sun on it without this hymn coming to us as a whisper from heaven."—J. BRIERLY.

353

Occasional Hymns
The Old and the New Year

A Collect for the Passing Year

We call to remembrance, O God, Thy loving-kindness through the year that is past, Thy tender mercies that have been ever of old. We thank Thee for anything we have been enabled to do to Thy praise, and pray Thee to forgive our manifold offenses and shortcomings, and to remember them no more against us. Make us deeply sensible of the passing of the years and the uncertainties of our mortal life, that we may do with all our present strength such duties as Thou hast intrusted to our hands. And grant that, in humble sincerity and cheerful hope, we may serve Thee more faithfully in such years as may remain: through Jesus Christ our Lord. Amen.

390 VALENTIA C. M.

Arranged from T. M. EBERWEIN, (1775–1831)
by GEORGE KINGSLEY, 1853

1 Break, new-born year, on glad eyes break, Me - lo - dious voi - ces move;
On, roll - ing time; thou canst not make The Fa - ther cease to love. A - MEN.

2 The parted year had wingèd feet;
The Saviour still doth stay:
The new year comes; but, Spirit sweet,
Thou goest not away.

3 Our hearts in tears may oft run o'er;
But, Lord, Thy smile still beams:
Our sins are swelling evermore,
But pardoning grace still streams.

4 Lord, from this year more service win,
More glory, more delight:

O make its hours less sad with sin,
Its days with Thee more bright.

5 Then we may bless its precious things
If earthly cheer should come,
Or gladsome mount on angel wings
If Thou wouldst take us home.

6 O golden then the hours must be;
The year must needs be sweet;
Yes, Lord, with happy melody
Thine opening grace we greet.

THOMAS H. GILL, 1855

391 (ST. BEES) 7. 7. 7. 7.

1 For Thy mercy and Thy grace,
Faithful through another year,
Hear our song of thankfulness;
Father, and Redeemer, hear.

2 Lo! our sins on Thee we cast,
Thee, our perfect Sacrifice;
And, forgetting all the past,
Press towards our glorious prize.

3 In our weakness and distress,
Rock of strength, be Thou our Stay;

In the pathless wilderness
Be our true and living Way.

4 Keep us faithful, keep us pure,
Keep us evermore Thine own;
Help, O help us to endure;
Fit us for the promised crown.

5 So with mingled prayer and praise
Would we seek the heavenly Friend
Who has loved us all our days
And will guide us to the end.

Verses 1-4 by Rev. HENRY DOWNTON, 1841:
verse 5 written for this book

The Old and the New Year

392 **MOZART L. M.**

Arranged from the "Kyrie" in the *Twelfth Mass*
attributed to MOZART

1 Ring out, wild bells, to the wild sky, The fly-ing cloud, the frost-y light:

The year is dy-ing in the night; Ring out, wild bells, and let him die. A-MEN.

2 Ring out the old, ring in the new,
 Ring, happy bells, across the snow:
 The year is going, let him go;
 Ring out the false, ring in the true.

3 Ring out the grief that saps the mind,
 For those that here we see no more;
 Ring out the feud of rich and poor,
 Ring in redress to all mankind.

4 Ring out old shapes of foul disease,
 Ring out the narrowing lust of gold;
 Ring out the thousand wars of old,
 Ring in the thousand years of peace.

5 Ring in the valiant man and free,
 The larger heart, the kindlier hand;
 Ring out the darkness of the land,
 Ring in the Christ that is to be.

From LORD TENNYSON's *In Memoriam*, 1849

ST. BEES 7. 7. 7. 7.

Rev. JOHN B. DYKES, 1862

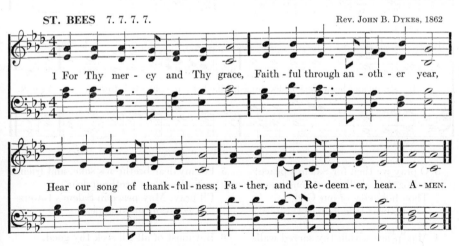

1 For Thy mer-cy and Thy grace, Faith-ful through an-oth-er year,

Hear our song of thank-ful-ness; Fa-ther, and Re-deem-er, hear. A-MEN.

The following Hymns are also suitable:

O God, the Rock of Ages, 52
Our God, our Help in ages past, 56
O God of Bethel, by whose hand, 88

The time is drawing near, 252
My days are gliding swiftly by, 388
Now rest, ye pilgrim host, 394

"O 'Twas a Joyful Sound to Hear"

393   **MOUNT ZION** C. M. D.   Horatio W. Parker, 1886

1 O 'twas a joy-ful sound to hear Our tribes de-vout-ly say,........
Our tribes

Up, Is-rael! to the tem-ple haste, And keep your fes-tal day.........
Our

2 At Sa-lem's courts we must ap-pear With our as-sem-bled powers,....

In strong and beauteous or-der ranged, Like her u-ni-ted towers.   A-MEN.

A PARAPHRASE OF PSALM CXXII

3 O pray we then for Salem's peace;
   For they shall prosperous be,
Thou holy city of our God,
   Who bear true love to thee.

4 May peace within thy sacred walls
   A constant guest be found;
With plenty and prosperity
   Thy palaces be crowned.

5 For my dear brethren's sake, and friends
   No less than brethren dear,
I'll pray, May peace in Salem's towers
   A constant guest appear.

6 But most of all I'll seek thy good,
   And ever wish thee well,
For Zion and the temple's sake,
   Where God vouchsafes to dwell.

TATE and BRADY's *New Version of the Psalms*, 1696, 1698

"Through all the bygone Years"

394 EVENING SHADOWS S. M. D.   JOHN T. MUSGRAVE, 1900

1 Now rest, ye pil-grim host, Look back up-on your way, The moun-tains climbed, the tor-rents crossed, Through many a wea-ry day. From this vic-to-rious height, How fair the past ap-pears, God's grace and glo-ry shi-ning bright On all the by-gone years. A-MEN.

Remember, O Lord, Thy tender mercies and Thy loving kindnesses; for they have been ever of old.—Ps. xxv, 6

2 How many, at His call,
   Have parted from our throng!
They watch us from the crystal wall,
   And echo back our song.
They rest, beyond complaints,
   Beyond all sighs and tears:
Praise be to God for all His saints
   Who wrought in bygone years.

3 The banners they upbore
   Our hands still lift on high;
The Lord they followed evermore
   To us is also nigh.

Arise, arise, and tread
   The future without fears;
He leadeth still, whose hand hath led
   Through all the bygone years.

4 When we have reached the home
   We seek with weary feet,
Our children's children still shall come
   To keep these ranks complete;
And He, whose host is one
   Throughout the countless spheres,
Will guide His marching servants on
   Through everlasting years.
ROSSITER W. RAYMOND, 1879 (his text of 1893)

"Marching with the Heroes"

395 ROSMORE 6. 5. 6. 5. 12 ll.

HENRY G. TREMBATH, 1893

1 Marching with the he - roes, Com-rades of the strong, Lift we hearts and voi - ces

As we march a - long; O the joy - ful mu - sic All in cho - rus raise!

Theirs the song of tri - umph, Ours the song of praise. Marching with the he - roes,

Com-rades of the strong, Lift we hearts and voi - ces As we march a - long. A-MEN.

2 Glory to the heroes,
　Who in days of old
Trod the path of duty,
　Faithful, wise, and bold,
For the right unflinching,
　Strong the weak to save,
Warriors all and freemen
　Fighting for the slave.
Glory to the heroes
　Who in days of old
Trod the path of duty,
　Faithful, wise, and bold.

3 So we sing the story
　Of the brave and true,
Till among the heroes
　We are heroes too;
Loyal to our Captain
　Like the men of yore,
Marching with the heroes
　Onward evermore.
O the joyful music
　All in chorus raise!
Theirs the song of triumph,
　Ours the song of praise.

Arranged from Rev. WILLIAM G. TARRANT (1853-　)

396 ST. COLUMBA 8. 7. 8. 7. Iambic   An ancient Irish hymn melody

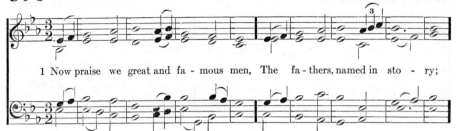

1 Now praise we great and fa - mous men, The fa - thers, named in sto - ry;

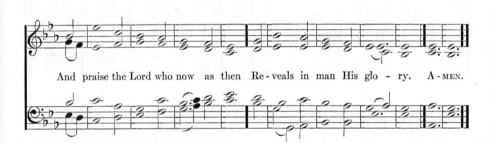

And praise the Lord who now as then Re - veals in man His glo - ry. A - MEN.

Alternative tune, BURG, No. 58

2 Praise we the wise and brave and strong,
  Who graced their generation;
Who helped the right, and fought the
And made our folk a nation. [wrong,

3 Praise we the great of heart and mind,
  The singers sweetly gifted,
Whose music like a mighty wind
The souls of men uplifted.

4 Praise we the peaceful men of skill
  Who builded homes of beauty,
And, rich in art, made richer still
The brotherhood of duty.

5 Praise we the glorious names we know;
  And they whose names have perished—
Lost in the haze of long ago—
  In silent love be cherished.

6 In peace their sacred ashes rest,
  Fulfilled their day's endeavor;
They blessed the earth, and they are blest
Of God and man for ever.

7 So praise we great and famous men,
  The fathers, named in story;
And praise the Lord who now as then
  Reveals in man His glory.

Rev. WILLIAM G. TARRANT (1853)

A Collect for Washington's Birthday

O God, who of old didst raise up leaders of Thy people and captains of Thy host, and didst not withhold the same good providence from our fathers in their need: We gratefully celebrate before Thee this day the singular excellence and the illustrious services of Thy servant, George Washington. And we pray that so long as this nation endures, his memory may abide in the hearts of all its citizens, and may shine steadfast in the places of their government, as a light which the hand of the Lord hath kindled. Amen.

"We Love the Venerable House"

397 MARTYRS C. M.

In the Scottish Psalter, 1635
(original form of the melody)

Slow and solemn. To be sung in unison.

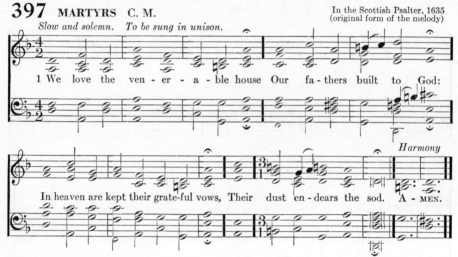

1 We love the ven - er - a - ble house Our fa - thers built to God:
In heaven are kept their grate-ful vows, Their dust en - dears the sod. A - MEN.

Lord, I have loved the habitation of Thy house, and the place where Thine honor dwelleth.—Ps. xxvi, 8

2 Here holy thoughts a light have shed
   From many a radiant face,
And prayers of humble virtue made
   The perfume of the place.

3 And anxious hearts have pondered here
   The mystery of life,
And prayed the eternal Light to clear
   Their doubts and aid their strife.

4 From humble tenements around
   Came up the pensive train,
And in the church a blessing found
   That filled their homes again;

5 For faith and peace and mighty love,
   That from the Godhead flow,
Showed them the life of heaven above
   Springs from the life below.

6 They live with God, their homes are dust;
   Yet here their children pray,
And in this fleeting life-time trust
   To find the narrow way.

7 On him who by the altar stands,
   On him Thy blessing fall;
Speak through his lips Thy pure com-
   Thou Heart that lovest all.   [mands,

RALPH WALDO EMERSON, at the ordination of his successor
in the Second Church, Boston, 1833

DUKE STREET L. M.

JOHN HATTON, 1793

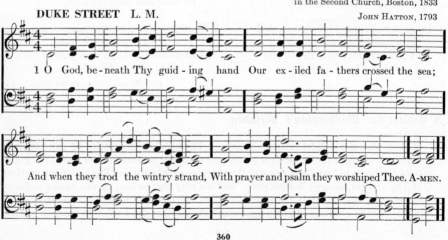

1 O God, be-neath Thy guid - ing hand Our ex - iled fa - thers crossed the sea;
And when they trod the wintry strand, With prayer and psalm they worshiped Thee. A-MEN.

"For Those in Peril on the Sea"

398 MELITA 8. 8. 8. 8. 8. 8.
Rev. John B. Dykes, 1861

1 E - ter - nal Fa - ther, strong to save, Whose arm doth bind the rest - less wave,

Who bidd'st the might - y o - cean deep Its own ap - point - ed lim - its keep:

O hear us when we cry to Thee For those in per - il on the sea. A-men.

Thou rulest the raging of the sea: when the waves thereof arise, Thou stillest them.—Ps. lxxxix, 9

2 O Saviour, whose almighty word
The winds and waves submissive heard,
Who walkedst on the foaming deep
And calm amid its rage didst sleep:
O hear us when we cry to Thee
For those in peril on the sea.

3 O Sacred Spirit, who didst brood
Upon the chaos dark and rude,
Who badd'st its angry tumult cease,

And gavest light and life and peace:
O hear us when we cry to Thee
For those in peril on the sea.

4 O Trinity of love and power,
Our brethren shield in danger's hour;
From rock and tempest, fired an foe,
Protect them wheresoe'er they go;
And ever let there rise to Thee
Glad hymns of praise from land and sea.

William Whiting, 1860 (his text of 1869)

"O God, Beneath Thy Guiding Hand"

399 (DUKE STREET) L. M.

1 O God, beneath Thy guiding hand
Our exiled fathers crossed the sea;
And when they trod the wintry strand,
With prayer and psalm they worshiped
Thee.

2 Thou heard'st, well pleased, the song, the
prayer:
Thy blessing came; and still its power
Shall onward, through all ages, bear
The memory of that holy hour.

3 Laws, freedom, truth, and faith in God
Came with those exiles o'er the waves;
And, where their pilgrim feet have trod,
The God they trusted guards their
graves.

4 And here Thy Name, O God of love,
Their children's children shall adore,
Till these eternal hills remove,
And spring adorns the earth no more.

Rev. Leonard Bacon, 1833 (his text of 1845)

361

400 **CROSSING THE BAR** Irregular

Sir Joseph Barnby, 1893

VERSE 1

Sun - set and eve - ning star, And one clear call for me!

And may there be no moan-ing of the bar When I put out to sea,

VERSE 2

But such a tide as mov-ing seems a-sleep, Too full for sound and foam,

rall.

When that which drew from out the bound-less deep Turns a - gain home...

home.

VERSE 3

.... Twi - light and eve - ning bell, And af - ter that the dark!

Twi - - - - - light and eve - ning bell,

And may there be no sad - ness of fare - well When I em - bark;

"Sunset and Evening Star" (Concluded)

VERSE 4 *cres - - - cen - - - - do   rit.*

For, though from out our bourne of time and place The flood may bear me far,

f

I hope to see my Pi - lot face to face When I have crost the bar. A - MEN.

ALFRED LORD TENNYSON, 1889

"Give Ear, Ye Children, to My Law"

401 ST. MARTIN'S C. M.   WILLIAM TANSUR, 1740

1 Give ear,   ye chil - dren, to   my law, De - vout   at - ten - tion lend;

Let   the in - struc - tions of   my mouth Deep in   your hearts de - scend. A - MEN.

2 My tongue, by inspiration taught,
  Shall parables unfold:
  Dark oracles, but understood,
  And owned for truths of old;

3 Which we from sacred registers
  Of ancient times have known,
  And our forefathers' pious care
  To us has handed down.

4 Let children learn the mighty deeds
  Which God performed of old;
  Which in our younger years we saw,
  And which our fathers told.

5 Our lips shall tell them to our sons,
  And they again to theirs;
  That generations yet unborn
  May teach them to their heirs.

A cento from various versions of Psalm LXXVIII, by Rev. JEREMY BELKNAP, 1795;
and sung at every Harvard commencement dinner since 1830

363

402   O FILII ET FILIAE   8. 8. 8. with Alleluias

The modern form of a
17th century French melody

To be sung in unison

Al - le - lu - ia!   Al - le - lu - ia!   Al - le -

lu - - - ia!   1 Ye sons and daugh - ters of the King,

Whom heaven - ly hosts in glo - ry sing, To - day the grave hath

D. S.

lost its sting.   Al - - le - lu - - ia.   A - MEN!

2 On that first morn, at break of day,
  The faithful Maries went their way
  To seek the tomb where Jesus lay.
    Alleluia!

3 An angel clad in white they see,
  Who sat, and spake unto the three,
  "Your Lord doth go to Galilee."
    Alleluia!

4 That night the apostles met in fear;
  Amidst them came their Lord most dear,
  And said, "My peace be on all here."
    Alleluia!

5 When Thomas first the tidings heard
  That Jesus had fulfilled His word,
  He doubted if it were the Lord.
    Alleluia!

6 "My piercèd side, O Thomas, see;
  My hands, My feet, I show to Thee;
  Not faithless but believing be."
    Alleluia!

7 No longer Thomas then denied;
  He saw the feet, the hands, the side;
  "Thou art my Lord and God," he cried.
    Alleluia!

"O Filii et Filiae" (Concluded)

8 How blest are they who have not seen,
And yet whose faith hath constant been,
For they eternal life shall win.
Alleluia!

9 On this most holy day of days,
To God your hearts and voices raise
In laud, and jubilee, and praise.
Alleluia!

A Latin hymn in the *Office de la Semaine Sainte*, Paris, 1674:
translated by Rev. JOHN M. NEALE, 1851: varied

"Christ is Made the Sure Foundation"

403 THE SURE FOUNDATION 8. 7. 8. 7. 8. 7. JAMES C. KNOX, 1911

1 Christ is made the sure Foun-da-tion, Christ the Head and Cor-ner-Stone,

Cho-sen of the Lord and pre-cious, Bind-ing all the Church in one;

Ho-ly Zi-on's help for ev-er, And her con-fi-dence a-lone. A-MEN.

ANGULARIS FUNDAMENTUM

2 All that dedicated city,
   Dearly loved of God on high,
In exultant jubilation
   Pours perpetual melody;
God the One in Three adoring
   In glad hymns eternally.

Hear Thy people as they pray;
And Thy fullest benediction
   Shed within its walls alway.

4 Here vouchsafe to all Thy servants
   What they ask of Thee to gain,
What they gain from Thee, for ever
   With the blessèd to retain,
And hereafter in Thy glory
   Evermore with Thee to reign.

3 To this temple, where we call Thee,
   Come, O Lord of Hosts, today:
With Thy wonted loving-kindness,

An anonymous 7th century Latin hymn translated by Rev. JOHN MASON NEALE, 1851,
as varied in *Hymns ancient and modern*, 1861

NOTE—*This hymn, especially associated with church dedications, is equally suitable to all occasions of public worship.*

"Now Thank We All Our God"

404 NUN DANKET 6. 7. 6. 7. 6. 6. 6. 6.   Johann Crüger, 1647

To be sung in unison

1 Now thank we all our God With heart and hands and voi - ces,

Who won-drous things hath done, In whom His world re - joi - ces;

Who, from our moth - ers' arms, Hath blessed us on our way

With count-less gifts of love, And still is ours to - day. A-men.

NUN DANKET ALLE GOTT

2 O may this bounteous God
Through all our life be near us,
With ever joyful hearts
And blessèd peace to cheer us;
And keep us in His grace,
And guide us when perplexed,
And free us from all ills
In this world and the next.

3 All praise and thanks to God
The Father now be given,
The Son, and Him who reigns
With them in highest heaven,
The One Eternal God
Whom earth and heaven adore;
For thus it was, is now,
And shall be evermore.

Rev. Martin Rinkart, c. 1636
Translated by Catherine Winkworth, 1858

366

"Now Again the World is Shaken"

405 CATHERINE 8. 7. 8. 7. 8. 7.   DAVID ROBERTS (1820–1872)

1 Now a-gain the world is sha-ken, Tem-pests break on sea and shore;
Earth, with ru - in o - ver - ta - ken, Trem - bles while the storm winds roar.
He a - bid - eth who con - fid - eth; God is God for ev - er - more. A - MEN.

Alternative tune, REGENT SQUARE, No. 50

Those things which cannot be shaken.—HEB. xii, 28

2 Thrones are falling, heathen raging,
　Peoples dreaming as of yore
Vain imaginations, waging,
　Man with man, unmeaning war.
　　He abideth who confideth;
　Christ is King for evermore.

3 Human wisdom in confusion
　Casts away the forms it wore;
Ancient error, new illusion,
　Lose the phantom fruit they bore.
　　He abideth who confideth;
　Truth is truth for evermore.

4 Right eternal, Love immortal,
　Built the House where we adore;
Mercy is its golden portal,
　Virtue its unshaken floor.
　　He abideth who confideth;
　God is God for evermore.

REV. HENRY VAN DYKE, 1922

367

406 SINE NOMINE 10. 10. 10. 4.

R. Vaughan Williams, 1906

Verses 1, 2, 3, and 7, 8.

Voices in unison. In moderate time. ♩ = 112

1 For all the saints who from their la-bors rest, Who Thee by faith be-
2 Thou wast their Rock, their Fort-ress and their Might; Thou, Lord, their Cap-tain
3 O may Thy sol-diers, faithful true and bold, Fight as the saints who
7 But lo! there breaks a yet more glorious day; The saints tri-um-phant
8 From earth's wide bounds, from ocean's farthest coast, Through gates of pearl streams

fore the world con-fessed, Thy Name, O Je-sus, be for ev-er blest.
in the well-fought fight; Thou, in the dark-ness drear, their one true Light.
no-bly fought of old, And win with them the vic-tor's crown of gold.
rise in bright ar-ray; The King of Glo-ry pass-es on His way.
in the count-less host, Sing-ing to Fa-ther, Son, and Ho-ly Ghost.

Harmony

Al-le-lu-ia, Al-le-lu-ia! A-men.

Harmony

368

"For All the Saints" (Concluded)

VERSES 4, 5, 6.

Voices in harmony

4 O blest com - mun - ion, fel - low - ship di - vine!
5 And when the strife is fierce, the war - fare long,
6 The gold - en eve - ning bright - ens in the west;

Org.

We fee - bly strug - gle; they in glo - ry shine; Yet
Steals on the ear the dis - tant tri - umph - song, And
Soon, soon to faith - ful war - riors comes their rest; —

all are one in Thee, for all are Thine.
hearts are brave a - gain, and arms are strong.
Sweet is the calm of Pa - ra - dise, the blest.

D.C. for Verses 7 and 8

Al - - le - lu - ia. Al - - le - lu - ia.

369

407 ABERYSTWYTH 7. 7. 7. 7. D.

JOSEPH PARRY, 1879

1 Jesus, Lover of my soul, Let me to Thy bosom fly,
While the nearer waters roll, While the tempest still is high:
Hide me, O my Saviour, hide, Till the storm of life is past;
Safe into the haven guide, O receive my soul at last. A-MEN.

2 Other refuge have I none;
    Hangs my helpless soul on Thee;
Leave, ah! leave me not alone,
    Still support and comfort me.
All my trust on Thee is stayed,
    All my help from Thee I bring;
Cover my defenceless head
    With the shadow of Thy wing.

3 Thou, O Christ, art all I want;
    More than all in Thee I find:
Raise the fallen, cheer the faint,
    Heal the sick, and lead the blind.

Just and holy is Thy Name;
    I am all unrighteousness;
False and full of sin I am,
    Thou art full of truth and grace.

4 Plenteous grace with Thee is found,
    Grace to cover all my sin;
Let the healing streams abound;
    Make and keep me pure within.
Thou of life the Fountain art,
    Freely let me take of Thee;
Spring Thou up within my heart,
    Rise to all eternity.

REV. CHARLES WESLEY, 1740

408 HYFRYDOL 8. 7. 8. 7. D.

R. H. PRICHARD, 1811–1887

1 Love Di - vine, all loves ex - cell - ing, Joy of heaven, to
  Fix in us Thy hum - ble dwell - ing, All Thy faith - ful

earth come down: Je - sus, Thou art all com - pas - sion,
mer - cies crown:

Pure, un - bound - ed love Thou art; Vis - it us with

Thy sal - va - tion, En - ter ev - ery trem - bling heart. A - MEN.

2 Breathe, O breathe Thy loving Spirit
  Into every troubled breast;
Let us all in Thee inherit,
  Let us find the promised rest:
Take away the love of sinning;
  Alpha and Omega be;
End of faith, as its Beginning,
  Set our hearts at liberty.

3 Come, Almighty to deliver,
  Let us all Thy life receive;
Suddenly return, and never,
  Never more Thy temples leave.

Thee we would be always blessing,
  Serve Thee as Thy hosts above,
Pray, and praise Thee, without ceasing,
  Glory in Thy perfect love.

4 Finish, then, Thy new creation;
  Pure and spotless let us be:
Let us see Thy great salvation
  Perfectly restored in Thee;
Changed from glory into glory,
  Till in heaven we take our place,
Till we cast our crowns before Thee,
  Lost in wonder, love, and praise.

Rev. CHARLES WESLEY, 1747: verse 2, lines 4 and 5, varied

"Of the Father's Heart Begotten"

409 **DIVINUM MYSTERIUM** 8. 7. 8. 7. 8. 7. 7.   In *Piae Cantiones*, 1582

1 Of the Fa-ther's heart be-got-ten, Ere the worlds be-gan to be,
He the Al-pha and O-me-ga, He the Source, the End-ing He,
Of the things that are, that have been, And that fu-ture years shall
see,...... Ev-er-more and ev-er-more. A-MEN.

CORDE NATUS EX PARENTIS

2 He is here, whom seers of old time
   Chanted of while ages ran,
Whom the faithful word of prophets
   Promised since the world began;
Long foretold, at length appearing,
   Praise Him, every child of man,
     Evermore and evermore.

3 Praise Him, O ye heaven of heavens,
   Praise Him, angels in the height;
All dominions, bow before Him
   And exalt His wondrous might.
Let no tongue of man be silent;
   Let each voice and heart unite,
     Evermore and evermore.

4 Thee let age, and Thee let manhood,
   Thee let choirs of infants sing;
Thee the matrons and the maidens,
   And the children answering:
Let their guileless song re-echo,
   And the heart its praises bring,
     Evermore and evermore.

5 Christ, to Thee, with God the Father,
   And, O Holy Ghost, to Thee,
Hymn, and chant, and high thanksgiving,
   And unwearied praises be,
Honor, glory, might, dominion,
   And eternal victory,
     Evermore and evermore.

Arranged from Rev. JOHN M. NEALE's translation
from the Latin of AURELIUS C. PRUDENTIUS, c. 348

"God Be With You Till We Meet Again"

410 GOD BE WITH YOU 9. 8. 8. 9. with Refrain   WILLIAM G. TOMER, 1880

1 God be with you till we meet a-gain, By His coun-sels guide, up-hold you,

With His sheep se-cure-ly fold you, God be with you till we meet a-gain.

REFRAIN

Till we meet,...... till we meet,   Till we meet at Je-sus' feet;

Till we meet, till we meet, till we meet,   till we meet,

Till we meet,...... till we meet,   God be with you till we meet a-gain.   A-MEN.

Till we meet, till we meet, till we meet,

2 God be with you till we meet again,
  'Neath His wings protecting hide you,
  Daily manna still divide you,
God be with you till we meet again.—REF.

3 God be with you till we meet again,
  When life's perils thick confound you,
  Put His arms unfailing round you,
God be with you till we meet again.—REF.

4 God be with you till we meet again,
  Keep love's banner floating o'er you,
  Smite death's threatening wave before you,
God be with you till we meet again.—REF.

Rev. JEREMIAH E. RANKIN, 1880

373

Canticles, Versicles, Etc.

411 BEFORE THE CONFESSION OF SINS

The Minister:

Our help is in the Name of the Lord.

Response:

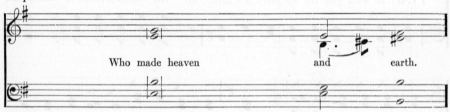

Who made heaven and earth.

The Minister:

I said, I will confess my transgressions unto the Lord.

Response:

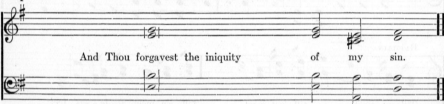

And Thou forgavest the iniquity of my sin.

412 DEUS MISEREATUR

LEWIS T. DOWNES (1827–1907)

1 God be merciful *unto* | us and | bless us || and show us the light of His countenance *
and be | merci • ful | unto | us;

2 That Thy *way* may be | known up • on | earth || Thy *saving* | health a | mong all |
nations.

3 Let the people *praise* | Thee O | God || *yea* let | all the | people | praise Thee.

4 O let the nations re*joice* | and be | glad || for Thou shalt judge the folk righteously *
and *govern* the | nations • up | on • = | earth.

5 Let the people *praise* | Thee O | God || *yea* let | all the | people | praise Thee.

6 Then shall the *earth* bring | forth her | increase || and God, even our own *God*, shall |
give • = | us His | blessing.

2nd Part 7 *God* shall | bless • = | us || and all the *ends* of the | world shall | fear • = | Him.

Glory be to the *Father* | and • to the | Son || *and* | to the | Holy | Ghost;

As it was in the beginning * is *now*, and | ever | shall be || *world* without | end • = |
A • = | men.

Canticles, Versicles, Etc.

413 LÆTATUS SUM

WILLIAM JACKSON, 1790

1 I was *glad* when they | said · unto | me || Let u*s go* | into · the | house · of the | Lord.

2 Our feet shall *stand* with | in thy | gates || O | = · Je | ru · sa | lem.

3 Jerusalem is *builded* | as a | city || *that* | is com | pact · to | gether:

4 Whither the tribes go up * the *tribes* | of the | Lord || unto the testimony of Israel *
to give *thanks* | unto · the | Name · of the | Lord.

5 For there are *set* | thrones of | judgment || the *thrones* | of the | house of | David.

6 Pray for the *peace* of Je | rusa | lem || *they* shall | prosper · that | love · = | thee.

7 *Peace* be with | in thy | walls || and prosperi*ty* with | in · = | thy = | palaces.

8 For my *breth*ren and com | panions' | sakes || I will now *say* | Peace · be with | in · = |
thee.

9 Because of the *house* of the | Lord · our | God || *I* will | seek · = | thy · = | good.

Glory be to the *Fa*ther | and · to the | Son || *and* | to the | Holy | Ghost;

As it was in the beginning * is *now*, and | ever | shall be || *world* without | end · = |
A · = | men.

414 JUBILATE DEO

JOHN ROBINSON (1682–1762)

1 O be joyful in the *Lord* | all ye | lands || serve the Lord with gladness * and come
be*fore* His | presence | with a | song.

2 Be ye sure that the Lord He is God * it is He that hath made us *and* not |
we our | selves || we are His people, *and* the | sheep of | His · = | pasture.

3 O go your way into His gates with thanksgiving * and *into* His | courts with | praise ||
be thankful unto *Him*, and | speak good | of His | Name.

4 For the Lord is gracious * His *mercy* is | ever | lasting || and His truth endureth
from *gener* | ation · to | gener | ation.

Glory be to the *Fa*ther | and · to the | Son || *and* | to the | Holy | Ghost;

As it was in the beginning * is *now*, and | ever | shall be || *world* without | end · = |
A · = | men.

Canticles, Versicles, Etc.

415 NUNC DIMITTIS

Sir Joseph Barnby (1838–1896)

1 Lord, now lettest Thou Thy *servant* de | part in | peace || *ac* | cording | to Thy | word:

2 *For* mine | eyes have | seen || *Thy* | = · sal | va · = | tion,

3 *Which* Thou | hast pre | pared || be*fore* the | face of | all · = | people;

4 To be a *light* to | lighten · the | Gentiles || and to be the *glory* | of Thy | people | Israel.

Glory be to the *Father* | and · to the | Son || *and* | to the | Holy | Ghost;

As it was in the beginning * is *now*, and |, ever | shall be || *world* without | end · = | A · = | men.

416 CANTATE DOMINO

Thomas Norris, 1770

1 O sing unto the *Lord* a | new · = | song || for *He* hath | done · = | marvellous | things.

2 With His own right hand * and *with* His | holy | arm || *hath* He | gotten · Him | self the | victory.

3 The Lord de*clared* | His sal | vation || His righteousness hath He openly *showed* in the | sight · = | of the | heathen.

4 He hath remembered His mercy and truth *toward* the | house of | Israel || and all the ends of the world have *seen* the sal | vation | of our | God.

5 Show yourselves joyful unto the *Lord* | all ye | lands || *sing*, re | joice and | give · = | thanks.

6 Praise the *Lord* up | on the | harp || sing to the *harp* with a | psalm of | thanks · = | giving.

7 With *trumpets* | also · and | shawms || O show yourselves *joy*ful be | fore the | Lord the | King.

8 Let the sea make a noise * and *all* that | therein | is || the round *world*, and | they that | dwell there | in.

9 Let the floods clap their hands * and let the hills be joyful to*gether* be | fore the | Lord || *for* He | cometh · to | judge the | earth.

10 With righteousness *shall* He | judge the | world || *and* the | people | with · = | equity.

Glory be to the *Father* | and · to the | Son || *and* | to the | Holy | Ghost;

As it was in the beginning * is *now*, and | ever | shall be || *world* without | end · = | A · = | men.

417 MAGNIFICAT   THOMAS ATTWOOD (1765–1838)

1 My soul doth *magni* | fy the | Lord || and my spirit *hath* re | joiced · in | God my | Saviour.

2 *For* He | hath re | garded || the *lowli* | ness of | His hand | maiden.

3 *For* be | hold from | henceforth || *all* gener | ations · shall | call me | blessed.

4 For He that is *mighty* hath | magni · fied | me || *and* | holy | is His | Name.

5 And His *mercy* is on | them that | fear Him || *through* | out all | gener | ations.

6 He hath showed *strength* | with His | arm || He hath scattered the proud in the ima*gin* | ation | of their | hearts.

7 He hath put down the *mighty* | from their | seat || and *hath* ex | alted · the | humble · and | meek.

8 He hath filled the *hungry* with | good · = | things || and the *rich* He hath | sent · = | empty · a | way.

2nd Part 9 He remembering His mercy hath *holp*en His | servant | Israel || as He promised to our forefathers * *A*braham | and his | seed for | ever.

Glory be to the *Father* | and · to the | Son || *and* | to the | Holy | Ghost;

As it was in the beginning * is *now*, and | ever | shall be || *world* without | end · = | A · = | men.

418 BENEDICTUS   Arranged from BEETHOVEN (1770–1827)

1 Blessed be the *Lord* | God of | Israel || for He hath *visited* | and re | deemed · His | people;

2 And hath raised up a *mighty* sal | vation | for us || in the *house* | of His | servant | David;

3 As He spake by the *mouth* of His | holy | prophets || which have *been* | since the | world be | gan;

4 That we should be *saved* | from our | enemies || and *from* the | hand of | all that | hate us.

Glory be to the *Father* | and · to the | Son || *and* | to the | Holy | Ghost;

As it was in the beginning * is *now*, and | ever | shall be || *world* without | end · = | A · = | men.

419 BENEDIC, ANIMA MEA

RICHARD LANGDON, 1774

1 Praise the *Lord* | O my | soul || and all that is with*in* me | praise His | holy | Name.

2 Praise the *Lord* | O my | soul || *and* for | get not | all His | benefits:

3 Who for*giv*eth | all thy | sin || and *heal*eth | all ˙ = | thine in | firmities;

4 Who saveth thy *life* | from de | struction || and crowneth *thee* with | mercy ˙ and | loving | kindness.

5 O praise the Lord ye angels of His * *ye* that ex | cel in | strength || ye that fulfil His commandment * and hearken *un* | to the | voice ˙ of His | word.

6 O praise the *Lord*, all | ye His | hosts || ye *serv*ants of | His that | do His | pleasure.

2nd Part 7 O speak good of the Lord, all ye works of His * in all *places* of | His do | minion || praise *thou* the | Lord ˙ = | O my | soul.

Glory be to the *Father* | and ˙ to the | Son || *and* | to the | Holy | Ghost;

As it was in the beginning * is *now*, and | ever | shall be || *world* without | end ˙ = | A ˙ = | men.

420 BONUM EST CONFITERI

JOHN RANDALL (1715–1799)

1 It is a good thing to give *thanks* un | to the | Lord || and to sing praises *unto* Thy | Name ˙ = | O Most | Highest;

2 To tell of Thy loving-kindness *early* | in the | morning || and of Thy *truth* | in the | night ˙ = | season;

3 Upon an instrument of ten strings * *and* up | on the | lute || upon a loud *in*strument | and up | on the | harp.

4 For Thou, Lord * hast made me *glad* | through Thy | works || and I will rejoice in giving *praise* * for the oper | ations | of Thy | hands.

Glory be to the *Father* | and ˙ to the | Son || *and* | to the | Holy | Ghost;

As it was in the beginning * is *now*, and | ever | shall be || *world* without | end ˙ =| A ˙ = | men.

Canticles, Versicles, Etc.

421 VENITE, EXULTEMUS DOMINO
William Boyce, 1740

1 O come, let us *sing* | unto · the | Lord || let us heartily re*joice* in the | strength of | our sal | vation.

2 Let us come before His *pres*ence with | thanks · = | giving || and show our*selves* | glad in | Him with | psalms.

3 For the *Lord* is a | great · = | God || and a *great* | King a | bove all | gods.

4 In His hand are all the *corners* | of the | earth || and the *strength* of the | hills is | His · = | also.

5 The sea is *His* | and He | made it || and His *hands* pre | pared · the | dry · = | land.

6 O come let us *worship* and | fall · = | down || and *kneel* be | fore the | Lord our | Maker.

7 For *He* is the | Lord our | God || and we are the people of His pasture * *and* the | sheep of | His · = | hand.

8 O worship the *Lord* in the | beauty · of | holiness || let the whole *earth* | stand in | awe of | Him.

2nd 9 For he cometh * for He *cometh* to | judge the | earth || and with righteousness
Part   to judge the *world* * and the | people | with His | truth.

Glory be to the *Father* | and · to the | Son || *and* | to the | Holy | Ghost;

As it was in the beginning * is *now*, and | ever | shall be || *world* without | end · = | A · = | men.

422 THE LORD'S PRAYER
Thomas Tallis, 1520

Our Father, who art in heaven, hallow*ed* | be Thy | Name; || Thy kingdom come; Thy will be *done* on | earth · as it | is in | heaven.

Give us this *day* our | daily | bread, || and forgive us our trespasses, as we for*give* | those who | trespass · a- | gainst us.

And lead us not into temptation, but de*liver* | us from | evil, || for Thine is the kingdom, and the power, and the *glory*, for | ever · and | ever. A- | men.

423 BEFORE THE PSALTER

The Minister: Now bless the Lord our God:

Response:

And praise His glo-rious Name.

The Minister: O give thanks unto the Lord, for He is good.

Response:

For His mer - cy en - dur - eth for ev - er.

424 OFFERTORY SENTENCE

Arranged from BEETHOVEN

All things *come* of Thee, O Lord; and of Thine *own* have we giv - en Thee. A - MEN.

425 RESPONSES TO THE BEATITUDES

ALFRED REGINALD ALLEN, 1911

After each Beautitude, except the last

Lord, be gra-cious un-to us,........ and help us to ob - tain this bless-ing.

After the last

Grant un - to us Thy Ho - ly Spir - it, O God, And en - a - ble us to ob-

tain all these bless - ings, through Je - sus Christ our Lord.

Canticles, Versicles, Etc.

426 KYRIE

1 *After each Commandment, except the 10th*

Lord, have mer-cy up-on us, and in-cline our hearts to keep this law.

After the 10th   *rit.*

Lord, have mer-cy up-on us, and write all these Thy laws in our hearts, we be-seech Thee.

Sir GEORGE J. ELVEY, (1816-1893)

2 *After each Commandment, except the 10th*

Lord, have mer-cy, have mer-cy up-on us, and in-cline our hearts to

After the 10th

keep this law. Lord, have mer-cy, have mer-cy up-on us, and write all

these Thy laws in our hearts, Thy laws in our hearts, we be-seech Thee.

Canticles, Versicles, Etc.

427   SURSUM CORDA and SANCTUS (longer form)

Minister. The Lord be with you.   *Minister.* Lift up your hearts.   *Minister.* Let us give thanks unto the Lord our God.

Response.   *Response.*   *Response.*

And with thy Spirit.   We lift them up un-to the Lord.   It is meet and right so to do.

SANCTUS   ALFRED REGINALD ALLEN, 1911

Ho - ly,   Ho - ly,   Ho - ly,   Lord God   of   Hosts;

Heav - en and earth are full   of   the   ma - jes - ty   of   Thy   glo - ry.   Ho -

san - na   in   the   high - est.   Bless - ed   is   He   that

com - eth in the Name of the Lord......   Ho - san - na   in   the   high - est.

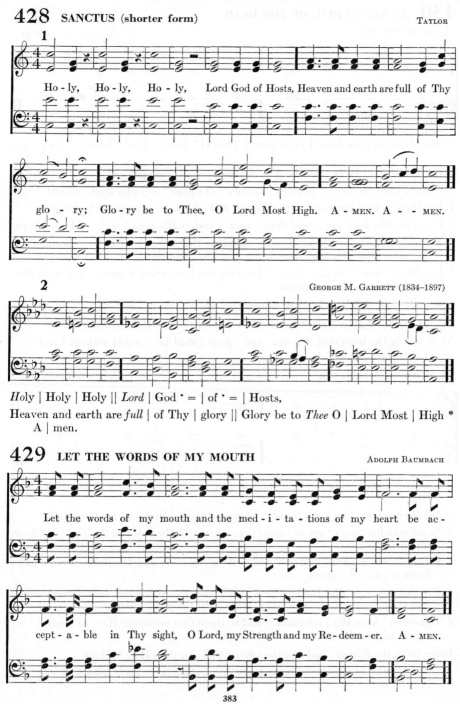

428 SANCTUS (shorter form)

TAYLOR

1

Ho - ly, Ho - ly, Ho - ly, Lord God of Hosts, Heaven and earth are full of Thy

glo - ry; Glo - ry be to Thee, O Lord Most High. A - MEN. A - - MEN.

2

GEORGE M. GARRETT (1834–1897)

Holy | Holy | Holy || *Lord* | God ˙ = | of ˙ = | Hosts,

Heaven and earth are *full* | of Thy | glory || Glory be to *Thee* O | Lord Most | High *
    A | men.

429 LET THE WORDS OF MY MOUTH

ADOLPH BAUMBACH

Let the words of my mouth and the med - i - ta - tions of my heart be ac -

cept - a - ble in Thy sight, O Lord, my Strength and my Re - deem - er. A - MEN.

383

430 AT THE BURIAL OF THE DEAD

1 DE PROFUNDIS

Rev. WILLIAM FELTON, 1740

1 Out of the depths have I *cried* unto | Thee O | Lord || *Lord* | hear ⋅ = | my ⋅ = | voice.

2 Let Thine *ears* | be at | tentive || to the *voice* | of my | suppli | cations.

3 If Thou Lord *should*est | mark in | iquities || O | Lord ⋅ = | who shall | stand?

4 But there *is* for | giveness ⋅ with | Thee || *that* | Thou ⋅ = | mayest ⋅ be | feared.

5 I wait for the *Lord* my | soul doth | wait || and in His *word* | do ⋅ = | I ⋅ = | hope.

6 My soul waiteth for the Lord more than *they* that | watch ⋅ for the | morning || I say, more than *they* that | watch ⋅ = | for the | morning.

7 Let *Is*rael | hope ⋅ in the | Lord || for with the Lord there is mercy, and with *Him* is | plente | ous re | demption.

8 And *He* shall re | deem ⋅ = | Israel || *from* | all ⋅ = | his in | iquities.

Glory be to the *Father* | and ⋅ to the | Son || *and* | to the | Holy | Ghost.

As it was in the beginning * is *now*, and | ever | shall be || *world* without | end ⋅ = | A ⋅ = | men.

2 QUOMODO MISERETUR

THOMAS TALLIS

1 Like as a *father* | pitieth ⋅ his | children || so the *Lord* | piti ⋅ eth | them that | fear Him.

2 For He *know*eth | our ⋅ = | frame || he re*mem*bereth | that we | are ⋅ = | dust.

3 As for *man* his | days ⋅ are as | grass || as a flower of the *field* | so ⋅ = | he ⋅ = | flour-isheth.

4 For the wind passeth *over* it | and ⋅ it is | gone || and the place there*of* shall | know it | no ⋅ = | more.

5 But the mercy of the Lord is from everlasting to everlasting up*on* | them that | fear Him || and His righteous*ness* | unto | chil ⋅ dren's | children;

6 To *such* as | keep His | covenant || and to those that re*mem*ber His com | mand ⋅ = | ments to | do them.

Glory be to the *Father* | and ⋅ to the | Son || *and* | to the | Holy | Ghost.

As it was in the beginning * is *now*, and | ever | shall be || *world* without | end ⋅ = | A ⋅ = | men.

Canticles, Versicles, Etc.

3 DOMINUS REGIT ME

HART

1 The *Lord* | is my | shepherd || *I* | shall = | not = | want.

2 He maketh me to lie *down* in | green = | pastures || He leadeth *me* be | side the | still = | waters.

3 *He* re- | storeth ˙ my | soul || He leadeth me in the paths of righteous*ness* | for His | Name's = | sake.

4 Yea though I walk through the valley of the shadow of *death* I will | fear no | evil || for Thou art with me; Thy *rod* and Thy | staff they | comfort | me.

5 Thou preparest a table before me in the *presence* | of mine | enemies || Thou anoint-est my head with *oil* my | cup = | runneth | over.

6 Surely goodness and mercy shall follow me all the *days* | of my | life || and I will dwell in the *house* | of the | Lord for- | ever.

Glory be to the *Father* | and ˙ to the | Son || *and* | to the | Holy | Ghost;

As it was in the beginning * is *now*, and | ever | shall be || *world* without | end ˙ = | A ˙ = | men.

431 ASCRIPTIONS

GREGORIAN: arranged

1

Unto Him that loved us and washed us from our *sins* in His | own ˙ = | blood || and hath made us kings and *priests* unto | God ˙ = | and His | Father.

To Him be *glory* | and do | minion || *for* | ever ˙ and | ever ˙ A | men.

2

GREGORIAN: arranged

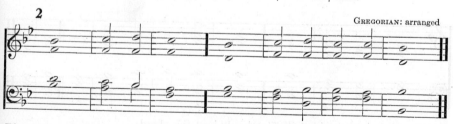

Blessing, and glory, and wisdom, and thanksgiving, and *honor* and | power ˙ and | might || be unto our *God* for | ever ˙ and | ever ˙ A | men.

432 GLORIA IN EXCELSIS

An old Chant

Glory *be* to | God on | high || and on *earth* | peace, good | will towards | men.

We praise Thee * we bless *Thee* * we | worship | Thee || we glorify Thee * we give *thanks* to | Thee for | Thy great | glory.

O Lord *God* | heavenly | King || *God* the | Father | Al ˙ = | mighty.

O Lord * the only-begotten *Son* | Jesus | Christ || O Lord God * Lamb of *God* * | Son ˙ = | of the | Father,

That takest *away* the | sins ˙ of the | world || have *mercy* up | on ˙ = | us.

Thou that takest *away* the | sins ˙ of the | world || *re* | ceive our | prayer.

Thou that sittest at the right *hand* of | God the | Father || have *mercy* up | on ˙ = | us.

For Thou *only* | art ˙ = | holy || *Thou* | only | art the | Lord.

Thou only, O *Christ* * with the | Holy | Ghost || art most *high* in the | glory ˙ of | God the | Father || A | men.

433 **DRESDEN AMEN**

Index of Authors

INCLUDING TRANSLATORS, REVISERS, AND SOURCES

Index of Composers

ARRANGERS, AND SOURCES OF THE TUNES

Index of Subjects and Occasions

NOTE.—The cross-references to titles in *Italics* refer to the heads in this Index.

395

The Psalter

SELECTION 1

A Morning Psalm

PSALM 5 : 1-7

1 GIVE ear to my words, O LORD; consider my meditation.

2 Hearken unto the voice of my cry, my King, and my God: for unto thee will I pray.

3 My voice shalt thou hear in the morning, O LORD; in the morning will I direct my prayer unto thee, and will look up.

4 For thou art not a God that hath pleasure in wickedness: neither shall evil dwell with thee.

5 The foolish shall not stand in thy sight: thou hatest all workers of iniquity.

6 Thou shalt destroy them that speak leasing: the Lord will abhor the bloody and deceitful man.

7 But as for me, I will come into thy house in the multitude of thy mercy: and in thy fear will I worship toward thy holy temple.

PSALM 19

8 THE heavens declare the glory of God; and the firmament showeth his handy-work.

9 Day unto day uttereth speech, and night unto night showeth knowledge.

10 There is no speech nor language, where their voice is not heard.

11 Their line is gone out through all the earth, and their words to the end of the world. In them hath he set a tabernacle for the sun,

12 Which is as a bridegroom coming out of his chamber, and rejoiceth as a strong man to run a race.

13 His going forth is from the end of the heaven, and his circuit unto the ends of it: and there 's nothing hid from the heat thereof.

14 The law of the Lord is perfect, converting the soul: the testimony of the Lord is sure, making wise the simple.

15 The statutes of the Lord are right, rejoicing the heart: the commandment of the Lord is pure, enlightening the eyes.

16 The fear of the Lord is clean, enduring for ever: the judgments of the Lord are true and righteous altogether.

17 More to be desired are they than gold, yea, than much fine gold: sweeter also than honey and the honeycomb.

18 Moreover by them is thy servant warned: and in keeping of them there is great reward.

19 Who can understand his errors? cleanse thou me from secret faults.

20 Keep back thy servant also from presumptuous sins; let them not have dominion over me:

21 Then shall I be upright, and I shall be innocent from the great transgression.

22 Let the words of my mouth, and the meditation of my heart, be acceptable in thy sight, O Lord, my strength, and my redeemer.

Glory be to the *Father* | and · to the | Son || *and* | to the | Holy | Ghost;
As it was in the beginning * is *now*, and | ever | shall be || *world* without | end · = | A · = | men.

SELECTION 2

An Evening Psalm

1 HEAR me when I call, O God of my righteousness: thou hast enlarged me when I was in distress; have mercy upon me, and hear my prayer.

2 O ye sons of men, how long will ye turn my glory into shame? how long will ye love vanity, and seek after leasing?

3 But know that the Lord hath set apart him that is godly for himself: the Lord will hear when I call unto him.

4 Stand in awe, and sin not; commune with your own heart upon your bed, and be still.

5 Offer the sacrifices of righteousness, and put your trust in the Lord.

6 There be many that say, Who will show us any good? Lord, lift thou up the light of thy countenance upon us.

7 Thou hast put gladness in my heart, more than in the time that their corn and their wine increased.

8 I will both lay me down in peace, and sleep: for thou, Lord, only makest me dwell in safety.

PSALM 31 (selected)

9 IN thee, O Lord, do I put my trust; let me never be ashamed: deliver me in thy righteousness.

10 Bow down thine ear to me; deliver me speedily: be thou my strong rock, for a house of defence to save me.

11 For thou art my rock and my fortress; therefore for thy name's sake lead me, and guide me.

12 Into thine hand I commit my spirit: thou hast redeemed me, O Lord God of truth.

13 My times are in thy hand: deliver me from the hand of mine enemies, and from them that persecute me.

14 Make thy face to shine upon thy servant: save me for thy mercies' sake.

15 Oh how great is thy goodness, which thou hast laid up for them that fear thee; which thou hast wrought for them that trust in thee before the sons of men !

16 Thou shalt hide them in the secret of thy presence from the pride of man: thou shalt keep them secretly in a pavilion from the strife of tongues.

17 O love the Lord, all ye his saints: for the Lord preserveth the faithful, and plentifully rewardeth the proud doer.

18 Be of good courage, and he shall strengthen your heart, all ye that hope in the Lord.

PSALM 134

19 BEHOLD, bless ye the Lord, all ye servants of the Lord, which by night stand in the house of the Lord.

20 Lift up your hands in the sanctuary, and bless the Lord.

21 The Lord that made heaven and earth bless thee out of Zion.

Glory be to the *Father* | and ˙ to the | Son || *and* | to the | Holy | Ghost;
As it was in the beginning * is *now*, and | ever | shall be || *world* without | end ˙ = | A ˙ = | men.

SELECTION 3

The Evening Sacrifice

PSALM 141 : 1-3

1 LORD, I cry unto thee: make haste unto me; give ear unto my voice, when I cry unto thee.

2 Let my prayer be set forth before thee as incense; and the lifting up of my hands as the evening sacrifice.

3 Set a watch, O Lord, before my mouth; keep the door of my lips.

PSALM 63 : 1-8

4 O GOD, thou art my God; early will I seek thee: my soul thirsteth for thee, my flesh longeth for thee in a dry and thirsty land, where no water is;

5 To see thy power and thy glory, so as I have seen thee in the sanctuary.

6 Because thy loving-kindness is better than life, my lips shall praise thee.

7 Thus will I bless thee while I live: I will lift up my hands in thy name.

8 My soul shall be satisfied as with marrow and fatness; and my mouth shall praise thee with joyful lips:

9 When I remember thee upon my bed, and meditate on thee in the night watches.

10 Because thou hast been my help, therefore in the shadow of thy wings will I rejoice.

11 My soul followeth hard after thee: thy right hand upholdeth me.

PSALM 56 : 3-4, 8-13

12 WHAT time I am afraid, I will trust in thee.

13 In God I will praise his word, in God I have put my trust; I will not fear what flesh can do unto me.

14 Thou tellest my wanderings: put thou my tears into thy bottle: are they not in thy book?

15 When I cry unto thee, then shall mine enemies turn back: this I know; for God is for me.

16 In God will I praise his word: in the Lord will I praise his word.

17 In God have I put my trust: I will not be afraid what man can do unto me.

18 Thy vows are upon me, O God: I will render praises unto thee; for thou hast delivered my soul from death:

19 Wilt not thou deliver my feet from falling, that I may walk before God in the light of the living?

Glory be to the *Father* | and ˙ to the | Son || *and* | to the | Holy | Ghost;
As it was in the beginning * is *now,* and | ever | shall be || *world* without |
   end ˙ = | A ˙ = | men.

SELECTION 4

God's Eternity and Life's Brief Span

PSALM 90

1 LORD, thou hast been our dwelling-place in all generations.

2 Before the mountains were brought forth, or ever thou hadst formed the earth and the world, even from everlasting to everlasting, thou art God.

3 Thou turnest man to destruction; and sayest, Return, ye children of men.

4 For a thousand years in thy sight are but as yesterday when it is past, and as a watch in the night.

5 Thou carriest them away as with a flood; they are as a sleep: in the morning they are like grass which groweth up.

6 In the morning it flourisheth, and groweth up; in the evening it is cut down, and withereth.

7 For we are consumed by thine anger. and by thy wrath are we troubled.

8 Thou hast set our iniquities before thee, our secret sins in the light of thy countenance.

9 For all our days are passed away in thy wrath: we spend our years as a tale that is told.

10 The days of our years are threescore years and ten; and if by reason of strength they be fourscore years, yet is their strength labor and sorrow; for it is soon cut off, and we fly away.

11 Who knoweth the power of thine anger? even according to thy fear, so is thy wrath.

12 So teach us to number our days, that we may apply our hearts unto wisdom.

13 Return, O Lord, how long? and let it repent thee concerning thy servants.

14 O satisfy us early with thy mercy; that we may rejoice and be glad all our days.

15 Make us glad according to the days wherein thou hast afflicted us, and the years wherein we have seen evil.

16 Let thy work appear unto thy servants, and thy glory unto their children.

17 And let the beauty of the Lord our God be upon us: and establish thou the work of our hands upon us; yea, the work of our hands establish thou it.

PSALM 73 : 25, 26

18 Whom have I in heaven but thee? and there is none upon earth that I desire besides thee.

19 My flesh and my heart faileth: but God is the strength of my heart, and my portion for ever.

Glory be to the *Fa*ther | and ˙ to the | Son || *and* | to the | Holy | Ghost;
As it was in the beginning * is *now,* and | ever | shall be || *world* without |
  end ˙ = | A ˙ = | men.

406

SELECTION 5

The Lord Reigneth

1   THE Lord reigneth, he is clothed with majesty;

2   The Lord is clothed with strength, wherewith he hath girded himself: the world also is stablished, that it cannot be moved.

3   Thy throne is established of old: thou art from everlasting.

4   The floods have lifted up, O Lord, the floods have lifted up their voice; the floods lift up their waves.

5   The Lord on high is mightier than the noise of many waters, yea, than the mighty waves of the sea.

6   Thy testimonies are very sure: holiness becometh thine house, O Lord, for ever.

7   THE Lord reigneth; let the earth rejoice; let the multitude of isles be glad thereof.

8   Clouds and darkness are round about him: righteousness and judgment are the habitation of his throne.

9   A fire goeth before him, and burneth up his enemies round about.

10   His lightnings enlightened the world: the earth saw, and trembled.

11   The hills melted like wax at the presence of the Lord, at the presence of the Lord of the whole earth.

12   The heavens declare his righteousness, and all the people see his glory.

13   Confounded be all they that serve graven images, that boast themselves of idols: worship him, all ye gods.

14   Zion heard, and was glad; and the daughters of Judah rejoiced because of thy judgments, O Lord.

15   For thou, Lord, art high above all the earth: thou art exalted far above all gods.

16   Ye that love the Lord, hate evil: he preserveth the souls of his saints; he delivereth them out of the hand of the wicked.

17   Light is sown for the righteous, and gladness for the upright in heart.

18   Rejoice in the Lord, ye righteous; and give thanks at the remembrance of his holiness.

19   THE Lord reigneth; let the people tremble: he sitteth between the cherubim; let the earth be moved.

20   The Lord is great in Zion; and he is high above all the people.

21   Let them praise thy great and terrible name; for it is holy.

22   Exalt ye the Lord our God, and worship at his footstool; for he is holy.

Glory be to the *Father* | and ˙ to the | Son || *and* | to the | Holy | Ghost;
As it was in the beginning * is *now*, and | ever | shall be || *world* without |
   end ˙ = | A ˙ = | men.

SELECTION 6

Let everything that hath breath praise the Lord

PSALM 148

1 PRAISE ye the Lord. Praise ye the Lord from the heavens: praise him in the heights.

2 Praise ye him, all his angels: praise ye him, all his hosts.

3 Praise ye him, sun and moon: praise him, all ye stars of light.

4 Praise him, ye heavens of heavens, and ye waters that be above the heavens.

5 Let them praise the name of the Lord: for he commanded, and they were created.

6 He hath also stablished them for ever and ever: he hath made a decree which shall not pass.

7 Praise the Lord from the earth, ye dragons, and all deeps:

8 Fire, and hail; snow, and vapors; stormy wind fulfilling his word:

9 Mountains, and all hills; fruitful trees, and all cedars:

10 Beasts, and all cattle; creeping things, and flying fowl:

11 Kings of the earth, and all people; princes, and all judges of the earth:

12 Both young men, and maidens; old men, and children:

13 Let them praise the name of the Lord: for his name alone is excellent; his glory is above the earth and heaven.

14 He also exalteth the horn of his people, the praise of all his saints; even of the children of Israel, a people near unto him. Praise ye the Lord.

PSALM 150

15 PRAISE ye the Lord. Praise God in his sanctuary: praise him in the firmament of his power.

16 Praise him for his mighty acts: praise him according to his excellent greatness.

17 Praise him with the sound of the trumpet: praise him with the psaltery and harp.

18 Praise him with the timbrel and dance: praise him with stringed instruments and organs.

19 Praise him upon the loud cymbals: praise him upon the high sounding cymbals.

20 Let everything that hath breath praise the Lord. Praise ye the Lord.

Glory be to the *Father* | and · to the | Son ‖ *and* | to the | Holy | Ghost;
As it was in the beginning * is *now*, and | ever | shall be ‖ *world* without | end · = | A · = | men.

SELECTION 7

A New Song to the Lord of all

PSALM 95 : 1-7

1 O COME, let us sing unto the Lord: let us make a joyful noise to the Rock of our salvation.

2 Let us come before his presence with thanksgiving, and make a joyful noise unto him with psalms.

3 For the Lord is a great God, and a great King above all gods.

4 In his hands are the deep places of the earth: the strength of the hills is his also.

5 The sea is his, and he made it: and his hands formed the dry land.

6 O come, let us worship and bow down: let us kneel before the Lord our maker.

7 For he is our God; and we are the people of his pasture, and the sheep of his hand.

8 O SING unto the Lord a new song: sing unto the Lord, all the earth.

9 Sing unto the Lord, bless his name; show forth his salvation from day to day.

10 Declare his glory amcng the heathen, his wonders among all people.

11 For the Lord is great, and greatly to be praised: he is to be feared above all gods.

12 For all the gods of the nations are idols: but the Lord made the heavens.

13 Honor and majesty are before him: strength and beauty are in his sanctuary.

14 Give unto the Lord, O ye kindreds of the people, give unto the Lord glory and strength.

15 Give unto the Lord the glory due unto his name: bring an offering, and come into his courts.

16 O worship the Lord in the beauty of holiness: fear before him, all the earth.

17 Say among the heathen that the Lord reigneth; the world also shall be established that it shall not be moved: he shall judge the people righteously.

18 Let the heavens rejoice, and let the earth be glad; let the sea roar, and the fulness thereof.

19 Let the field be joyful, and all that is therein: then shall all the trees of the wood rejoice

20 Before the Lord: for he cometh, for he cometh to judge the earth: he shall judge the world with righteousness, and the people with his truth.

21 MAKE a joyful noise unto the Lord, all ye lands.

22 Serve the Lord with gladness: come before his presence with singing.

23 Know ye that the Lord he is God: it is he that hath made us, and not we ourselves; we are his people, and the sheep of his pasture.

24 Enter into his gates with thanksgiving, and into his courts with praise: be thankful unto him, and bless his name.

25 For the Lord is good; his mercy is everlasting; and his truth endureth to all generations.

Glory be to the *Father* | and · to the | Son || *and* | to the | Holy | Ghost;
As it was in the beginning * is *now*, and | ever | shall be || *world* without |
    end · = | A · = | men.

SELECTION 8

A Congregational Hymn to God's Praise

PSALM 33

1 REJOICE in the Lord, O ye righteous: for praise is comely for the upright.

2 Praise the Lord with harp: sing unto him with the psaltery and an instrument of ten strings.

3 Sing unto him a new song; play skilfully with a loud noise.

4 For the word of the Lord is right; and all his works are done in truth.

5 He loveth righteousness and judgment: the earth is full of the goodness of the Lord.

6 By the word of the Lord were the heavens made; and all the host of them by the breath of his mouth.

7 He gathereth the waters of the sea together as a heap: he layeth up the depth in storehouses.

8 Let all the earth fear the Lord: let all the inhabitants of the world stand in awe of him.

9 For he spake, and it was done; he commanded, and it stood fast.

10 The Lord bringeth the counsel of the heathen to nought: he maketh the devices of the people of none effect.

11 The counsel of the Lord standeth for ever, the thoughts of his heart to all generations.

12 Blessed is the nation whose God is the Lord; and the people whom he hath chosen for his own inheritance.

13 The Lord looketh from heaven; he beholdeth all the sons of men.

14 From the place of his habitation he looketh upon all the inhabitants of the earth.

15 He fashioneth their hearts alike; he considereth all their works.

16 There is no king saved by the multitude of a host: a mighty man is not delivered by much strength.

17 A horse is a vain thing for safety: neither shall he deliver any by his great strength.

18 Behold, the eye of the Lord is upon them that fear him, upon them that hope in his mercy;

19 To deliver their soul from death, and to keep them alive in famine.

20 Our soul waiteth for the Lord: he is our help and our shield.

21 For our heart shall rejoice in him, because we have trusted in his holy name.

22 Let thy mercy, O Lord, be upon us, according as we hope in thee.

Glory be to the *Father* | and · to the | Son || *and* | to the | Holy | Ghost;
As it was in the beginning * is *now,* and | ever | shall be || *world* without |
     end · = | A · = | men.

SELECTION 9

A Psalm of God's Sovereignty and Grace

PSALM 66

1   MAKE a joyful noise unto God, all ye lands:

2   Sing forth the honor of his name: make his praise glorious.

3   Say unto God, How terrible art thou in thy works! through the greatness of thy power shall thine enemies submit themselves unto thee.

4   All the earth shall worship thee, and shall sing unto thee; they shall sing to thy name.

5   Come and see the works of God: he is terrible in his doing toward the children of men.

6   He turned the sea into dry land: they went through the flood on foot: there did we rejoice in him.

7   He ruleth by his power for ever; his eyes behold the nations: let not the rebellious exalt themselves.

8   O bless our God, ye people, and make the voice of his praise to be heard:

9   Which holdeth our soul in life, and suffereth not our feet to be moved.

10   For thou, O God, hast proved us: thou hast tried us, as silver is tried.

11   Thou broughtest us into the net; thou laidst affliction upon our loins.

12   Thou hast caused men to ride over our heads; we went through fire and through water: but thou broughtest us out into a wealthy place.

13   I will go into thy house with burnt offerings: I will pay thee my vows,

14   Which my lips have uttered, and my mouth hath spoken, when I was in trouble.

15   Come and hear, all ye that fear God, and I will declare what he hath done for my soul.

16   I cried unto him with my mouth, and he was extolled with my tongue.

17   If I regard iniquity in my heart, the Lord will not hear me:

18   But verily God hath heard me; he hath attended to the voice of my prayer.

19   Blessed be God, which hath not turned away my prayer, nor his mercy from me.

Glory be to the *F*ather | and ᐧ to the | Son || *and* | to the | Holy | Ghost;
As it was in the beginning * is *now*, and | ever | shall be || *world* without |
 end ᐧ = | A ᐧ = | men.

411

SELECTION 10

God's Greatness and Mercy

PSALM 145

1 I WILL extol thee, my God, O King; and I will bless thy name for ever and ever.

   2 Every day will I bless thee; and I will praise thy name for ever and ever.

3 Great is the Lord, and greatly to be praised; and his greatness is unsearchable.

   4 One generation shall praise thy works to another, and shall declare thy mighty acts.

5 I will speak of the glorious honor of thy majesty, and of thy wondrous works.

   6 And men shall speak of the might of thy terrible acts: and I will declare thy greatness.

7 They shall abundantly utter the memory of thy great goodness, and shall sing of thy righteousness.

   8 The Lord is gracious, and full of compassion; slow to anger, and of great mercy.

9 The Lord is good to all: and his tender mercies are over all his works.

   10 All thy works shall praise thee, O Lord; and thy saints shall bless thee.

11 They shall speak of the glory of thy kingdom, and talk of thy power;

   12 To make known to the sons of men his mighty acts, and the glorious majesty of his kingdom.

13 Thy kingdom is an everlasting kingdom, and thy dominion endureth throughout all generations.

   14 The Lord upholdeth all that fall, and raiseth up all those that be bowed down.

15 The eyes of all wait upon thee; and thou givest them their meat in due season.

   16 Thou openest thine hand, and satisfiest the desire of every living thing.

17 The Lord is righteous in all his ways, and holy in all his works.

   18 The Lord is nigh unto all them that call upon him, to all that call upon him in truth.

19 He will fulfil the desire of them that fear him: he also will hear their cry, and will save them.

   20 The Lord preserveth all them that love him: but all the wicked will he destroy.

21 My mouth shall speak the praise of the Lord: and let all flesh bless his holy name for ever and ever.

Glory be to the *Father* | and · to the | Son || *and* | to the | Holy | Ghost;
As it was in the beginning * is *now*, and | ever | shall be || *world* without |
    end · = | A · = | men.

SELECTION 11

God in His World

PSALM 104 : 1–15, 19–24, 31–33

1 BLESS the Lord, O my soul. O Lord my God, thou art very great; thou art clothed with honor and majesty:

2 Who coverest thyself with light as with a garment: who stretchest out the heavens like a curtain:

3 Who layeth the beams of his chambers in the waters: who maketh the clouds his chariot: who walketh upon the wings of the wind:

4 Who maketh his angels spirits; his ministers a flaming fire:

5 Who laid the foundations of the earth, that it should not be removed for ever.

6 Thou coveredst it with the deep as with a garment: the waters stood above the mountains.

7 At thy rebuke they fled; at the voice of thy thunder they hasted away.

8 They go up by the mountains; they go down by the valleys unto the place which thou hast founded for them.

9 Thou hast set a bound that they may not pass over; that they turn not again to cover the earth.

10 He sendeth the springs into the valleys, which run among the hills.

11 They give drink to every beast of the field: the wild asses quench their thirst.

12 By them shall the fowls of the heaven have their habitation, which sing among the branches.

13 He watereth the hills from the clouds: the earth is satisfied with the fruit of thy works.

14 He causeth the grass to grow for the cattle, and herb for the service of man: that he may bring forth food out of the earth;

15 And wine that maketh glad the heart of man, and oil to make his face to shine, and bread which strengtheneth man's heart.

16 He appointed the moon for seasons: the sun knoweth his going down.

17 Thou makest darkness, and it is night: wherein all the beasts of the forest do creep forth.

18 The young lions roar after their prey, and seek their meat from God.

19 The sun ariseth, they gather themselves together, and lay them down in their dens.

20 Man goeth forth unto his work and to his labor until the evening.

21 O Lord, how manifold are thy works ! in wisdom hast thou made them all: the earth is full of thy riches.

22 The glory of the Lord shall endure for ever: the Lord shall rejoice in his works.

23 He looketh on the earth, and it trembleth: he toucheth the hills, and they smoke.

24 I will sing unto the Lord as long as I live: I will sing praise to my God while I have my being.

Glory be to the *Father* | and ˙ to the | Son || *and* | to the | Holy | Ghost;
As it was in the beginning * is *now*, and | ever | shall be || *world* without |
    end ˙ = | ˙ A ˙ = | men.

SELECTION 12

God's Power in Nature and His Goodness to Man

PSALM 29

· 1 GIVE unto the Lord, O ye mighty, give unto the Lord glory and strength.

2 Give unto the Lord the glory due unto his name; worship the Lord in the beauty of holiness.

3 The voice of the Lord is upon the waters: the God of glory thundereth: the Lord is upon many waters.

4 The voice of the Lord is powerful; the voice of the Lord is full of majesty.

5 The voice of the Lord breaketh the cedars; yea, the Lord breaketh the cedars of Lebanon.

6 He maketh them also to skip like a calf; Lebanon and Sirion like a young unicorn.

7 The voice of the Lord divideth the flames of fire.

8 The voice of the Lord shaketh the wilderness; the Lord shaketh the wilderness of Kadesh.

9 The voice of the Lord maketh the hinds to calve, and discovereth the forests: and in his temple doth every one speak of his glory.

10 The Lord sitteth upon the flood; yea, the Lord sitteth King for ever.

11 The Lord will give strength unto his people; the Lord will bless his people with peace.

PSALM 36 : 5–10

12 Thy mercy, O Lord is in the heavens; and thy faithfulness reacheth unto the clouds.

13 Thy righteousness is like the great mountains; thy judgments are a great deep: O Lord, thou preservest man and beast.

14 How excellent is thy loving-kindness, O God ! therefore the children of men put their trust under the shadow of thy wings.

15 They shall be abundantly satisfied with the fatness of thy house; and thou shalt make them drink of the river of thy pleasures.

16 For with thee is the fountain of life: in thy light shall we see light.

17 O continue thy loving-kindness unto them that know thee; and thy righteousness to the upright in heart.

Glory be to the *Father* | and · to the | Son || *and* | to the | Holy | Ghost;
As it was in the beginning * is *now*, and | ever | shall be || *world* without | end · = | A · = | men.

SELECTION 13

A Psalm of the Earth's Abundance and Man's Dominion

PSALM 65

1 PRAISE waiteth for thee, O God, in Zion: and unto thee shall the vow be performed.

2 O thou that hearest prayer, unto thee shall all flesh come.

3 Iniquities prevail against me: as for our transgressions, thou shalt purge them away.

4 Blessed is the man whom thou choosest, and causest to approach unto thee, that he may dwell in thy courts:

5 We shall be satisfied with the goodness of thy house, even of thy holy temple.

6 By terrible things in righteousness wilt thou answer us, O God of our salvation;

7 Who art the confidence of all the ends of the earth, and of them that are afar off upon the sea:

8 Which by his strength setteth fast the mountains; being girded with power:

9 Which stilleth the noise of the seas, the noise of their waves, and the tumult of the people.

10 They also that dwell in the uttermost parts are afraid at thy tokens:

11 Thou makest the outgoings of the morning and evening to rejoice.

12 Thou visitest the earth, and waterest it: thou greatly enrichest it with the river of God, which is full of water:

13 Thou preparest them corn, when thou hast so provided for it.

14 Thou waterest the ridges thereof abundantly: thou settlest the furrows thereof:

15 Thou makest it soft with showers: thou blessest the springing thereof.

16 Thou crownest the year with thy goodness; and thy paths drop fatness.

17 They drop upon the pastures of the wilderness: and the little hills rejoice on every side.

18 The pastures are clothed with flocks; the valleys also are covered over with corn; they shout for joy, they also sing.

PSALM 8

19 O LORD our Lord, how excellent is thy name in all the earth ! who hast set thy glory above the heavens.

20 Out of the mouth of babes and sucklings hast thou ordained strength because of thine enemies, that thou mightest still the enemy and the avenger.

21 When I consider thy heavens, the work of thy fingers, the moon and the stars, which thou hast ordained;

22 What is man, that thou art mindful of him? and the son of man, that thou visitest him?

23 For thou hast made him a little lower than the angels, and hast crowned him with glory and honor.

24 Thou madest him to have dominion over the works of thy hands; thou hast put all things under his feet:

25 All sheep and oxen, yea, and the beasts of the field;

26 The fowl of the air, and the fish of the sea, and whatsoever passeth through the paths of the seas.

27 O Lord our Lord, how excellent is thy name in all the earth !

Glory be to the *Father* | and · to the | Son || *and* | to the | Holy | Ghost;
As it was in the beginning * is *now*, and | ever | shall be || *world* without | end · = | A · = | men.

415

SELECTION 14

God's Praise in the Assembly of His People

Psalm 92 : 1–9, 12, 13

1 IT is a good thing to give thanks unto the Lord, and to sing praises unto thy name, O Most High:

2 To show forth thy loving-kindness in the morning, and thy faithfulness every night,

3 Upon an instrument of ten strings, and upon the psaltery; upon the harp with a solemn sound.

4 For thou, Lord, hast made me glad through thy work: I will triumph in the works of thy hands.

5 O Lord, how great are thy works ! and thy thoughts are very deep.

6 A brutish man knoweth not; neither doth a fool understand this.

7 When the wicked spring as the grass, and when all the workers of iniquity do flourish; it is that they shall be destroyed for ever:

8 But thou, Lord, art most high for evermore.

9 For, lo, thine enemies, O Lord, for, lo, thine enemies shall perish; all the workers of iniquity shall be scattered.

10 The righteous shall flourish like the palm tree: he shall grow like a cedar in Lebanon.

11 Those that be planted in the house of the Lord shall flourish in the courts of our God.

Psalm 111

12 PRAISE ye the Lord. I will praise the Lord with my whole heart, in the assembly of the upright, and in the congregation.

13 The works of the Lord are great, sought out of all them that have pleasure therein.

14 His work is honorable and glorious: and his righteousness endureth for ever.

15 He hath made his wonderful works to be remembered: the Lord is gracious and full of compassion.

16 He hath given meat unto them that fear him: he will ever be mindful of his covenant.

17 He hath showed his people the power of his works, that he may give them the heritage of the heathen.

18 The works of his hands are verity and judgment; all his commandments are sure.

19 They stand fast for ever and ever, and are done in truth and uprightness.

20 He sent redemption unto his people: he hath commanded his covenant for ever: holy and reverend is his name.

21 The fear of the Lord is the beginning of wisdom:

22 A good understanding have all they that do his commandments: his praise endureth for ever.

Glory be to the *Father* | and · to the | Son || *and* | to the | Holy | Ghost;
As it was in the beginning * is *now*, and | ever | shall be || *world* without | end · = | A · = | men.

416

SELECTION 15

A Psalm of the manifold Mercies of God

PSALM 103

1 BLESS the Lord, O my soul: and all that is within me, bless his holy name.

2 Bless the Lord, O my soul, and forget not all his benefits:

3 Who forgiveth all thine iniquities; who healeth all thy diseases;

4 Who redeemeth thy life from destruction; who crowneth thee with loving-kindness and tender mercies;

5 Who satisfieth thy mouth with good things; so that thy youth is renewed like the eagle's.

6 The Lord executeth righteousness and judgment for all that are oppressed.

7 He made known his ways unto Moses, his acts unto the children of Israel.

8 The Lord is merciful and gracious, slow to anger, and plenteous in mercy.

9 He will not always chide: neither will he keep his anger for ever.

10 He hath not dealt with us after our sins; nor rewarded us according to our iniquities.

11 For as the heaven is high above the earth, so great is his mercy toward them that fear him.

12 As far as the east is from the west, so far hath he removed our transgressions from us.

13 Like as a father pitieth his children, so the Lord pitieth them that fear him.

14 For he knoweth our frame; he remembereth that we are dust.

15 As for man, his days are as grass: as a flower of the field, so he flourisheth.

16 For the wind passeth over it, and it is gone; and the place thereof shall know it no more.

17 But the mercy of the Lord is from everlasting to everlasting upon them that fear him, and his righteousness unto children's children;

18 To such as keep his covenant, and to those that remember his commandments to do them.

19 The Lord hath prepared his throne in the heavens; and his kingdom ruleth over all.

20 Bless the Lord, ye his angels, that excel in strength, that do his commandments, hearkening unto the voice of his word.

21 Bless ye the Lord, all ye his hosts; ye ministers of his, that do his pleasure.

22 Bless the Lord, all his works in all places of his dominion: bless the Lord, O my soul.

Glory be to the *Father* | and · to the | Son || *and* | to the | Holy | Ghost;
As it was in the beginning * is *now*, and | ever | shall be || *world* without |
    end · = | A · = | men.

SELECTION 16

O that men would praise the Lord for His Goodness

PSALM 107 : 1–22

1 O GIVE thanks unto the Lord, for he is good: for his mercy endureth for ever.

2 Let the redeemed of the Lord say so, whom he hath redeemed from the hand of the enemy;

3 And gathered them out of the lands, from the east, and from the west, from the north, and from the south.

4 They wandered in the wilderness in a solitary way; they found no city to dwell in.

5 Hungry and thirsty, their soul fainted in them.

6 Then they cried unto the Lord in their trouble, and he delivered them out of their distresses.

7 And he led them forth by the right way, that they might go to a city of habitation.

8 Oh that men would praise the Lord for his goodness, and for his wonderful works to the children of men !

9 For he satisfieth the longing soul, and filleth the hungry soul with goodness.

10 Such as sit in darkness and in the shadow of death, being bound in affliction and iron;

11 Because they rebelled against the words of God, and contemned the counsel of the Most High:

12 Therefore he brought down their heart with labor; they fell down, and there was none to help.

13 Then they cried unto the Lord in their trouble, and he saved them out of their distresses.

14 He brought them out of darkness and the shadow of death, and brake their bands in sunder.

15 Oh that men would praise the Lord for his goodness, and for his wonderful works to the children of men !

16 For he hath broken the gates of brass, and cut the bars of iron in sunder.

17 Fools, because of their transgression, and because of their iniquities, are afflicted.

18 Their soul abhorreth all manner of meat; and they draw near unto the gates of death.

19 Then they cry unto the Lord in their trouble, and he saveth them out of their distresses.

20 He sent his word, and healed them, and delivered them from their destructions.

21 Oh that men would praise the Lord for his goodness, and for his wonderful works to the children of men !

22 And let them sacrifice the sacrifices of thanksgiving, and declare his works with rejoicing.

Glory be to the *Father* | and ˙ to the | Son ‖ *and* | to the | Holy | Ghost;
As it was in the beginning * is *now,* and | ever | shall be ‖ *world* without |
end ˙ = | A ˙ = | men.

SELECTION 17

God's Goodness on Sea and Land

PSALM 107 : 23–43

1 THEY that go down to the sea in ships, that do business in great waters;

2 These see the works of the Lord, and his wonders in the deep.

3 For he commandeth, and raiseth the stormy wind, which lifteth up the waves thereof.

4 They mount up to the heaven, they go down again to the depths: their soul is melted because of trouble.

5 They reel to and fro, and stagger like a drunken man, and are at their wit's end.

6 Then they cry unto the Lord in their trouble, and he bringeth them out of their distresses.

7 He maketh the storm a calm, so that the waves thereof are still.

8 Then are they glad because they be quiet; so he bringeth them unto their desired haven.

9 Oh that men would praise the Lord for his goodness, and for his wonderful works to the children of men !

10 Let them exalt him also in the congregation of the people, and praise him in the assembly of the elders.

11 He turneth rivers into a wilderness, and the watersprings into dry ground;

12 A fruitful land into barrenness, for the wickedness of them that dwell therein.

13 He turneth the wilderness into a standing water, and dry ground into watersprings.

14 And there he maketh the hungry to dwell, that they may prepare a city for habitation;

15 And sow the fields, and plant vineyards, which may yield fruits of increase.

16 He blesseth them also, so that they are multiplied greatly; and suffereth not their cattle to decrease.

17 Again, they are minished and brought low through oppression, affliction, and sorrow.

18 He poureth contempt upon princes, and causeth them to wander in the wilderness, where there is no way.

19 Yet setteth he the poor on high from affliction, and maketh him families like a flock.

20 The righteous shall see it, and rejoice: and all iniquity shall stop her mouth.

21 Whoso is wise, and will observe these things, even they shall understand the lovingkindness of the Lord.

Glory be to the *Father* | and · to the | Son || *and* | to the | Holy | Ghost;
As it was in the beginning * is *now*, and | ever | shall be || *world* without |
end · = | A · = | men.

419

SELECTION 18

His Mercy endureth for ever

PSALM 136 : 1–9, 23–26

1 O GIVE thanks unto the Lord; for he is good: for his mercy endureth for ever.

2 O give thanks unto the God of gods: for his mercy endureth for ever.

3 O give thanks to the Lord of lords: for his mercy endureth for ever.

4 To him who alone doeth great wonders: for his mercy endureth for ever.

5 To him that by wisdom made the heavens: for his mercy endureth for ever.

6 To him that stretched out the earth above the waters: for his mercy endureth for ever.

7 To him that made great lights: for his mercy endureth for ever:

8 The sun to rule by day: for his mercy endureth for ever:

9 The moon and stars to rule by night: for his mercy endureth for ever.

10 Who remembered us in our low estate: for his mercy endureth for ever:

11 And hath redeemed us from our enemies: for his mercy endureth for ever.

12 Who giveth food to all flesh: for his mercy endureth for ever.

13 O give thanks unto the God of heaven: for his mercy endureth for ever.

PSALM 138

14 I WILL praise thee with my whole heart: before the gods will I sing praise unto thee.

15 I will worship toward thy holy temple, and praise thy name for thy loving-kindness and for thy truth:

16 For thou hast magnified thy word above all thy name.

17 In the day when I cried thou answeredst me, and strengthenedst me with strength in my soul.

18 All the kings of the earth shall praise thee, O Lord, when they hear the words of thy mouth.

19 Yea, they shall sing in the ways of the Lord: for great is the glory of the Lord.

20 Though the Lord be high, yet hath he respect unto the lowly: but the proud he knoweth afar off.

21 Though I walk in the midst of trouble, thou wilt revive me:

22 Thou shalt stretch forth thine hand against the wrath of mine enemies, and thy right hand shall save me.

23 The Lord will perfect that which concerneth me:

24 Thy mercy, O Lord, endureth for ever: forsake not the works of thine own hands.

Glory be to the *Father* | and ˙ to the | Son || *and* | to the | Holy | Ghost;
As it was in the beginning * is *now,* and | ever | shall be || *world* without |
    end ˙ = | A ˙ ≍ | men.

SELECTION 19

The Lord is my Shepherd

Psalm 20

1 THE Lord hear thee in the day of trouble; the name of the God of Jacob defend thee;

2 Send thee help from the sanctuary, and strengthen thee out of Zion;

3 Remember all thy offerings, and accept thy burnt sacrifice;

4 Grant thee according to thine own heart, and fulfil all thy counsel.

5 We will rejoice in thy salvation, and in the name of our God we will set up our banners: the Lord fulfil all thy petitions.

6 Now know I that the Lord saveth his anointed;

7 He will hear him from his holy heaven with the saving strength of his right hand.

8 Some trust in chariots, and some in horses: but we will remember the name of the Lord our God.

9 They are brought down and fallen: but we are risen, and stand upright.

10 Save, Lord: let the king hear us when we call.

Psalm 121

11 I WILL lift up mine eyes unto the hills, from whence cometh my help.

12 My help cometh from the Lord, which made heaven and earth.

13 He will not suffer thy foot to be moved: he that keepeth thee will not slumber.

14 Behold, he that keepeth Israel shall neither slumber nor sleep.

15 The Lord is thy keeper: the Lord is thy shade upon thy right hand.

16 The sun shall not smite thee by day, nor the moon by night.

17 The Lord shall preserve thee from all evil: he shall preserve thy soul.

18 The Lord shall preserve thy going out and thy coming in from this time forth, and even for evermore.

Psalm 23

19 THE Lord is my shepherd; I shall not want.

20 He maketh me to lie down in green pastures: he leadeth me beside the still waters.

21 He restoreth my soul: he leadeth me in the paths of righteousness for his name's sake.

22 Yea, though I walk through the valley of the shadow of death, I will fear no evil: for thou art with me; thy rod and thy staff they comfort me.

23 Thou preparest a table before me in the presence of mine enemies: thou anointest my head with oil; my cup runneth over.

24 Surely goodness and mercy shall follow me all the days of my life: and I will dwell in the house of the Lord for ever.

Glory be to the *Father* | and ˙ to the | Son || *and* | to the | Holy | Ghost;
As it was in the beginning * is *now*, and | ever | shall be || *world* without |
    end ˙ = | A ˙ = | men.

SELECTION 20

Our Help is in the Name of the Lord

PSALM 124

1 IF it had not been the Lord who was on our side, now may Israel say;

    2 If it had not been the Lord who was on our side, when men rose up against us:

3 Then they had swallowed us up quick, when their wrath was kindled against us:

    4 Then the waters had overwhelmed us, the stream had gone over our soul:

5 Then the proud waters had gone over our soul.

    6 Blessed be the Lord, who hath not given us as a prey to their teeth.

7 Our soul is escaped as a bird out of the snare of the fowlers: the snare is broken, and we are escaped.

    8 Our help is in the name of the Lord, who made heaven and earth.

PSALM 135 : 1–5, 15–21

9 PRAISE ye the Lord. Praise ye the name of the Lord; praise him, O ye servants of the Lord.

    10 Ye that stand in the house of the Lord, in the courts of the house of our God,

11 Praise the Lord; for the Lord is good: sing praises unto his name; for it is pleasant.

    12 For the Lord hath chosen Jacob unto himself, and Israel for his peculiar treasure.

13 For I know that the Lord is great, and that our Lord is above all gods.

    14 The idols of the heathen are silver and gold, the work of men's hands.

15 They have mouths, but they speak not; eyes have they, but they see not;

    16 They have ears, but they hear not; neither is there any breath in their mouths.

17 They that make them are like unto them: so is every one that trusteth in them.

    18 Bless the Lord, O house of Israel: bless the Lord, O house of Aaron:

19 Bless the Lord, O house of Levi: ye that fear the Lord, bless the Lord.

    20 Blessed be the Lord out of Zion, which dwelleth at Jerusalem. Praise ye the Lord.

PSALM 57 : 7–11

21 MY heart is fixed, O God, my heart is fixed: I will sing and give praise.

    22 Awake up, my glory; awake, psaltery and harp: I myself will awake early.

23 I will praise thee, O Lord, among the people: I will sing unto thee among the nations.

    24 For thy mercy is great unto the heavens, and thy truth unto the clouds.

25 Be thou exalted, O God, above the heavens: let thy glory be above all the earth.

Glory be to the *Father* | and ⋅ to the | Son ‖ *and* | to the | Holy | Ghost;
As it was in the beginning * is *now*, and | ever | shall be ‖ *world* without |
    end ⋅ = | A ⋅ = | men.

422

SELECTION 21

A Prayer that our God will vindicate His Name

PSALM 113 : 1-6

1 PRAISE ye the Lord. Praise, O ye servants of the Lord, praise the name of the Lord.

2 Blessed be the name of the Lord from this time forth and for evermore.

3 From the rising of the sun unto the going down of the same the Lord's name is to be praised.

4 The Lord is high above all nations, and his glory above the heavens.

5 Who is like unto the Lord our God, who dwelleth on high,

6 Who humbleth himself to behold the things that are in heaven, and in the earth !

PSALM 115

7 NOT unto us, O Lord, not unto us, but unto thy name give glory, for thy mercy, and for thy truth's sake.

8 Wherefore should the heathen say, Where is now their God?

9 But our God is in the heavens: he hath done whatsoever he hath pleased.

10 Their idols are silver and gold, the work of men's hands.

11 They have mouths, but they speak not: eyes have they, but they see not:

12 They have ears, but they hear not: noses have they, but they smell not:

13 They have hands, but they handle not: feet have they, but they walk not: neither speak they through their throat.

14 They that make them are like unto them; so is every one that trusteth in them.

15 O Israel, trust thou in the Lord: he is their help and their shield.

16 O house of Aaron, trust in the Lord: he is their help and their shield.

17 Ye that fear the Lord, trust in the Lord: he is their help and their shield.

18 The Lord hath been mindful of us: he will bless us; he will bless the house of Israel; he will bless the house of Aaron.

19 He will bless them that fear the Lord, both small and great.

20 The Lord shall increase you more and more, you and your children.

21 Ye are blessed of the Lord which made heaven and earth.

22 The heaven, even the heavens, are the Lord's: but the earth hath he given to the children of men.

23 The dead praise not the Lord, neither any that go down into silence.

24 But we will bless the Lord from this time forth and for evermore. Praise the Lord.

Glory be to the *Father* | and ˙ to the | Son || *and* | to the | Holy | Ghost;
As it was in the beginning * is *now*, and | ever | shall be || *world* without |
　　end ˙ = | A ˙ = | men.

SELECTION 22

A Prayer for God's Protection and His Peace

PSALM 25

1 UNTO thee, O Lord, do I lift up my soul.

2 O my God, I trust in thee: let me not be ashamed, let not mine enemies triumph over me.

3 Yea, let none that wait on thee be ashamed: let them be ashamed which transgress without cause.

4 Show me thy ways, O Lord; teach me thy paths.

5 Lead me in thy truth, and teach me: for thou art the God of my salvation; on thee do I wait all the day.

6 Remember, O Lord, thy tender mercies and thy loving-kindnesses; for they have been ever of old.

7 Remember not the sins of my youth, nor my transgressions:

8 According to thy mercy remember thou me for thy goodness' sake, O Lord.

9 Good and upright is the Lord: therefore will he teach sinners in the way.

10 The meek will he guide in judgment: and the meek will he teach his way.

11 All the paths of the Lord are mercy and truth unto such as keep his covenant and his testimonies.

12 For thy name's sake, O Lord, pardon mine iniquity; for it is great.

13 What man is he that feareth the Lord? him shall he teach in the way that he shall choose.

14 His soul shall dwell at ease; and his seed shall inherit the earth.

15 The secret of the Lord is with them that fear him; and he will show them his covenant.

16 Mine eyes are ever toward the Lord; for he shall pluck my feet out of the net.

17 Turn thee unto me, and have mercy upon me; for I am desolate and afflicted.

18 The troubles of my heart are enlarged: O bring thou me out of my distresses.

19 Look upon mine affliction and my pain; and forgive all my sins.

20 Consider mine enemies; for they are many; and they hate me with cruel hatred.

21 O keep my soul, and deliver me: let me not be ashamed; for I put my trust in thee.

22 Let integrity and uprightness preserve me; for I wait on thee.

23 Redeem Israel, O God, out of all his troubles.

Glory be to the *Father* | and · to the | Son || *and* | to the | Holy | Ghost;
As it was in the beginning * is *now*, and | ever | shall be || *world* without |
    end · = | A · = | men.

SELECTION 23

In the secret place of God's Presence

PSALM 91

1 HE that dwelleth in the secret place of the Most High shall abide under the shadow of the Almighty.

2 I will say of the Lord, He is my refuge and my fortress: my God; in him will I trust.

3 Surely he shall deliver thee from the snare of the fowler, and from the noisome pestilence.

4 He shall cover thee with his feathers, and under his wings shalt thou trust: his truth shall be thy shield and buckler.

5 Thou shalt not be afraid for the terror by night; nor for the arrow that flieth by day;

6 Nor for the pestilence that walketh in darkness; nor for the destruction that wasteth at noonday.

7 A thousand shall fall at thy side, and ten thousand at thy right hand; but it shall not come nigh thee.

8 Only with thine eyes shalt thou behold and see the reward of the wicked.

9 Because thou hast made the Lord, which is my refuge, even the Most High, thy habitation;

10 There shall no evil befall thee, neither shall any plague come nigh thy dwelling.

11 For he shall give his angels charge over thee, to keep thee in all thy ways.

12 They shall bear thee up in their hands, lest thou dash thy foot against a stone.

13 Thou shalt tread upon the lion and adder: the young lion and the dragon shalt thou trample under feet.

14 Because he hath set his love upon me, therefore will I deliver him: I will set him on high, because he hath known my name.

15 He shall call upon me, and I will answer him: I will be with him in trouble; I will deliver him, and honor him.

16 With long life will I satisfy him, and show him my salvation.

Glory be to the *Father* | and · to the | Son || *and* | to the | Holy | Ghost;
As it was in the beginning * is *now*, and | ever | shall be || *world* without |
    end · = | A · = | men.

SELECTION 24

The Grounds of our Confidence in Prayer

Psalm 86

1 BOW down thine ear, O Lord, hear me: for I am poor and needy.

2 Preserve my soul; for I am holy: O thou my God, save thy servant that trusteth in thee.

3 Be merciful unto me, O Lord: for I cry unto thee daily.

4 Rejoice the soul of thy servant: for unto thee, O Lord, do I lift up my soul.

5 For thou, Lord, art good, and ready to forgive; and plenteous in mercy unto all them that call upon thee.

6 Give ear, O Lord, unto my prayer; and attend to the voice of my supplications.

7 In the day of my trouble I will call upon thee: for thou wilt answer me.

8 Among the gods there is none like unto thee, O Lord; neither are there any works like unto thy works.

9 All nations whom thou hast made shall come and worship before thee, O Lord; and shall glorify thy name.

10 For thou art great, and doest wondrous things: thou art God alone.

11 Teach me thy way, O Lord; I will walk in thy truth: unite my heart to fear thy name.

12 I will praise thee, O Lord my God, with all my heart: and I will glorify thy name for evermore.

13 For great is thy mercy toward me: and thou hast delivered my soul from the lowest hell.

14 O God, the proud are risen against me, and the assemblies of violent men have sought after my soul; and have not set thee before them.

15 But thou, O Lord, art a God full of compassion, and gracious, long suffering, and plenteous in mercy and truth.

16 O turn unto me, and have mercy upon me; give thy strength unto thy servant, and save the son of thine handmaid.

17 Show me a token for good; that they wh'ch hate me may see it, and be ashamed: because thou, Lord, hast helped me, and comforted me.

Psalm 28 : 6–9

18 BLESSED be the Lord, because he hath heard the voice of my supplications.

19 The Lord is my strength and my shield; my heart trusted in him, and I am helped: therefore my heart greatly rejoiceth; and with my song will I praise him.

20 The Lord is their strength, and he is the saving strength of his anointed.

21 Save thy people, and bless thine inheritance: feed them also, and lift them up for ever.

Glory be to the *Father* | and ' to the | Son || *and* | to the | Holy | Ghost;
As it was in the beginning * is *now*, and | ever | shall be || *world* without |
  end ' = | A ' = | men.

SELECTION 25

A Song of answered Prayer and life-long Praise

PSALM 116

1 I LOVE the Lord, because he hath heard my voice and my supplications.

2 Because he hath inclined his ear unto me, therefore will I call upon him as long as I live.

3 The sorrows of death compassed me, and the pains of hell gat hold upon me: I found trouble and sorrow.

4 Then called I upon the name of the Lord; O Lord, I beseech thee, deliver my soul.

5 Gracious is the Lord, and righteous; yea, our God is merciful.

6 The Lord preserveth the simple: I was brought low, and he helped me.

7 Return unto thy rest, O my soul; for the Lord hath dealt bountifully with thee.

8 For thou hast delivered my soul from death, mine eyes from tears, and my feet from falling.

9 I will walk before the Lord in the land of the living.

10 I believed, therefore have I spoken: I was greatly afflicted:

11 I said in my haste, All men are liars.

12 What shall I render unto the Lord for all his benefits toward me?

13 I will take the cup of salvation, and call upon the name of the Lord.

14 I will pay my vows unto the Lord now in the presence of all his people.

15 Precious in the sight of the Lord is the death of his saints.

16 O Lord, truly I am thy servant; I am thy servant, and the son of thine handmaid: thou hast loosed my bonds.

17 I will offer to thee the sacrifice of thanksgiving, and will call upon the name of the Lord.

18 I will pay my vows unto the Lord now in the presence of all his people,

19 In the courts of the Lord's house, in the midst of thee, O Jerusalem. Praise ye the Lord.

PSALM 117

20 O PRAISE the Lord, all ye nations: praise him, all ye people.

21 For his merciful kindness is great toward us: and the truth of the Lord endureth for ever. Praise ye the Lord.

Glory be to the *Father* | and ˙ to the | Son || *and* | to the | Holy | Ghost;
As it was in the beginning * is *now*, and | ever | shall be || *world* without |
    end ˙ = | A ˙ = | men.

SELECTION 26

The Song of a Faith that has proved God's Goodness

PSALM 71 : 1–5, 8–9, 12, 14–24

1 IN thee, O Lord, do I put my trust: let me never be put to confusion.

2 Deliver me in thy righteousness, and cause me to escape: incline thine ear unto me, and save me.

3 Be thou my strong habitation, whereunto I may continually resort:

4 Thou hast given commandment to save me; for thou art my rock and my fortress.

5 Deliver me, O my God, out of the hand of the wicked, out of the hand of the unrighteous and cruel man.

6 For thou art my hope, O Lord God: thou art my trust from my youth.

7 Let my mouth be filled with thy praise and with thy honor all the day.

8 Cast me not off in the time of old age; forsake me not when my strength faileth.

9 O God, be not far from me: O my God, make haste for my help.

10 But I will hope continually, and will yet praise thee more and more.

11 My mouth shall show forth thy righteousness and thy salvation all the day; for I know not the numbers thereof.

12 I will go in the strength of the Lord God: I will make mention of thy righteousness, even of thine only.

13 O God, thou hast taught me from my youth: and hitherto have I declared thy wondrous works.

14 Now also when I am old and gray-headed, O God, forsake me not; until I have showed thy strength unto this generation, and thy power to every one that is to come.

15 Thy righteousness also, O God, is very high, who hast done great things: O God, who is like unto thee !

16 Thou, which hast showed me great and sore troubles, shalt quicken me again, and shalt bring me up again from the depths of the earth.

17 Thou shalt increase my greatness, and comfort me on every side.

18 I will also praise thee with the psaltery, even thy truth, O my God:

19 Unto thee will I sing with the harp, O thou Holy One of Israel.

20 My lips shall greatly rejoice when I sing unto thee; and my soul, which thou hast redeemed.

21 My tongue also shall talk of thy righteousness all the day long:

22 For they are confounded, for they are brought unto shame, that seek my hurt.

Glory be to the *F*ather | and ˙ to the | Son || *and* | to the | Holy | Ghost;
As it was in the beginning * is *now*, and | ever | shall be || *world* without |
end ˙ ⚓ | A ˙ = | men.

SELECTION 27

The Searcher of Hearts

Psalm 139 : 1–12, 14–18, 23, 24

1   O LORD, thou hast searched me, and known me.

2   Thou knowest my downsitting and mine uprising; thou understandest my thought afar off.

3   Thou compassest my path and my lying down, and art acquainted with all my ways.

4   For there is not a word in my tongue, but, lo, O Lord, thou knowest it altogether.

5   Thou hast beset me behind and before, and laid thine hand upon me.

6   Such knowledge is too wonderful for me; it is high, I cannot attain unto it.

7   Whither shall I go from thy Spirit? or whither shall I flee from thy presence?

8   If I ascend up into heaven, thou art there: if I make my bed in hell, behold, thou art there.

9   If I take the wings of the morning, and dwell in the uttermost parts of the sea;

10   Even there shall thy hand lead me, and thy right hand shall hold me.

11   If I say, Surely the darkness shall cover me; even the night shall be light about me.

12   Yea, the darkness hideth not from thee; but the night shineth as the day: the darkness and the light are both alike to thee.

13   I will praise thee; for I am fearfully and wonderfully made: marvellous are thy works; and that my soul knoweth right well.

14   My substance was not hid from thee, when I was made in secret, and curiously wrought in the lowest parts of the earth.

15   Thine eyes did see my substance, yet being unperfect;

16   And in thy book all my members were written, which in continuance were fashioned, when as yet there was none of them.

17   How precious also are thy thoughts unto me, O God ! how great is the sum of them !

18   If I should count them, they are more in number than the sand: when I awake, I am still with thee.

19   Search me, O God, and know my heart: try me, and know my thoughts:

20   And see if there be any wicked way in me, and lead me in the way everlasting.

Glory be to the *Father* | and ˙ to the | Son || *and* | to the | Holy | Ghost;
As it was in the beginning * is *now*, and | ever | shall be || *world* without |
    end ˙ = | A ˙ = | men.

SELECTION 28

God's saving Help

1 I WILL bless the Lord at all times: his praise shall continually be in my mouth.

2 My soul shall make her boast in the Lord: the humble shall hear thereof, and be glad.

3 O magnify the Lord with me, and let us exalt his name together.

4 I sought the Lord, and he heard me, and delivered me from all my fears.

5 They looked unto him, and were l'ghtened: and their faces were not ashamed.

6 This poor man cried, and the Lord heard him, and saved him out of all his troubles.

7 The angel of the Lord encampeth round about them that fear him, and delivereth them.

8 O taste and see that the Lord is good: blessed is the man that trusteth in him.

9 O fear the Lord, ye his saints: for there is no want to them that fear him.

10 The young lions do lack, and suffer hunger: but they that seek the Lord shall not want any good thing.

11 Come, ye children, hearken unto me: I will teach you the fear of the Lord.

12 What man is he that desireth life, and loveth many days, that he may see good?

13 Keep thy tongue from evil, and thy lips from speaking guile.

14 Depart from evil, and do good; seek peace, and pursue it.

15 The eyes of the Lord are upon the righteous, and his ears are open unto their cry.

16 The face of the Lord is against them that do evil, to cut off the remembrance of them from the earth.

17 The righteous cry, and the Lord heareth, and delivereth them out of all their troubles.

18 The Lord is nigh unto them that are of a broken heart; and saveth such as be of a contrite spirit.

19 Many are the afflictions of the righteous: but the Lord delivereth him out of them all.

20 He keepeth all his bones: not one of them is broken.

21 Evil shall slay the wicked: and they that hate the righteous shall be desolate.

22 The Lord redeemeth the soul of his servants: and none of them that trust in him shall be desolate.

Glory be to the *Father* | and ꞏ to the | Son || *and* | to the | Holy | Ghost;
As it was in the beginning * is *now*, and | ever | shall be || *world* without |
    end ꞏ = | A ꞏ = | men.

SELECTION 29

The Rock that is higher than I

PSALM 61

1 HEAR my cry, O God; attend unto my prayer.

2 From the end of the earth will I cry unto thee, when my heart is overwhelmed: lead me to the rock that is higher than I.

3 For thou hast been a shelter for me, and a strong tower from the enemy.

4 I will abide in thy tabernacle for ever: I will trust in the covert of thy wings.

5 For thou, O God, hast heard my vows: thou hast given me the heritage of those that fear thy name.

6 Thou wilt prolong the king's life: and his years as many generations.

7 He shall abide before God for ever: O prepare mercy and truth, which may preserve him.

8 So will I sing praise unto thy name for ever, that I may daily perform my vows.

PSALM 62

9 TRULY my soul waiteth upon God: from him cometh my salvation.

10 He only is my rock and my salvation; he is my defence; I shall not be greatly moved.

11 How long will ye imagine mischief against a man? ye shall be slain all of you: as a bowing wall shall ye be, and as a tottering fence.

12 They only consult to cast him down from his excellency: they delight in lies: they bless with their mouth, but they curse inwardly.

13 My soul, wait thou only upon God; for my expectation is from him.

14 He only is my rock and my salvation: he is my defence; I shall not be moved.

15 In God is my salvation and my glory: the rock of my strength, and my refuge, is in God.

16 Trust in him at all times; ye people, pour out your heart before him: God is a refuge for us.

17 Surely men of low degree are vanity, and men of high degree are a lie: to be laid in the balance, they are altogether lighter than vanity.

18 Trust not in oppression, and become not vain in robbery: if riches increase, set not your heart upon them.

19 God hath spoken once; twice have I heard this; that power belongeth unto God.

20 Also unto thee, O Lord, belongeth mercy: for thou renderest to every man according to his work.

Glory be to the *Father* | and · to the | Son || *and* | to the | Holy | Ghost;
As it was in the beginning * is *now,* and | ever | shall be || *world* without |
  end · = | A · = | men.

SELECTION 30

Happy the People whose God is the Lord

PSALM 144 : 3-15

1 LORD, what is man, that thou takest knowledge of him ! or the son of man, that thou makest account of him !

2 **Man is like to vanity: his days are as a shadow that passeth away.**

3 Bow thy heavens, O Lord, and come down: touch the mountains, and they shall smoke.

4 **Cast forth lightning, and scatter them: shoot out thine arrows, and destroy them.**

5 Send thine hand from above; rid me, and deliver me out of great waters, from the hand of strange children;

6 **Whose mouth speaketh vanity, and their right hand is a right hand of falsehood.**

7 I will sing a new song unto thee, O God: upon a psaltery and an instrument of ten strings will I sing praises unto thee.

8 **It is he that giveth salvation unto kings: who delivereth David his servant from the hurtful sword.**

9 Rid me, and deliver me from the hand of strange children, whose mouth speaketh vanity, and their right hand is a right hand of falsehood:

10 **That our sons may be as plants grown up in their youth; that our daughters may be as corner stones, polished after the similitude of a palace:**

11 That our garners may be full, affording all manner of store; that our sheep may bring forth thousands and ten thousands in our streets:

12 **That our oxen may be strong to labor; that there be no breaking in, nor going out; that there be no complaining in our streets.**

13 Happy is that people, that is in such a case: yea, happy is that people, whose God is the Lord.

PSALM 146

14 **PRAISE ye the Lord. Praise the Lord, O my soul.**

15 While I live will I praise the Lord: I will sing praises unto my God while I have any being.

16 **Put not your trust in princes, nor in the son of man, in whom there is no help.**

17 His breath goeth forth, he returneth to his earth; in that very day his thoughts perish.

18 **Happy is he that hath the God of Jacob for his help, whose hope is in the Lord his God:**

19 Which made heaven, and earth, the sea, and all that therein is: which keepeth truth for ever:

20 **Which executeth judgment for the oppressed: which giveth food to the hungry. The Lord looseth the prisoners:**

21 The Lord openeth the eyes of the blind: the Lord raiseth them that are bowed down: the Lord loveth the righteous:

22 **The Lord preserveth the strangers; he relieveth the fatherless and widow: but the way of the wicked he turneth upside down.**

23 The Lord shall reign for ever, even thy God, O Zion, unto all generations. Praise ye the Lord.

Glory be to the *Father* | and ˙ to the | Son || *and* | to the | Holy | Ghost;
As it was in the beginning * is *now*, and | ever | shall be || *world* without |
  end ˙ = | A ˙ = | men

SELECTION 31

A Prayer for Forgiveness

PSALM 51

1 HAVE mercy upon me, O God, according to thy lovingkindness: according unto the multitude of thy tender mercies blot out my transgressions.

2 Wash me thoroughly from mine iniquity, and cleanse me from my sin.

3 For I acknowledge my transgressions: and my sin is ever before me.

4 Against thee, thee only, have sinned, and done this evil in thy sight:

5 That thou mightest be justified when thou speakest, and be clear when thou judgest.

6 Behold, thou desirest truth in the inward parts: and in the hidden part thou shalt make me to know wisdom.

7 Purge me with hyssop, and I shall be clean: wash me, and I shall be whiter than snow.

8 Make me to hear joy and gladness; that the bones which thou hast broken may rejoice.

9 Hide thy face from my sins, and blot out all mine iniquities.

10 Create in me a clean heart, O God; and renew a right spirit within me.

11 Cast me not away from thy presence; and take not thy Holy Spirit from me.

12 Restore unto me the joy of thy salvation; and uphold me with thy free Spirit.

13 Then will I teach transgressors thy ways; and sinners shall be converted unto thee.

14 Deliver me from bloodguiltiness, O God, thou God of my salvation: and my tongue shall sing aloud of thy righteousness.

15 O Lord, open thou my lips; and my mouth shall show forth thy praise.

16 For thou desirest not sacrifice; else would I give it: thou delightest not in burnt offering.

17 The sacrifices of God are a broken spirit: a broken and a contrite heart, O God, thou wilt not despise.

18 Do good in thy good pleasure unto Zion: build thou the walls of Jerusalem.

19 Then shalt thou be pleased with the sacrifices of righteousness.

Glory be to the *Father* | and ˙ to the | Son || *and* | to the | Holy | Ghost;
As it was in the beginning * is *now*, and | ever | shall be || *world* without |
   end ˙ = | A ˙ = | men.

SELECTION 32

The Blessedness of the Righteous

1 BLESSED is the man that walketh not in the counsel of the ungodly, nor standeth in the way of sinners, nor sitteth in the seat of the scornful.

2 But his delight is in the law of the Lord; and in his law doth he meditate day and night.

3 And he shall be like a tree planted by the rivers of water, that bringeth forth his fruit in his season;

4 His leaf also shall not wither; and whatsoever he doeth shall prosper.

5 The ungodly are not so: but are like the chaff which the wind driveth away.

6 Therefore the ungodly shall not stand in the judgment, nor sinners in the congregation of the righteous.

7 For the Lord knoweth the way of the righteous: but the way of the ungodly shall perish.

8 LORD, who shall abide in thy tabernacle? who shall dwell in thy holy hill?

9 He that walketh uprightly, and worketh righteousness, and speaketh the truth in his heart.

10 He that backbiteth not with his tongue, nor doeth evil to his neighbor, nor taketh up a reproach against his neighbor.

11 In whose eyes a vile person is contemned; but he honoreth them that fear the Lord.

12 He that sweareth to his own hurt, and changeth not.

13 He that putteth not out his money to usury, nor taketh reward against the innocent.

14 He that doeth these things shall never be moved.

15 PRAISE ye the Lord. Blessed is the man that feareth the Lord, that delighteth greatly in his commandments.

16 His seed shall be mighty upon earth: the generation of the upright shall be blessed.

17 Wealth and riches shall be in his house: and his righteousness endureth for ever.

18 Unto the upright there ariseth light in the darkness: he is gracious, and full of compassion, and righteous.

19 A good man showeth favor, and lendeth: he will guide his affairs with discretion.

20 Surely he shall not be moved for ever: the righteous shall be in everlasting remembrance.

Glory be to the *Father* | and ˙ to the | Son || *and* | to the | Holy | Ghost;
As it was in the beginning * is *now*, and | ever | shall be || *world* without | end ˙ = | A ˙ = | men.

SELECTION 33

Loyalty to God's Word Life's Safeguard and its Joy

PSALM 119 : 1–24

1 BLESSED are the undefiled in the way, who walk in the law of the Lord.

2 Blessed are they that keep his testimonies, and that seek him with the whole heart.

3 They also do no iniquity: they walk in his ways.

4 Thou hast commanded us to keep thy precepts diligently.

5 O that my ways were directed to keep thy statutes !

6 Then shall I not be ashamed, when I have respect unto all thy commandments.

7 I will praise thee with uprightness of heart, when I shall have learned thy righteous judgments.

8 I will keep thy statutes: O forsake me not utterly.

9 Wherewithal shall a young man cleanse his way? by taking heed thereto according to thy word.

10 With my whole heart have I sought thee: O let me not wander from thy commandments.

11 Thy word have I hid in mine heart, that I might not sin against thee.

12 Blessed art thou, O Lord: teach me thy statutes.

13 With my lips have I declared all the judgments of thy mouth.

14 I have rejoiced in the way of thy testimonies, as much as in all riches.

15 I will meditate in thy precepts, and have respect unto thy ways.

16 I will delight myself in thy statutes: I will not forget thy word.

17 Deal bountifully with thy servant, that I may live, and keep thy word.

18 Open thou mine eyes, that I may behold wondrous things out of thy law.

19 I am a stranger in the earth: hide not thy commandments from me.

20 My soul breaketh for the longing that it hath unto thy judgments at all times.

21 Thou hast rebuked the proud that are cursed, which do err from thy commandments.

22 Remove from me reproach and contempt; for I have kept thy testimonies.

23 Princes also did sit and speak against me: but thy servant did meditate in thy statutes.

24 Thy testimonies also are my delight, and my counsellors.

Glory be to the *Father* | and ˙ to the | Son || *and* | to the | Holy | Ghost;
As it was in the beginning * is *now*, and | ever | shall be || *world* without | end ˙ = | A ˙ = men.

SELECTION 34

In the keeping of Thy Law is Liberty

PSALM 119 : 33–48, 89–96

1 TEACH me, O Lord, the way of thy statutes; and I shall keep it unto the end.

2 Give me understanding, and I shall keep thy law; yea, I shall observe it with my whole heart.

3 Make me to go in the path of thy commandments; for therein do I delight.

4 Incline my heart unto thy testimonies, and not to covetousness.

5 Turn away mine eyes from beholding vanity; and quicken thou me in thy way.

6 Stablish thy word unto thy servant, who is devoted to thy fear.

7 Turn away my reproach which I fear: for thy judgments are good.

8 Behold, I have longed after thy precepts: quicken me in thy righteousness.

9 Let thy mercies come also unto me, O Lord, even thy salvation, according to thy word.

10 So shall I have wherewith to answer him that reproacheth me: for I trust in thy word.

11 And take not the word of truth utterly out of my mouth; for I have hoped in thy judgments.

12 So shall I keep thy law continually for ever and ever.

13 And I will walk at liberty: for I seek thy precepts.

14 I will speak of thy testimonies also before kings, and will not be ashamed.

15 And I will delight myself in thy commandments, which I have loved.

16 My hands also will I lift up unto thy commandments, which I have loved; and I will meditate in thy statutes.

17 For ever, O Lord, thy word is settled in heaven.

18 Thy faithfulness is unto all generations: thou hast established the earth, and it abideth.

19 They continue this day according to thine ordinances: for all are thy servants.

20 Unless thy law had been my delights, I should then have perished in mine affliction.

21 I will never forget thy precepts: for with them thou hast quickened me.

22 I am thine, save me; for I have sought thy precepts.

23 The wicked have waited for me to destroy me: but I will consider thy testimonies.

24 I have seen an end of all perfection: but thy commandment is exceeding broad.

Glory be to the *Fa*ther | and ˙ to the | Son || *and* | to the | Holy | Ghost;
As it was in the beginning * is *now*, and | ever | shall be || *world* without |
    end ˙ = | A ˙ = | men.

SELECTION 35

Trust in the Lord, and do good

Psalm 37 : 1–9, 23–31, 34–37

1 FRET not thyself because of evil doers, neither be thou envious against the workers of iniquity.

2 For they shall soon be cut down like the grass, and wither as the green herb.

3 Trust in the Lord, and do good; so shalt thou dwell in the land, and verily thou shalt be fed.

4 Delight thyself also in the Lord; and he shall give thee the desires of thine heart.

5 Commit thy way unto the Lord; trust also in him; and he shall bring it to pass.

6 And he shall bring forth thy righteousness as the light, and thy judgment as the noonday.

7 Rest in the Lord, and wait patiently for him:

8 Fret not thyself because of him who prospereth in his way, because of the man who bringeth wicked devices to pass.

9 Cease from anger, and forsake wrath: fret not thyself in any wise to do evil.

10 For evil doers shall be cut off: but those that wait upon the Lord, they shall inherit the earth.

11 The steps of a good man are ordered by the Lord: and he delighteth in his way.

12 Though he fall, he shall not be utterly cast down: for the Lord upholdeth him with his hand.

13 I have been young, and now am old; yet have I not seen the righteous forsaken, nor his seed begging bread.

14 He is ever merciful, and lendeth; and his seed is blessed.

15 Depart from evil, and do good; and dwell for evermore.

16 For the Lord loveth judgment, and forsaketh not his saints; they are preserved for ever: but the seed of the wicked shall be cut off.

17 The righteous shall inherit the land, and dwell therein for ever.

18 The mouth of the righteous speaketh wisdom, and his tongue talketh of judgment.

19 The law of his God is in his heart; none of his steps shall slide.

20 Wait on the Lord, and keep his way, and he shall exalt thee to inherit the land:

21 When the wicked are cut off, thou shalt see it.

22 I have seen the wicked in great power, and spreading himself like a green bay tree.

23 Yet he passed away, and, lo, he was not: yea, I sought him, but he could not be found.

24 Mark the perfect man, and behold the upright: for the end of that man is peace.

Glory be to the *F*ather | and ˙ to the | Son ‖ *and* | to the | Holy | Ghost;
As it was in the beginning * is *now*, and | ever | shall be ‖ *world* without |
    end ˙ = | A ˙ = | men.

SELECTION 36

Forgiven and Forgiving

Psalm 32

1 BLESSED is he whose transgression is forgiven, whose sin is covered.

2 Blessed is the man unto whom the Lord imputeth not iniquity, and in whose spirit there is no guile.

3 When I kept silence, my bones waxed old through my roaring all the day long.

4 For day and night thy hand was heavy upon me: my moisture is turned into the drought of summer.

5 · I acknowledged my sin unto thee, and mine iniquity have I not hid.

6 I said, I will confess my transgressions unto the Lord; and thou forgavest the iniquity of my sin.

7 For this shall every one that is godly pray unto thee in a time when thou mayest be found:

8 Surely in the floods of great waters they shall not come nigh unto him.

9 Thou art my hiding place; thou shalt preserve me from trouble; thou shalt compass me about with songs of deliverance.

10 I will instruct thee and teach thee in the way which thou shalt go: I will guide thee with mine eye.

11 Be ye not as the horse, or as the mule, which have no understanding: whose mouth must be held in with bit and bridle, lest they come near unto thee.

12 Many sorrows shall be to the wicked: but he that trusteth in the Lord, mercy shall compass him about.

13 Be glad in the Lord, and rejoice, ye righteous: and shout for joy, all ye that are upright in heart.

Psalm 18 : 25–35

14 WITH the merciful thou wilt show thyself merciful; with an upright man thou wilt show thyself upright;

15 With the pure thou wilt show thyself pure; and with the froward thou wilt show thyself froward.

16 For thou wilt save the afflicted people; but wilt bring down high looks.

17 For thou wilt light my candle: the Lord my God will enlighten my darkness.

18 For by thee I have run through a troop; and by my God have I leaped over a wall.

19 As for God, his way is perfect: the word of the Lord is tried: he is a buckler to all those that trust in him.

20 For who is God save the Lord? or who is a rock save our God?

21 It is God that girdeth me with strength, and maketh my way perfect.

22 He maketh my feet like hinds' feet, and setteth me upon my high places.

23 He teacheth my hands to war, so that a bow of steel is broken by mine arms.

24 Thou hast also given me the shield of thy salvation: and thy right hand hath holden me up, and thy gentleness hath made me great.

Glory be to the *Father* | and ⋅ to the | Son || *and* | to the | Holy | Ghost;
As it was in the beginning * is *now,* and | ever | shall be || *world* without |
    end ⋅ = | A ⋅ = | men.

438

SELECTION 37

Hope thou in God

1 AS the hart panteth after the water brooks, so panteth my soul after thee, O God.

2 My soul thirsteth for God, for the living God: when shall I come and appear before God?

3 My tears have been my meat day and night, while they continually say unto me, where is thy God?

4 When I remember these things, I pour out my soul in me: for I had gone with the multitude.

5 I went with them to the house of God, with the voice of joy and praise, with a multitude that kept holyday.

6 Why art thou cast down, O my soul? and why art thou disquieted in me?

7 Hope thou in God: for I shall yet praise him for the help of his countenance.

8 O my God, my soul is cast down within me: therefore will I remember thee from the land of Jordan, and of the Hermonites, from the hill Mizar.

9 Deep calleth unto deep at the noise of thy waterspouts: all thy waves and thy billows are gone over me.

10 Yet the Lord will command his loving-kindness in the daytime, and in the night his song shall be with me, and my prayer unto the God of my life.

11 I will say unto God my rock, Why hast thou forgotten me? why go I mourning because of the oppression of the enemy?

12 As with a sword in my bones, mine enemies reproach me; while they say daily unto me, Where is thy God?

13 Why art thou cast down, O my soul? and why art thou disquieted within me?

14 Hope thou in God: for I shall yet praise him, who is the health of my countenance, and my God.

15 JUDGE me, O God, and plead my cause against an ungodly nation: O deliver me from the deceitful and unjust man.

16 For thou art the God of my strength: why dost thou cast me off?

17 Why go I mourning because of the oppression of the enemy?

18 O send out thy light and thy truth: let them lead me; let them bring me unto thy holy hill, and to thy tabernacles.

19 Then will I go unto the altar of God, unto God my exceeding joy:

20 Yea, upon the harp will I praise thee, O God my God.

21 Why art thou cast down, O my soul? and why art thou disquieted within me?

22 Hope in God: for I shall yet praise him, who is the health of my countenance, and my God.

Glory be to the *Father* | and ˙ to the | Son ‖ *and* | to the | Holy | Ghost;
As it was in the beginning * is *now*, and | ever | shall be ‖ *world* without |
    end ˙ = | A ˙ = | men.

SELECTION 38

The Ark of God's Presence enters the Gates of His Sanctuary

PSALM 132

1 LORD, remember David, and all his afflictions:

2 How he sware unto the Lord, and vowed unto the mighty God of Jacob;

3 Surely I will not come into the tabernacle of my house, nor go up into my bed;

4 I will not give sleep to mine eyes, or slumber to mine eyelids,

5 Until I find out a place for the Lord, a habitation for the mighty God of Jacob.

6 Lo, we heard of it at Ephratah: we found it in the fields of the wood.

7 We will go into his tabernacles: we will worship at his footstool.

8 Arise, O Lord, into thy rest; thou, and the ark of thy strength.

9 Let thy priests be clothed with righteousness; and let thy saints shout for joy.

10 For thy servant David's sake turn not away the face of thine anointed.

11 The Lord hath sworn in truth unto David; he will not turn from it; Of the fruit of thy body will I set upon thy throne.

12 If thy children will keep my covenant and my testimony that I shall teach them, their children shall also sit upon thy throne for evermore.

13 For the Lord hath chosen Zion; he hath desired it for his habitation.

14 This is my rest for ever: here will I dwell; for I have desired it.

15 I will abundantly bless her provision: I will satisfy her poor with bread.

16 I will also clothe her priests with salvation: and her saints shall shout aloud for joy.

17 There will I make the horn of David to bud: I have ordained a lamp for mine anointed.

18 His enemies will I clothe with shame: but upon himself shall his crown flourish.

PSALM 24

19 THE earth is the Lord's, and the fulness thereof; the world, and they that dwell therein.

20 For he hath founded it upon the seas, and established it upon the floods.

21 Who shall ascend into the hill of the Lord? or who shall stand in his holy place?

22 He that hath clean hands, and a pure heart; who hath not lifted up his soul unto vanity, nor sworn deceitfully.

23 He shall receive the blessing from the Lord, and righteousness from the God of his salvation.

24 This is the generation of them that seek him, that seek thy face, O Jacob.

25 Lift up your heads, O ye gates; and be ye lifted up, ye everlasting doors; and the King of glory shall come in.

26 Who is this King of glory? The Lord strong and mighty, the Lord mighty in battle.

27 Lift up your heads, O ye gates; even lift them up, ye everlasting doors; and the King of glory shall come in.

28 Who is this King of glory? The Lord of hosts, he is the King of glory.

Glory be to the *Father* | and ꞏ to the | Son || *and* | to the | Holy | Ghost;
As it was in the beginning * is *now*, and | ever | shall be || *world* without | end ꞏ = | A ꞏ = | men.

SELECTION 39

God the Strength of His Church

PSALM 46

1 GOD is our refuge and strength, a very present help in trouble.

2 Therefore will we not fear, though the earth be removed, and though the mountains be carried into the midst of the sea;

3 Though the waters thereof roar and be troubled, though the mountains shake with the swelling thereof.

4 There is a river, the streams whereof shall make glad the city of God, the holy place of the tabernacles of the Most High.

5 God is in the midst of her; she shall not be moved: God shall help her, and that right early.

6 The heathen raged, the kingdoms were moved: he uttered his voice, the earth melted.

7 The Lord of hosts is with us; the God of Jacob is our refuge.

8 Come, behold the works of the Lord, what desolations he hath made in the earth.

9 He maketh wars to cease unto the end of the earth; he breaketh the bow, and cutteth the spear in sunder; he burneth the chariot in the fire.

10 Be still, and know that I am God: I will be exalted among the heathen, I will be exalted in the earth.

11 The Lord of hosts is with us; the God of Jacob is our refuge.

PSALM 48 : 1–3, 8–14

12 GREAT is the Lord, and greatly to be praised in the city of our God, in the mountain of his holiness.

13 Beautiful for situation, the joy of the whole earth, is mount Zion, on the sides of the north, the city of the great King.

14 God is known in her palaces for a refuge.

15 As we have heard, so have we seen in the city of the Lord of hosts, in the city of our God: God will establish it for ever.

16 We have thought of thy lovingkindness, O God, in the midst of thy temple.

17 According to thy name, O God, so is thy praise unto the ends of the earth: thy right hand is full of righteousness.

18 Let mount Zion rejoice, let the daughters of Judah be glad, because of thy judgments.

19 Walk about Zion, and go round about her: tell the towers thereof.

20 Mark ye well her bulwarks, consider her palaces; that ye may tell it to the generation following.

21 For this God is our God for ever and ever: he will be our guide even unto death.

Glory be to the *Father* | and ˙ to the | Son || *and* | to the | Holy | Ghost;
As it was in the beginning * is *now*, and | ever | shall be || *world* without | end ˙ = | A ˙ = | men.

SELECTION 40

The Gates of Zion

1 I WAS glad when they said unto me, Let us go into the house of the Lord.

2 Our feet shall stand within thy gates, O Jerusalem.

3 Jerusalem is builded as a city that is compact together:

4 Whither the tribes go up, the tribes of the Lord, unto the testimony of Israel, to give thanks unto the name of the Lord.

5 For there are set thrones of judgment, the thrones of the house of David.

6 Pray for the peace of Jerusalem: they shall prosper that love thee.

7 Peace be within thy walls, and prosperity within thy palaces.

8 For my brethren and companions' sakes, I will now say, Peace be within thee.

9 Because of the house of the Lord our God I will seek thy good.

10 HIS foundation is in the holy mountains.

11 The Lord loveth the gates of Zion more than all the dwellings of Jacob.

12 Glorious things are spoken of thee, O city of God.

13 I will make mention of Rahab and Babylon to them that know me:

14 Behold Philistia, and Tyre, with Ethiopia; this man was born there.

15 And of Zion it shall be said, This and that man was born in her: and the Highest himself shall establish her.

16 The Lord shall count, when he writeth up the people, that this man was born there.

17 As well the singers as the players on instruments shall be there: all my springs are in thee.

18 THEY that trust in the Lord shall be as mount Zion, which cannot be removed, but abideth for ever.

19 As the mountains are round about Jerusalem, so the Lord is round about his people from henceforth even for ever.

20 For the rod of the wicked shall not rest upon the lot of the righteous; lest the righteous put forth their hands unto iniquity.

21 Do good, O Lord, unto those that be good, and to them that are upright in their hearts.

22 As for such as turn aside unto their crooked ways, the Lord shall lead them forth with the workers of iniquity:

23 But peace shall be upon Israel.

Glory be to the *Father* | and · to the | Son || *and* | to the | Holy | Ghost;
As it was in the beginning * is *now*, and | ever | shall be || *world* without |
  end · = | A · = | men.

442

SELECTION 41

The House of the Lord

PSALM 26 : 8, 12

1 LORD, I have loved the habitation of thy house, and the place where thine honor dwelleth.

2 My foot standeth in an even place: in the congregations will I bless the Lord.

PSALM 27 : 1, 3–14

3 THE Lord is my light and my salvation; whom shall I fear? the Lord is the strength of my life; of whom shall I be afraid?

4 Though an host should encamp against me, my heart shall not fear: though war should rise against me, in this will I be confident.

5 One thing have I desired of the Lord, that will I seek after; that I may dwell in the house of the Lord all the days of my life, to behold the beauty of the Lord, and to inquire in his temple.

6 For in the time of trouble he shall hide me in his pavilion: in the secret of his tabernacle shall he hide me; he shall set me up upon a rock.

7 And now shall mine head be lifted up above mine enemies round about me:

8 Therefore will I offer in his tabernacle sacrifices of joy; I will sing, yea, I will sing praises unto the Lord.

9 Hear, O Lord, when I cry with my voice: have mercy also upon me, and answer me.

10 When thou saidst, Seek ye my face; my heart said unto thee, Thy face, Lord, will I seek.

11 Hide not thy face far from me; put not thy servant away in anger: thou hast been my help; leave me not, neither forsake me, O God of my salvation.

12 When my father and my mother forsake me, then the Lord will take me up.

13 I had fainted, unless I had believed to see the goodness of the Lord in the land of the living.

14 Wait on the Lord: be of good courage, and he shall strengthen thine heart: wait, I say, on the Lord.

PSALM 84

15 HOW amiable are thy tabernacles, O Lord of hosts!

16 My soul longeth, yea, even fainteth for the courts of the Lord: my heart and my flesh crieth out for the living God.

17 Yea, the sparrow hath found a house, and the swallow a nest for herself, where she may lay her young, even thine altars, O Lord of hosts, my King, and my God.

18 Blessed are they that dwell in thy house: they will be still praising thee.

19 Blessed is the man whose strength is in thee; in whose heart are the ways of them.

20 Who passing through the valley of Baca make it a well; the rain also filleth the pools.

21 They go from strength to strength, every one of them in Zion appeareth before God.

22 O Lord God of hosts, hear my prayer: give ear, O God of Jacob.

23 Behold, O God our shield, and look upon the face of thine anointed.

24 For a day in thy courts is better than a thousand. I had rather be a door-keeper in the house of my God, than to dwell in the tents of wickedness.

25 For the Lord God is a sun and shield: the Lord will give grace and glory: no good thing will be withhold from them that walk uprightly.

26 O Lord of hosts, blessed is the man that trusteth in thee.

Glory be to the *Father* | and · to the | Son || *and* | to the | Holy | Ghost;
As it was in the beginning * is *now,* and | ever | shall be || *world* without | end · = | A · = | men.

SELECTION 42

A Wedding Hymn of Christ and His Church

PSALM 45

1 MY heart is inditing a good matter: I speak of the things which I have made touching the King: my tongue is the pen of a ready writer.

2 Thou art fairer than the children of men: grace is poured into thy lips: therefore God hath blessed thee for ever.

3 Gird thy sword upon thy thigh, O most Mighty, with thy glory and thy majesty.

4 And in thy majesty ride prosperously, because of truth and meekness and righteousness; and thy right hand shall teach thee terrible things.

5 Thine arrows are sharp in the heart of the King's enemies; whereby the people fall under thee.

6 Thy throne, O God, is for ever and ever: the sceptre of thy kingdom is a right sceptre.

7 Thou lovest righteousness, and hatest wickedness: therefore God, thy God, hath anointed thee with the oil of gladness above thy fellows.

8 All thy garments smell of myrrh, and aloes, and cassia, out of the ivory palaces, whereby they have made thee glad.

9 Kings' daughters were among thy honorable women: upon thy right hand did stand the queen in gold of Ophir.

10 Hearken, O daughter, and consider, and incline thine ear; forget also thine own people, and thy father's house;

11 So shall the King greatly desire thy beauty: for he is thy Lord; and worship thou him.

12 And the daughter of Tyre shall be there with a gift; even the rich among the people shall entreat thy favor.

13 The King's daughter is all glorious within: her clothing is of wrought gold.

14 She shall be brought unto the King in raiment of needlework: the virgins her companions that follow her shall be brought unto thee.

15 With gladness and rejoicing shall they be brought: they shall enter into the King's palace.

16 Instead of thy fathers shall be thy children, whom thou mayest make princes in all the earth.

17 I will make thy name to be remembered in all generations: therefore shall the people praise thee for ever and ever.

Glory be to the *Fa*ther | and · to the | Son || *and* | to the | Holy | Ghost;
As it was in the beginning * is *now*, and | ever | shall be || *world* without |
    end · = | A · = | men.

SELECTION 43

A Prayer for the Church's Revival

PSALM 80

1   GIVE ear, O Shepherd of Israel, thou that leadest Joseph like a flock; thou that dwellest between the cherubim, shine forth.

2   Before Ephraim and Benjamin and Manasseh stir up thy strength, and come and save us.

3   Turn us again, O God, and cause thy face to shine; and we shall be saved.

4   O Lord God of hosts, how long wilt thou be angry against the prayer of thy people?

5   Thou feedest them with the bread of tears; and givest them tears to drink in great measure.

6   Thou makest us a strife unto our neighbors: and our enemies laugh among themselves.

7   Turn us again, O God of hosts, and cause thy face to shine; and we shall be saved.

8   Thou hast brought a vine out of Egypt: thou hast cast out the heathen, and planted it.

9   Thou preparedst room before it, and didst cause it to take deep root, and it filled the land.

10   The hills were covered with the shadow of it, and the boughs thereof were like the goodly cedars.

11   She sent out her boughs unto the sea, and her branches unto the river.

12   Why hast thou then broken down her hedges, so that all they which pass by the way do pluck her?

13   The boar out of the wood doth waste it, and the wild beast of the field doth devour it.

14   Return, we beseech thee, O God of hosts: look down from heaven, and behold, and visit this vine;

15   And the vineyard which thy right hand hath planted, and the branch that thou madest strong for thyself.

16   It is burned with fire, it is cut down: they perish at the rebuke of thy countenance.

17   Let thy hand be upon the man of thy right hand, upon the son of man whom thou madest strong for thyself.

18   So will not we go back from thee: quicken us, and we will call upon thy name.

19   Turn us again, O Lord God of hosts, cause thy face to shine; and we shall be saved.

Glory be to the *Father* | and ˙ to the | Son || *and* | to the | Holy | Ghost;
As it was in the beginning * is *now*, and | ever | shall be || *world* without |
    end ˙ = | A ˙ = | men.

SELECTION 44

PSALM 137 : 1-6

1 BY the rivers of Babylon, there we sat down, yea, we wept, when we remembered Zion.

2 We hanged our harps upon the willows in the midst thereof.

3 For there they that carried us away captive required of us a song;

4 And they that wasted us required of us mirth, saying, Sing us one of the songs of Zion.

5 How shall we sing the Lord's song in a strange land?

6 If I forget thee, O Jerusalem, let my right hand forget her cunning.

7 If I do not remember thee, let my tongue cleave to the roof of my mouth; if I prefer not Jerusalem above my chief joy.

PSALM 126

8 WHEN the Lord turned again the captivity of Zion, we were like them that dream.

9 Then was our mouth filled with laughter, and our tongue with singing:

10 Then said they among the heathen, The Lord hath done great things for them.

11 The Lord hath done great things for us; whereof we are glad.

12 Turn again our captivity, O Lord, as the streams in the south.

13 They that sow in tears shall reap in joy.

14 He that goeth forth and weepeth, bearing precious seed, shall doubtless come again with rejoicing, bringing his sheaves with him.

PSALM 85

15 LORD, thou hast been favorable unto thy land: thou hast brought back the captivity of Jacob.

16 Thou hast forgiven the iniquity of thy people; thou hast covered all their sin.

17 Thou hast taken away all thy wrath: thou hast turned thyself from the fierceness of thine anger.

18 Turn us, O God of our salvation, and cause thine anger toward us to cease.

19 Wilt thou be angry with us for ever? wilt thou draw out thine anger to all generations?

20 Wilt thou not revive us again: that thy people may rejoice in thee?

21 Show us thy mercy, O Lord, and grant us thy salvation.

22 I will hear what God the Lord will speak: for he will speak peace unto his people, and to his saints: but let them not turn again to folly.

23 Surely his salvation is nigh them that fear him; that glory may dwell in our land.

24 Mercy and truth are met together; righteousness and peace have kissed each other.

25 Truth shall spring out of the earth; and righteousness shall look down from heaven.

26 Yea, the Lord shall give that which is good; and our land shall yield her increase.

27 Righteousness shall go before him; and shall set us in the way of his steps.

Glory be to the *Father* | and · to the | Son || *and* | to the | Holy | Ghost;
As it was in the beginning * is *now*, and | ever | shall be || *world* without | end · = | A · = | men.

SELECTION 45

A Psalm of the great Messianic Promise to David

Psalm 89 (selected)

1   I WILL sing of the mercies of the Lord for ever: with my mouth will I make known thy faithfulness to all generations.

2   For I have said, Mercy shall be built up for ever: thy faithfulness shalt thou establish in the very heavens.

3   I have made a covenant with my chosen, I have sworn unto David my servant.

4   Thy seed will I establish for ever, and build up thy throne to all generations.

5   And the heavens shall praise thy wonders, O Lord: thy faithfulness also in the congregation of the saints.

6   Blessed is the people that know the joyful sound: they shall walk, O Lord, in the light of thy countenance.

7   For the Lord is our defence; and the Holy One of Israel is our King.

8   Then thou spakest in vision to thy Holy One, and saidst, I have laid help upon one that is mighty; I have exalted one chosen out of the people.

9   I have found David my servant; with my holy oil have I anointed him:

10   With whom my hand shall be established: mine arm also shall strengthen him.

11   And I will beat down his foes before his face, and plague them that hate him.

12   Also I will make him my firstborn, higher than the kings of the earth.

13   My mercy will I keep for him for evermore, and my covenant shall stand fast with him.

14   His seed also will I make to endure for ever, and his throne as the days of heaven.

15   If his children forsake my law, and walk not in my judgments;

16   If they break my statutes, and keep not my commandments;

17   Then will I visit their transgression with the rod, and their iniquity with stripes.

18   Nevertheless my loving-kindness will I not utterly take from him, nor suffer my faithfulness to fail.

19   My covenant will I not break, nor alter the thing that is gone out of my lips.

20   Once have I sworn by my holiness that I will not lie unto David.

21   His seed shall endure for ever, and his throne as the sun before me.

22   It shall be established for ever as the moon, and as a faithful witness in heaven.

Glory be to the *F*ather | and ˙ to the | Son ‖ *and* | to the | Holy | Ghost;
As it was in the beginning * is *now,* and | ever | shall be ‖ *world* without |
    end ˙ = | A ˙ = | men.

SELECTION 46

A Psalm of the Patient Christ

1 I WAITED patiently for the Lord; and he inclined unto me, and heard my cry.

2 He brought me up also out of a horrible pit, out of the miry clay, and set my feet upon a rock, and established my goings.

3 And he hath put a new song in my mouth, even praise unto our God:

4 Many shall see it, and fear, and shall trust in the Lord.

5 Blessed is that man that maketh the Lord his trust, and respecteth not the proud, nor such as turn aside to lies.

6 Many, O Lord my God, are thy wonderful works which thou hast done, and thy thoughts which are to us-ward:

7 They cannot be reckoned up in order unto thee: if I would declare and speak of them, they are more than can be numbered.

8 Sacrifice and offering thou didst not desire; mine ears hast thou opened:

9 Burnt offering and sin offering hast thou not required.

10 Then said I, Lo, I come: in the volume of the book it is written of me,

11 I delight to do thy will, O my God: yea, thy law is within my heart.

12 I have preached righteousness in the great congregation: lo, I have not refrained my lips, O Lord, thou knowest.

13 I have not hid thy righteousness within my heart; I have declared thy faithfulness and thy salvation:

14. I have not concealed thy loving-kindness and thy truth from the great congregation.

15 Withhold not thou thy tender mercies from me, O Lord: let thy loving-kindness and thy truth continually preserve me.

16 For innumerable evils have compassed me about: mine iniquities have taken hold upon me, so that I am not able to look up;

17 They are more than the hairs of mine head: therefore my heart faileth me.

18 Be pleased, O Lord, to deliver me: O Lord, make haste to help me.

19 Let them be ashamed and confounded together that seek after my soul to destroy it;

20 Let them be driven backward and put to shame that wish me evil.

21 Let them be desolate for a reward of their shame that say unto me Aha, Aha.

22 Let all those that seek thee rejoice and be glad in thee: let such as love thy salvation say continually, The Lord be magnified.

23 But I am poor and needy; yet the Lord thinketh upon me: thou art my help and my deliverer; make no tarrying, O my God.

Glory be to the *Father* | and ˙ to the | Son ‖ *and* | to the | Holy | Ghost;
As it was in the beginning * is *now,* and | ever | shall be ‖ *world* without
    end ˙ = | A ˙ = | men.

SELECTION 47

God's Deliverance of His Anointed One

PSALM 18 : 1–19

1 I WILL love thee, O Lord, my strength.

2 The Lord is my rock, and my fortress, and my deliverer;

3 My God, my strength, in whom I will trust; my buckler, and the horn of my salvation, and my high tower.

4 I will call upon the Lord, who is worthy to be praised: so shall I be saved from mine enemies.

5 The sorrows of death compassed me, and the floods of ungodly men made me afraid.

6 The sorrows of hell compassed me about: the snares of death prevented me.

7 In my distress I called upon the Lord, and cried unto my God:

8 He heard my voice out of his temple, and my cry came before him, even into his ears.

9 Then the earth shook and trembled; the foundations also of the hills moved and were shaken, because he was wroth.

10 There went up a smoke out of his nostrils, and fire out of his mouth devoured: coals were kindled by it.

11 He bowed the heavens also, and came down: and darkness was under his feet.

12 And he rode upon a cherub, and did fly: yea, he did fly upon the wings of the wind.

13 He made darkness his secret place; his pavilion round about him were dark waters and thick clouds of the skies.

14 At the brightness that was before him his thick clouds passed, hail stones and coals of fire.

15 The Lord also thundered in the heavens, and the Highest gave his voice; hail stones and coals of fire.

16 Yea, he sent out his arrows, and scattered them; and he shot out lightnings, and discomfited them.

17 Then the channels of waters were seen, and the foundations of the world were discovered at thy rebuke, O Lord, at the blast of the breath of thy nostrils.

18 He sent from above, he took me, he drew me out of many waters.

19 He delivered me from my strong enemy, and from them which hated me: for they were too strong for me.

20 They prevented me in the day of my calamity: but the Lord was my stay.

21 He brought me forth also into a large place; he delivered me, because he delighted in me.

Glory be to the *Father* | and · to the | Son || *and* | to the | Holy | Ghost;
As it was in the beginning * is *now*, and | ever | shall be || *world* without |
    end · = | A · = men.

SELECTION 48

A Summons to all Nations to worship God as King

PSALM 2

1 WHY do the heathen rage, and the people imagine a vain thing?

2 **The kings of the earth set themselves, and the rulers take counsel together, against the Lord, and against his Anointed, saying,**

3 Let us break their bands asunder, and cast away their cords from us.

4 **He that sitteth in the heavens shall laugh: the Lord shall have them in derision.**

5 Then shall he speak unto them in his wrath, and vex them in his sore displeasure.

6 **Yet have I set my King upon my holy hill of Zion.**

7 I will declare the decree: the Lord hath said unto me, Thou art my Son; this day have I begotten thee.

8 **Ask of me, and I shall give thee the heathen for thine inheritance, and the uttermost parts of the earth for thy possession.**

9 Thou shalt break them with a rod of iron; thou shalt dash them in pieces like a potter's vessel.

10 **Be wise now therefore, O ye kings: be instructed, ye judges of the earth.**

11 Serve the Lord with fear, and rejoice with trembling.

12 **Kiss the Son, lest he be angry, and ye perish from the way, when his wrath is kindled but a little.**

13 Blessed are all they that put their trust in him.

PSALM 47 : 1-3, 6-8

14 **O CLAP your hands, all ye people; shout unto God with the voice of triumph.**

15 For the Lord most high is terrible; he is a great King over all the earth.

16 **He shall subdue the people under us, and the nations under our feet.**

17 Sing praises to God, sing praises: sing praises unto our King, sing praises.

18 **For God is the King of all the earth: sing ye praises with understanding.**

19 God reigneth over the heathen: God sitteth upon the throne of his holiness.

PSALM 67

20 **GOD be merciful unto us, and bless us; and cause his face to shine upon us;**

21 That thy way may be known upon earth, thy saving health among all nations.

22 **Let the people praise thee, O God; let all the people praise thee.**

23 O let the nations be glad and sing for joy: for thou shalt judge the people righteously, and govern the nations upon earth.

24 **Let the people praise thee, O God; let all the people praise thee.**

25 Then shall the earth yield her increase; and God, even our own God, shall bless us.

26 **God shall bless us; and all the ends of the earth shall fear him.**

Glory be to the *Father* | and · to the | Son || *and* | to the | Holy | Ghost;

As it was in the beginning * ·is *now*, and | ever | shall be || *world* without | end · = | A · = | men.

450

SELECTION 49

A Vision of Christ's Kingdom

PSALM 72

1 GIVE the king thy judgments, O God, and thy righteousness unto the king's son.

2 He shall judge thy people with righteousness, and thy poor with judgment.

3 The mountains shall bring peace to the people, and the little hills, by righteousness.

4 He shall judge the poor of the people, he shall save the children of the needy, and shall break in pieces the oppressor.

5 They shall fear thee as long as the sun and moon endure, throughout all generations.

6 He shall come down like rain upon the mown grass: as showers that water the earth.

7 In his days shall the righteous flourish; and abundance of peace so long as the moon endureth.

8 He shall have dominion also from sea to sea, and from the river unto the ends of the earth.

9 They that dwell in the wilderness shall bow before him; and his enemies shall lick the dust.

10 The kings of Tarshish and of the isles shall bring presents: the kings of Sheba and Seba shall offer gifts.

11 Yea, all kings shall fall down before him: all nations shall serve him.

12 For he shall deliver the needy when he crieth; the poor also, and him that hath no helper.

13 He shall spare the poor and needy, and shall save the souls of the needy.

14 He shall redeem their soul from deceit and violence: and precious shall their blood be in his sight.

15 And he shall live, and to him shall be given of the gold of Sheba: prayer also shall be made for him continually; and daily shall he be praised.

16 There shall be a handful of corn in the earth upon the top of the mountains;

17 The fruit thereof shall shake like Lebanon: and they of the city shall flourish like grass of the earth.

18 His name shall endure for ever: his name shall be continued as long as the sun:

19 And men shall be blessed in him: all nations shall call him blessed.

20 Blessed be the Lord God, the God of Israel, who only doeth wondrous things.

21 And blessed be his glorious name for ever: and let the whole earth be filled with his glory. Amen, and Amen.

Glory be to the *Father* | and · to the | Son || *and* | to the | Holy | Ghost;
As it was in the beginning * is *now*, and | ever | shall be || *world* without |
    end · = | A · = | men.

SELECTION 50

He hath not dealt so with any Nation

1 PRAISE ye the Lord: for it is good to sing praises unto our God; for it is pleasant; and praise is comely.

2 The Lord doth build up Jerusalem: he gathereth together the outcasts of Israel.

3 He healeth the broken in heart, and bindeth up their wounds.

4 He telleth the number of the stars; he calleth them all by their names.

5 Great is our Lord, and of great power: his understanding is infinite.

6 The Lord lifteth up the meek: he casteth the wicked down to the ground.

7 Sing unto the Lord with thanksgiving; sing praise upon the harp unto our God:

8 Who covereth the heaven with clouds, who prepareth rain for the earth, who maketh grass to grow upon the mountains.

9 He giveth to the beast his food, and to the young ravens which cry.

10 He delighteth not in the strength of the horse: he taketh not pleasure in the legs of a man.

11 The Lord taketh pleasure in them that fear him, in those that hope in his mercy.

12 Praise the Lord, O Jerusalem; praise thy God, O Zion.

13 For he hath strengthened the bars of thy gates; he hath blessed thy children within thee.

14 He maketh peace in thy borders, and filleth thee with the finest of the wheat.

15 He sendeth forth his commandment upon earth: his word runneth very swiftly.

16 He giveth snow like wool: he scattereth the hoar frost like ashes.

17 He casteth forth his ice like morsels: who can stand before his cold?

18 He sendeth out his word, and melteth them: he causeth his wind to blow, and the waters flow.

19 He showeth his word unto Jacob, his statutes and his judgments unto Israel.

20 He hath not dealt so with any nation: and as for his judgments, they have not known them. Praise ye the Lord.

Glory be to the *Father* | and ˙ to the | Son || *and* | to the | Holy | Ghost;
As it was in the beginning * is *now*, and | ever | shall be || *world* without |
    end ˙ = | A ˙ = | men.

SELECTION 51

A Festival Psalm: The Day the Lord hath made

PSALM 118 : 1–9, 14–29

1   O GIVE thanks unto the Lord; for he is good: because his mercy endureth for ever.

2   Let Israel now say, that his mercy endureth for ever.

3   Let the house of Aaron now say, that his mercy endureth for ever.

4   Let them now that fear the Lord say, that his mercy endureth for ever.

5   I called upon the Lord in distress: the Lord answered me, and set me in a large place.

6   The Lord is on my side; I will not fear: what can man do unto me?

7   The Lord taketh my part with them that help me: therefore shall I see my desire upon them that hate me.

8   It is better to trust in the Lord than to put confidence in man.

9   It is better to trust in the Lord than to put confidence in princes.

10   The Lord is my strength and song, and is become my salvation.

11   The voice of rejoicing and salvation is in the tabernacles of the righteous: the right hand of the Lord doeth valiantly.

12   The right hand of the Lord is exalted: the right hand of the Lord doeth valiantly.

13   I shall not die, but live, and declare the works of the Lord.

14   The Lord hath chastened me sore: but he hath not given me over unto death.

15   Open to me the gates of righteousness: I will go into them, and I will praise the Lord:

16   This gate of the Lord, into which the righteous shall enter.

17   1 will praise thee: for thou hast heard me, and art become my salvation.

18   The stone which the builders refused is become the head stone of the corner.

19   This is the Lord's doing; it is marvellous in our eyes.

20   This is the day which the Lord hath made; we will rejoice and be glad in it.

21   Save now, I beseech thee, O Lord: O Lord, I beseech thee, send now prosperity.

22   Blessed be he that cometh in the name of the Lord: we have blessed you out of the house of the Lord.

23   God is the Lord, which hath showed us light: bind the sacrifice with cords, even unto the horns of the altar.

24   Thou art my God, and I will praise thee: thou art my God, I will exalt thee.

25   O give thanks unto the Lord; for he is good: for his mercy endureth for ever.

Glory be to the *Father* | and · to the | Son || *and* | to the | Holy | Ghost;
As it was in the beginning * is *now*, and | ever | shall be || *world* without |
    end · = | A · = | men.

SELECTION 52

A Festival Psalm: Our Fathers have told us

1 WHEN Israel went out of Egypt, the house of Jacob from a people of strange language;

2 Judah was his sanctuary, and Israel his dominion.

3 The sea saw it, and fled: Jordan was driven back.

4 The mountains skipped like rams, and the little hills like lambs.

5 What ailed thee, O thou sea, that thou fleddest? thou Jordan, that thou wast driven back?

6 Ye mountains, that ye skipped like rams; and ye little hills, like lambs?

7 Tremble, thou earth, at the presence of the Lord, at the presence of the God of Jacob;

8 Which turned the rock into a standing water, the flint into a fountain of waters.

9 WE have heard with our ears, O God, our fathers have told us, what work thou didst in their days, in the times of old.

10 How thou didst drive out the heathen with thy hand, and plantedst them;

11 How thou didst afflict the people, and cast them out.

12 For they got not the land in possession by their own sword, neither did their own arm save them:

13 But thy right hand, and thine arm, and the light of thy countenance, because thou hadst a favor unto them.

14 Thou art my King, O God: command deliverances for Jacob.

15 Through thee will we push down our enemies: through thy name will we tread them under that rise up against us.

16 For I will not trust in my bow, neither shall my sword save me.

17 But thou hast saved us from our enemies, and hast put them to shame that hated us.

18 In God we boast all the day long, and praise thy name for ever.

19 PRAISE ye the Lord. Sing unto the Lord a new song, and his praise in the congregation of saints.

20 Let Israel rejoice in him that made him: let the children of Zion be joyful in their King.

21 Let them praise his name in the dance: let them sing praises unto him with the timbrel and harp.

22 For the Lord taketh pleasure in his people: he will beautify the meek with salvation.

23 Let the saints be joyful in glory: let them sing aloud upon their beds.   Praise ye the Lord.

Glory be to the *Father* | and ˙ to the | Son || *and* | to the | Holy | Ghost;
As it was in the beginning * is *now*, and | ever | shall be || *world* without |
    end ˙ = | A ˙ = | men.

SELECTION 53

A Festival Psalm: God's March to Victory

PSALM 68 (selected)

1 LET God arise, let his enemies be scattered: let them also that hate him flee before him.

2 As smoke is driven away, so drive them away: as wax melteth before the fire, so let the wicked perish at the presence of God.

3 But let the righteous be glad; let them rejoice before God: yea, let them exceedingly rejoice.

4 Sing unto God, sing praises to his name:

5 Extol him that rideth upon the heavens by his name JAH, and rejoice before him.

6 A father of the fatherless, and a judge of the widows, is God in his holy habitation.

7 God setteth the solitary in families: he bringeth out those which are bound with chains: but the rebellious dwell in a dry land.

8 O God, when thou wentest forth before thy people, when thou didst march through the wilderness;

9 The earth shook, the heavens also dropped at the presence of God:

10 Even Sinai itself was moved at the presence of God, the God of Israel.

11 Thou, O God, didst send a plentiful rain, whereby thou didst confirm thine inheritance, when it was weary.

12 Thy congregation hath dwelt therein: thou, O God, hast prepared of thy goodness for the poor.

13 The Lord gave the word: great was the company of those that published it.

14 Kings of armies did flee apace: and she that tarried at home divided the spoil.

15 The hill of God is as the hill of Bashan; a high hill as the hill of Bashan.

16 Why leap ye, ye high hills? this is the hill which God desireth to dwell in; yea, the Lord will dwell in it for ever.

17 The chariots of God are twenty thousand, even thousands of angels: the Lord is among them, as in Sinai, in the holy place.

18 Thou hast ascended on high, thou hast led captivity captive: thou hast received gifts for men;

19 Yea, for the rebellious also, that the Lord God might dwell among them.

20 Blessed be the Lord, who daily loadeth us with benefits, even the God of our salvation.

21 Thy God hath commanded thy strength: strengthen, O God, that which thou hast wrought for us.

22 Sing unto God, ye kingdoms of the earth; O sing praises unto the Lord;

23 To him that rideth upon the heavens of heavens, which were of old; lo, he doth send out his voice, and that a mighty voice.

24 Ascribe ye strength unto God: his excellency is over Israel, and his strength is in the clouds.

25 O God, thou art terrible out of thy holy places: the God of Israel is he that giveth strength and power unto his people. Blessed be God.

Glory be to the *F*ather | and ˙ to the | Son || *and* | to the | Holy | Ghost;
As it was in the beginning * is *now*, and | ever | shall be || *world* without |
   end ˙ = | A ˙ = | men.

SELECTION 54

A Good Friday Psalm

PSALM 22 : 1–8, 11–19

1 MY God, my God, why hast thou forsaken me? why art thou so far from helping me, and from the words of my roaring?

2 O my God, I cry in the daytime, but thou hearest not; and in the night season, and am not silent.

3 But thou art holy, O thou that inhabitest the praises of Israel.

4 Our fathers trusted in thee: they trusted, and thou didst deliver them.

5 They cried unto thee, and were delivered: they trusted in thee, and were not confounded.

6 But I am a worm, and no man; a reproach of men, and despised of the people.

7 All they that see me laugh me to scorn: they shoot out the lip, they shake the head, saying,

8 He trusted on the Lord that he would deliver him: let him deliver him, seeing he delighted in him.

9 Be not far from me; for trouble is near; for there is none to help.

10 Many bulls have compassed me: strong bulls of Bashan have beset me round.

11 They gaped upon me with their mouths, as a ravening and a roaring lion.

12 I am poured out like water, and all my bones are out of joint: my heart is like wax; it is melted in the midst of my distresses.

13 My strength is dried up like a potsherd; and my tongue cleaveth to my jaws; and thou hast brought me into the dust of death.

14 For dogs have compassed me: the assembly of the wicked have inclosed me: they pierced my hands and my feet.

15 I may tell all my bones: they look and stare upon me.

16 They part my garments among them, and cast lots upon my vesture.

17 But be not thou far from me, O Lord: O my strength, haste thee to help me.

PSALM 69 : 18–21, 29–30

18 Draw nigh unto my soul, and redeem it: deliver me because of mine enemies.

19 Thou hast known my reproach, and my shame, and my dishonour: mine adversaries are all before thee.

20 Reproach hath broken my heart; and I am full of heaviness: and I looked for some to take pity, but there was none; and for comforters, but I found none.

21 They gave me also gall for my meat; and in my thirst they gave me vinegar to drink.

22 But I am poor and sorrowful: let thy salvation, O God, set me up on high.

23 I will praise the name of God with a song, and will magnify him with thanksgiving.

Glory be to the *Father* | and ˙ to the | Son || *and* | to the | Holy | Ghost;
As it was in the beginning * is *now*, and | ever | shall be || *world* without |
    end ˙ = | A ˙= | men.

SELECTION 55

The Song of the Three Children

<small>Benedicite, Omnia Opera Domini</small>

1   O ALL ye works of the Lord, bless ye the Lord: praise him, and magnify him for ever.

2   O ye angels of the Lord, bless ye the Lord: praise him, and magnify him for ever.

3   O ye heavens, bless ye the Lord: praise him, and magnify him for ever.

4   O ye sun and moon, bless ye the Lord: praise him, and magnify him for ever.

5   O ye stars of heaven, bless ye the Lord: praise him, and magnify him for ever.

6   O ye winds of God, bless ye the Lord: praise him, and magnify him for ever.

7   O ye winter and summer, bless ye the Lord: praise him, and magnify him for ever.

8   O ye dews and frosts, bless ye the Lord: praise him, and magnify him for ever.

9   O ye nights and days, bless ye the Lord: praise him, and magnify him for ever.

10   O ye light and darkness, bless ye the Lord: praise him, and magnify him for ever.

11   O ye lightnings and clouds, bless ye the Lord: praise him, and magnify him for ever.

12   O let the earth bless the Lord: yea, let it praise him, and magnify him for ever.

13   O ye mountains and hills, bless ye the Lord: praise him, and magnify him for ever.

14   O all ye green things upon the earth, bless ye the Lord: praise him, and magnify him for ever.

15   O ye seas and floods, bless ye the Lord: praise him, and magnify him for ever.

16   O all ye fowls of the air, bless ye the Lord: praise him, and magnify him for ever.

17   O all ye beasts and cattle, bless ye the Lord: praise him, and magnify him for ever.

18   O ye children of men, bless ye the Lord: praise him, and magnify him for ever.

19   O let Israel bless the Lord: praise him, and magnify him for ever.

20   O ye servants of the Lord, bless ye the Lord: praise him, and magnify him for ever.

21   O ye spirits and souls of the righteous, bless ye the Lord: praise him, and magnify him for ever.

22   O ye holy and humble men of heart, bless ye the Lord: praise him, and magnify him for ever.

Glory be to the *Father* | and · to the | Son || *and* | to the | Holy | Ghost;
As it was in the beginning * is *now*, and | ever | shall be || *world* without |
    end · = | A · = | men.

SELECTION 56

The Psalms of the Nativity

MAGNIFICAT

1 MY soul doth magnify the Lord, and my spirit hath rejoiced in God my Saviour.

   2 For he hath regarded the lowliness of his handmaiden.

3 For, behold, from henceforth all generations shall call me blessed.

   4 For he that is mighty hath magnified me: and holy is his name.

5 And his mercy is on them that fear him throughout all generations.

   6 He hath showed strength with his arm: he hath scattered the proud in the imagination of their hearts.

7 He hath put down the mighty from their seat, and hath exalted the humble and meek.

   8 He hath filled the hungry with good things: and the rich he hath sent empty away.

9 He, remembering his mercy, hath holpen his servant Israel: as he promised to our forefathers, Abraham and his seed, for ever.

BENEDICTUS

   10 Blessed be the Lord God of Israel: for he hath visited and redeemed his people;

11 And hath raised up a mighty salvation for us in the house of His servant David;

   12 As he spake by the mouth of his holy prophets, which have been since the world began;

13 That we should be saved from our enemies, and from the hand of all that hate us.

   14 To perform the mercy promised to our forefathers, and to remember his holy covenant;

15 To perform the oath which he sware to our forefather Abraham, that he would give us;

   16 That we, being delivered out of the hand of our enemies, might serve him without fear;

17 In holiness and righteousness before him, all the days of our life.

   18 And thou, child, shalt be called the prophet of the Highest: for thou shalt go before the face of the Lord to prepare his ways;

19 To give knowledge of salvation unto his people, for the remission of their sins,

   20 Through the tender mercy of our God: whereby the dayspring from on high hath visited us;

21 To give light to them that sit in darkness, and in the shadow of death: and to guide our feet into the way of peace.

Glory be to the *Father* | and · to the | Son || *and* | to the | Holy | Ghost;
As it was in the beginning * is *now,* and | ever | shall be || *world* without | end · = | A · = | men.

SELECTION 57

A Psalm of the Early Church

Te Deum Laudamus

1 WE praise thee, O God: we acknowledge thee to be the Lord.

2 All the earth doth worship thee, the Father everlasting.

3 To thee all angels cry aloud: the heavens, and all the powers therein;

4 To thee cherubim and seraphim continually do cry,

5 Holy, holy, holy, Lord God of Sabaoth;

6 Heaven and earth are full of the majesty of thy glory.

7 The glorious company of the apostles praise thee.

8 The goodly fellowship of the prophets praise thee.

9 The noble army of martyrs praise thee.

10 The holy church throughout all the world doth acknowledge thee;

11 The Father of an infinite majesty;

12 Thine adorable, true, and only Son;

13 Also the Holy Ghost, the Comforter.

14 Thou art the king of glory, O Christ.

15 Thou art the everlasting Son of the Father.

16 When thou tookest upon thee to deliver man, thou didst humble thyself to be born of a virgin.

17 When thou hadst overcome the sharpness of death, thou didst open the kingdom of heaven to all believers.

18 Thou sittest at the right hand of God, in the glory of the Father.

19 We believe that thou shalt come to be our judge.

20 We therefore pray thee, help thy servants, whom thou hast redeemed with thy precious blood.

21 Make them to be numbered with thy saints in glory everlasting.

22 O Lord, save thy people, and bless thine heritage.

23 Govern them, and lift them up for ever.

24 Day by day we magnify thee;

25 And we worship thy name ever, world without end.

26 Vouchsafe, O Lord, to keep us this day without sin.

27 O Lord, have mercy upon us, have mercy upon us.

28 O Lord, let thy mercy be upon us, as our trust is in thee.

29 O Lord, in thee have I trusted: let me never be confounded.

Index of Occasions

	Selection		Selection
Morning	1	Thanksgiving 10, 11, 12, 13, 15, 16	
Evening	2, 3	Christmas	45, 49, 56, 57
Advent	7	Epiphany and Missions	48, 49
New Years 4, 7, 10, 15, 18, 22, 41		Preparatory Service	36
Ash Wednesday	31	The Communion 38, 40, 41, 42	
Good Friday	46, 54	Dedication of Church	38
Easter 6, 8, 14, 47, 51, 53, 57		National Days 16, 30, 50, 52, 57	
Ascension 47, 53, 57		In Time of Trouble	19
Whitsuntide	27	Festival Psalms 6, 18, 51, 52, 53, 55	

Index of Psalms

Psalm	Selection	Psalm	Selection	Psalm	Selection	Psalm	Selection
1	32	37	35	86	24	121	19
2	48	40	46	87	40	122	40
4	2	42, 43	37	89	45	124	20
5	1	44	52	90	4	125	40
8	13	45	42	91	23	126	44
15	32	46	39	92	14	130	Cant. 430
18	36, 47	47	48	93	5	132	38
19	1	48	39	95, 96	7	134	2
20	19	51	31	97	5	135	20
22	54	56	3	98	Cant. 416	136	18
23	19	57	20	99	5	137	44
24	38	61, 62	29	100	7	138	18
25	22	63	3	103	15	139	27
26, 27	41	65	13	104	11	141	3
28	24	66	9	107	16, 17	144	30
29	12	67	48	111	14	145	10
31	2	68	53	112	32	146	30
32	36	69	54	113	21	147	50
33	8	71	26	114	52	148	6
34	28	72	49	115	21	149	52
36	12	80	43	116, 117	25	150	6
		84	41	118	51	Song of the Three Children	55
		85	44	119	33, 34	Magnificat	56
						Benedictus	56
						Te Deum	57

Gloria Patri

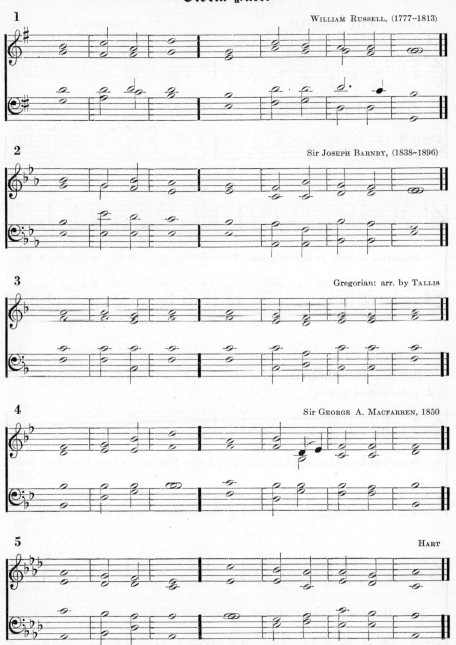

1   WILLIAM RUSSELL, (1777–1813)

2   Sir JOSEPH BARNBY, (1838–1896)

3   Gregorian: arr. by TALLIS

4   Sir GEORGE A. MACFARREN, 1850

5   HART

Glory be to the *Father* | and · to the Son || *and* | to the Holy | Ghost;

As it was in the beginning * is *now*, and | ever | shall be || *world* without | end ·
= | A · = | men.

The Doxology

In the Genevan Psalter, 1551

THE OLD HUNDREDTH

1 In the modern rhythm

Praise God, from whom all bless-ings flow; Praise Him, all crea-tures here be-low;

Praise Him a-bove, ye heavenly host; Praise Father, Son, and Ho-ly Ghost. A-MEN.

THE OLD HUNDREDTH

As arranged by LOUIS BOURGEOIS, 1551

2 In the original rhythm

Praise God, from whom all bless-ings flow; Praise Him, all crea-tures here be-low;

Praise Him a-bove, ye heaven-ly host: Praise Fa-ther, Son, and Ho-ly Ghost. A-MEN.

NOTE—*The melody was set to Psalm CXXXIV in the Genevan Psalter, but to Psalm C in the old English Psalter.*